THE HUMAN NATURE
OF SCIENCE

STEWART E. PERRY

The HUMAN NATURE of SCIENCE

Researchers at Work in Psychiatry

With a Foreword by John P. Spiegel, M.D.

THE FREE PRESS, NEW YORK

COLLIER-MACMILLAN LIMITED, LONDON

THIS BOOK IS DEDICATED TO

the late Gordon Keith Chalmers
who first showed me a vision of the
romance of the intellect

AND TO

Helen Swick Perry
who makes that vision and much else of our
common humanity wonderfully real

FOREWORD

❦

In our age of technology, everything changes rapidly. Governments, political parties, and nations are transformed before our eyes; populations explode, peoples migrate, urban centers decay and are rebuilt almost before we have had time to take note of what is happening. Revolutions in specialized branches of knowledge occur overnight, usually triggered by a technical invention such as the electron microscope or the high-speed computer. The arts, too, undergo lightening alterations of form, content, and style, while religion, abandoning its customary conservatism, struggles to keep up with changing times.

In the hustle and confusion of change, we are likely to pin the responsibility for whatever discomfort we feel upon the sciences. Science promotes the technological invention that so alarmingly transforms time and space and the world as we have known it. It is easy to forget—or perhaps never to recognize—that science is a human affair, subject to the same social influences that are at work in every other area of life, responding to the very processes of change in which it plays such a leading role. Even if one has a strong sense that science is not always one step ahead of change, perpetually generating new truths through error-free procedures, one is seldom in a position to witness for oneself the operations of social demands, institutional pressures, professional pride, and sheer necessity on the advances and retreats that science undergoes in its daily rounds. Scientists are their own best image-makers and they would have us believe in the characterization of science as an intellectual adventure, a proud and relentless advance into the unknown. In the usual course, their errors go unpublished, their blind-spots are overlooked. The layman has little opportunity to see in detail what he probably suspects: that the scientist, like most others, is fallible, but keeps working at his problems, only in the long run making any headway; that he is always responsive to the social process in which he is embedded and is often blindly propelled by it.

What this book does is to provide an eyewitness report on the human side of the scientist's work. The result is not always pretty and at times is fairly depressing. The author is a social scientist and his procedure is to observe, record, and analyze the day-to-day workings of a group of scientists. Often the work goes in the wrong direction, it comes to nothing, the scientists get involved in arrangements that are doomed from the start, or seem just plain foolish and possibly dangerous. Then things improve a bit and the work seems to creep forward. The reader is likely to experience vicariously the frustrations of the scientists, to be appalled at their blunders, and to reproach them for their apparent inability to take a more sensible course.

But one is soon persuaded that attitudes of irritation, blame, and fault-finding are out of order. The criticisms that leap to mind are softened and perhaps stilled by the author's ability to show how the plans, the concepts, and the procedures of the scientists are shaped by the pressures of the social system of which they are members. It is Stewart Perry's special gift, as a social-science observer of human frailty, that he is able to switch the reader's attention away from the failings of the men as individuals and to force concentrated attention to fall upon minute fluctuations in the social currents in which they become immersed. In the end, we are left without fools, or villains, or heroes, despite our tendency to invent such roles for people in trouble. The trouble-maker—if it can be called that—is a perfectly natural, historically conditioned conflict of interest, aims, and purposes among the personnel of the organization in which the scientists work. Concealed or ignored for the most part, this conflict only emerges into the light of day as a result of the

author's studies. As it emerges, the reader's reaction switches
from a sense of futility at the waste of time, money, and effort
in the name of science to a feeling of hope. How, if ever, will
the conflict be resolved? What effect on the efficiency of the
work will its resolution have? What implications for scientific
work in general can be drawn from the particular problems that
had to be faced within this organization?

It is well to have frustration and progress set in so general a
framework. For, in this case, the scientists are psychiatrists, they
work in a newly organized Medical Research Center within a
university, and their conflict involves the frequent incompatibility between the pursuit of research goals and the obligation to
take good care of the patient. Given the dubious standing of
psychiatry as therapy, on the one hand, and as research, on the
other, we can be grateful for the objectivity and insight that
this study brings to bear upon the obstacles that the psychiatrist
encounters when he tries to behave like a scientist.

Psychiatry is widely regarded as an important if somewhat
backward field, having an important role to play on the national
scene. Because of its potential though still unrealized capacity to
relieve human suffering, great hopes center upon it. It also stimu-
lates great doubts. Both laymen and scientists in other fields are
unsure what it consists of and whether it can deliver the improved mental health that it publicly advocates. Much of the
public's confidence in its ability to carry out its promises rests
upon its status as a science. The public would like to know that
its methods of treatment and its explanations of the causes of
mental illness are based upon firm, scientifically validated knowledge. If not, there is at least the wish that it head in this direction with as much speed and energy as possible.

Accordingly, a book such as this, which throws a searchlight
on the questionable procedures taking place in a mental health
research program, on the problems, failures, and partial solutions
within the program, carries an important message to a variety of
audiences. It can be considered as a contribution to the sociology
of science, of institutions, and of professions and this, in fact,
is the chief aim of the author. But in view of its factual content,

it may well be regarded as a candid account of disorders endemic to the profession of psychiatry. Such a view could well provide fodder for those who think ill of the mental health movement and expect little good to come of it. To be sure, a psychiatrist could make the self-serving defense that every scientific discipline, no matter how sophisticated, has its share of failures, problems, defeats, and general foolishness. Indeed, in an aroused mood, one could go further and protest that the accounts of "participant-observer" conversations between the author and members of the staff of the Center constitute nothing but the sort of backstairs gossip and exaggerated *schrechlichkeit* to be found between the seams of any well-run organization. But neither the accusation of chronic, scientific ineptness in the field of psychiatry nor the defensive cry of "Unfair!" are to the point.

I am a psychiatrist and I doubt whether any psychiatrist can read the account of the research projects reported in this book without experiencing acute discomfort. It strikes to the heart of the problem in our profession. I would predict that the malaise I felt will also be experienced by many, many nonpsychiatrists. The anxiety is likely to become so acute that one is tempted to cry, "But this is neither good research nor good therapy!" The cry will be stifled before it is uttered if one asks: What is good research and what is good therapy in this field? What are the canons that determine the answers to these questions? Why is it so difficult to come up with the answers? These are the questions to which the author directs our attention. And it is these questions for which he provides some solutions.

This is not the place to discuss the nature of his solutions. Suffice it to say that they are both practical and of considerable interest to a theory of social systems. The problem inheres in the way in which research is believed to interfere with treatment, and treatment to interfere with research. It is a stubborn problem, with many ramifications outside the confines of a hospital or research institute. The research that is examined in this book was carried out over ten years ago. In the meantime, a decade of psychiatric research generously supported by government funding and by private foundations has passed by. Yet the same problems, often in new forms, crop up repeatedly. Just as ten years ago research methods were unwisely resisted and then ineptly used by therapists in hospitals, so they now are being resisted by service organizations involved in the community psychiatry and community mental health and poverty programs so characteristic of the present scene. Because of the intensity of the resistance and the pressure to implement new programs as rapidly as possible, it is difficult to discover whether the programs have been based upon sound planning and ascertainable fact and whether they are producing fruitful results. Until those who plan and implement such service programs no longer feel threatened by the basic research methods and the evaluation studies that are needed to determine the rationale and efficacy of the services, we can expect to find in these areas the same sorts of misadventures and awkward dilemmas as are reported herein for clinical and hospital psychiatry.

Because this book discusses in a dispassionate, scholarly, and creative fashion the issues that hobble psychiatric research, it deserves detailed attention by policy makers, planners, practitioners, and researchers in the mental health field.

John P. Spiegel, M.D.

Harvard University

PREFACE

ONE REASON that I have wanted to write this book is to combat a common and sturdy misapprehension about science that has two mutually reinforcing parts: (1) Science is a pure interaction of theory, reason, and intelligence, combined with careful observation, search, or experimentation; and (2) the proper combination of these ingredients, with perhaps a bit of luck, can lead to a firm and unassailable truth. Surely, I may have oversimplified this misapprehension, yet it is as widespread as science itself. In this century particularly, its limitations have been exposed on rational, logical, and historical grounds, and some commentators have also pointed out that it is a misinterpretation of the original and fertile conceptions of Bacon and others. Yet it survives, and may even be immortal, perhaps because it is a useful view of science. Nevertheless, I want in this book to join those who have argued against it, although I shall use a somewhat different approach. I shall describe some of the scientific projects that I have had an opportunity to observe as they developed, and use these as a way of presenting a competing view of science: I shall take for granted that science includes theory, logic, empirical study—and luck. I shall insist that (1) it also includes social pressures, personal emotions, and cultural predispositions; and (2) *without them it could not exist.*

When one seeks to argue for the essential importance of non-intellectual forces in the life of the intellect, one willy-nilly enters into an irrationalist tradition. That tradition has a long history and eminent leaders, and for purposes of brevity in this book I must steadfastly ignore that tradition. Nevertheless, I must say what many have said before: To insist that irrational forces are an integral part of our knowledge-producing process may seem to derogate thought or the intellect itself, but we must examine the part played by those forces in order to maintain the intellect in the position in which it, too, is a subject for rational analysis and not merely an object of blind faith.

I hope that this book will be useful to the practicing scientist in psychiatry and the other studies of human behavior—sociology, psychology, anthropology, and so on—because I have also tried to describe simply the events in the projects that I watched unfold. I have suggested simple ways in which the scientist who studies his fellow human beings can do so with full respect for them and less wear and tear on himself, and I have tried to link these suggestions up with a respectable conception of scientific knowledge that commentators have constructed, in various forms, in a tradition that stems from the Greek skeptics through Nietzsche to James, Dewey, Whitehead, Bridgman, and Polanyi in our own time.

Finally, I have, in a most sketchy way, pointed to some conceptions for describing the ways in which scientists and others try to honor the competing demands of a conflicting and complex scheme of values in our society. This book itself is one prime illustration of the attempt to achieve a balance between a good many competing values, for it by no means represents a pure distillation of the scientific process. Such purity, I believe, is nonexistent.

Much time has passed since the events described in this book took place. All of us involved in them have learned a good deal in the meantime. A sophisticated reader will recognize numerous limitations of all sorts, including scientific standards, in the research projects, as described here; but that same reader must also recognize that these limitations are apparent because they were not hidden from my inquiries. The limitations and the disturbing or tension-provoking events of the projects are now insignificant history, but the problems they illustrate remain with medicine, psychiatry, and science—in any field in which men try to unfold the endless charts of our world. At the University Medical Research Center, as I call it for this book, I had a rare opportunity to watch that unfolding in full and open view, including some distressing episodes. Such episodes seem to occur everywhere, and I would not join anyone who sought to throw the first stone at the work undertaken at the Center. Yet at the Center, as elsewhere, the committed scientist must be committed also to the perfection of his craft as a humane endeavor. He cannot ignore a human problem because it has already been researched and well understood and no longer presents as much challenge to scientific inquiry.

The human problems of science are greater when scientific inquiry focuses upon man himself, rather than upon his non-human environment. In this sense, then, there are greater burdens placed upon the medical researcher, the psychiatric researcher, and the behavioral scientist in the development of their work. I cannot offer a ready solution to the basic difficulty of human experimentation, for example, although in the final chapter I suggest some ways of easing that difficulty. I would stress only that whatever may be the opportunities for pure curiosity in investigations of the nonhuman world, research upon people can have no more overriding goal than to obtain knowledge for the improvement of the conditions of human life. Maintaining the primacy of that goal does not, however, solve the inevitable conflicts that must arise between what is good for people in the present and what is good for people in the future in the calculus of that goal. Excruciating choices will be made. Our only mechanism for the optimal process of choice is that the process be carried out in openness and clarity and that the responsibility be not only accepted, but sought, by those who participate in making the choices. Moreover, we need to recognize that the responsibility must also be borne by those of us who are willing to be benefitted by the advances stemming from research on medical patients.

STEWART E. PERRY

ACKNOWLEDGMENTS

&

I AM ACUTELY aware that this book owes an essential debt to a number of social scientists and psychiatrists who have given me over the years the benefit of their ideas and criticisms. I owe no one, however, more than I owe Helen Swick Perry, my wife, who has interpreted for me (as for many others) the seminal structure in the theories of Harry Stack Sullivan. Without some way to bring together the insights of psychiatry and social science, as Sullivan so significantly constructed in his work, it would be hard indeed to understand the human nature of science or any other of man's activities. I have found essential conceptual tools in Sullivan's work, but for me as for many others their significance would have been missed without Helen Swick Perry's concern with making the tools both available and meaningful, especially in the interpretations she has provided in *The Fusion of Psychiatry and Social Science.** Of course, I am indebted to her in so many other ways in the research and writing of this book that the dedication can express my appreciation only by its intent.

If, from psychiatry, Sullivan has offered me one means for the melding of psychiatric and social science that this book required, Talcott Parsons' broad sociological vision provided another. In some ways I have not used Parsons' formulations as explicitly as I have Sullivan's; nevertheless, I remain deeply indebted to him intellectually and personally in the making of this book.

I have benefitted greatly from the encouragement of John R. Seely and Leslie Farber, M.D., each of whom in differing ways offered an outsider's viewpoint when I especially needed it. To Lyman

* Harry Stack Sullivan, *The Fusion of Psychiatry and Social Science* (with introduction and commentaries by Helen Swick Perry), New York: Norton, 1964.

C. Wynne, M.D., a psychiatrist who also received training at Harvard's Department of Social Relations, and to Charlotte Green Schwartz, a sociologist who also used the training opportunities of the Washington School of Psychiatry, I owe a heavy debt that I shall not go on to describe in detail here, but their interest and ideas are implicit in much of this book.

There are others, though, whose special help must be described in part: My colleagues at the University Medical Research Center may take credit for much that is useful in this book, and like all the persons already mentioned, they can accurately leave to me the responsibility for anything that is lacking. I shall not name these colleagues, but they must know that I am indebted to them in more than the usual manner that a social or psychological researcher is indebted to his research subjects: I had the added advantage of studying people who conventionally made the effort to be scientifically self-observant and who were articulate about what they observed. We had some stormy weather, but my work was made easier by their own attention to the very problems I describe in this book. I am grateful to them, and I will always be especially grateful to the psychiatrist-in-chief who gave me the opportunity to examine whatever I wanted to. I hope I have repaid my fellow staff members in small part for their help, by this book, because I have made a strenuous effort to provide an analysis of the events that would be practically useful, as well as theoretically meaningful.

Of course I have taken considerable precautions to maintain a degree of anonymity for fellow staff members. Interestingly enough I have discovered, with previously published papers, that these precautions allow only those immediately involved in a particular case to recognize themselves, while other colleagues, remarking on the same materials, are apt to attribute events from one person's project to a different person or to a project not studied by me. This may be evidence of a certain generality in what I have observed and described. Indeed I hope that is true, of course, but I have deliberately mixed identities and constructed new ones when that was possible without interfering with the significance of the events.

Many of the chapters of this book are drawn from earlier versions in a dissertation and in published papers. I want to acknowledge with thanks permission from the William Alanson White Psychiatric Foundation to make use of copyrighted material from a paper jointly authored with Gertrude N. Shea, "Social Controls and Psychiatric Theory in a Ward Setting," *Psychiatry* (1957) 20: 221-47. I want to thank Mrs. Shea for her courtesy in allowing me to use this material. I also acknowledge with thanks permission from *Behavioral Science* to use copyrighted material appearing in "Observations on Social

Processes in Psychiatric Research," *Behavioral Science* (1956) 1: 290-302. The dissertation (*Social Processes in Psychiatric Research: A Study in the Sociology of Science*) was prepared for a doctoral degree in the Department of Social Relations, Harvard University, 1963.

The almost interminable editorial and secretarial tasks involved in the making of this book would have been virtually overwhelming without the interest, competence, and energy of Mrs. Irene Paull and Mrs. Victoria Hicks. I am grateful to each of them.

I am grateful to Mrs. Hicks especially for her assistance in the preparation of the index and the other final tasks on this book.

CONTENTS

(x x i)

ᴥ§

IT IS CERTAIN, however, that to gain an exact idea of a science one must practice it, and, so to speak, live with it. That is because it does not entirely consist of some propositions which have been definitely proved. Along side this actual, realized science, there is another, concrete and living, which is in part ignorant of itself and yet seeks itself; besides acquired results, there are hopes, habits, instincts, needs, presentiments so obscure that they cannot be expressed in words, yet so powerful that they sometimes dominate the whole life of the scholar. All this is still science; it is even its best and largest part, for the discovered truths are a little thing in comparison with those that remain to be discovered. . . . Each science has, so to speak, a soul which lives in the conscience of scholars. Only a part of this soul assumes sensible bodily form. The formulas which express it, being general, are easily transmitted. But such is not the case with this other part of science which no symbol translates without. Here, all is personal and must be acquired through personal experience. To take part in it, one must put oneself to work and place oneself before the facts.

—Emile Durkheim, *The Division of Labor*, 1893.

THE HUMAN NATURE
OF SCIENCE

૭ई

One

ALL SCIENCE HAS
A SOCIAL CONTEXT—
ESPECIALLY PSYCHIATRY

❧

As I walked down a corridor of our new research hospital, shortly after it opened, I passed a colleague, a young research psychiatrist, who startled me with a sardonic question, grinning crookedly as he sidled by. "Discovered anything recently?" That greeting came to be familiar to us in the psychiatric research program, and we never found an adequate rejoinder. How could we answer his neat flicking of our tenderest vulnerabilities? It made no difference that he did not exclude himself from sharing those vulnerabilities. What a mordantly unsettling question to toss out so casually! We all knew that none of us from the most junior person like myself to the senior director was ever likely to answer that question with a serious and accurate "Yes."

Significant clear-cut discoveries are rare anywhere in science, but they are virtually inconceivable in most of the frustrating, baffling field of mental health research. Medicine in general may occasionally produce a new effective vaccine or life-saving treatment, but in psychiatry the chances for similar success are painfully small. I do not mean that the fundamental secrets of man's physical ills are easily bared while his mental ills remain mysterious. I mean, though, that the knowledgeable scientist in cancer research, for example, is being quite realistic if he predicts that shortly we shall know just exactly how to cure or prevent certain cancer conditions, but no such optimism can attach itself realistically to the researcher who works on the prevention and cure of those psychological and social disturbances of personal living that today are conceptualized as mental illness.

There are a number of quite respectable scientific and theoretical reasons why the mental health researcher must today tolerate the fact that he will be "discovering" very little as he plods along. Yet no matter how significant these reasons may be and no matter how they exculpate his lack of clear success, the mental health researcher will still feel vulnerable to the pressures —social, psychological, cultural—surrounding the kind of work that cannot be easily defended as successful in a success-filled, success-oriented society.[1] The intellectually sound explanations for his slow progress cannot fully protect the researcher from his own painful recognition of that slow progress.

And yet is he really so different in his quest from any other scientist? Are not all scientists bound to a Sisyphean task, laboriously moving up the slopes of knowledge but doomed never to reach the summit? I rather doubt that other research scientists— in medicine or elsewhere—would be willing to cede to the mental health researcher the dubious right to the most baffling scientific problems. All scientists, everywhere, must accept a fate that can promise only a temporary sense of achievement and a rather permanent sense of alienation from the sort of success that occurs in the world around them.

I make no brief here for the special burdens of the psychiatric researcher. If he cannot today announce triumphantly that he has discovered something really significant, he, like all other re-

---

1. Perhaps it is these pressures that help make the field of mental illness subject to swift enthusiasms; thus, every so often some new fact is interpreted as the true clue to control of the mind. For example, thirty years ago rats seemed to be smarter after an induced fever and this was supposed to be the clue to a higher I.Q. for everyone; today a certain drug is getting the same publicity. The enthusiastic interpretations of the effect of one or another new drug as offering opportunities for controlling behavior are probably best seen in the light of the long-known, mind-controlling drug, alcohol. Careful evaluation will put each "discovery" in a more appropriate if less exciting perspective.

searchers, works in a task that rewards for its own sake much of the time. That, in fact, is the core of the scientific life—the enjoyment of the quest itself. But a scientist is not merely a scientist; he is a man—feeling, thinking, desiring, in other realms besides science. He is part of a greater context than the small world of science, for science itself is part of that greater context of all the living that men do. Thus, the researcher's work gets shaped not only by the forces and motivations inherent in the structure of science itself but also by the forces inherent in the whole structure of human living.

It is about this human nature of scientific research that I want to write—the human nature that poses and responds to sardonic questions as well as scientific ones, the human nature that makes science possible, the human nature that roughs out the basic shapes that all scientific research takes. To describe this real science, I need not tell the biographical histories of this or that researcher; I want instead to describe the intimate work relationships and pressures that take place in the microcosm of science—the small group of interacting colleagues who bring to each other the experiences, shared or unshared, that create the work they do. These experiences are sometimes common to all walks of life—the unsatisfied need, for example, to achieve in the eyes of others as well as one's self. At other times they take forms particular to the branch of science concerned, although they are based upon that common humanity of the scientist and layman. The forms particular to psychiatric science are my special interest.

For five years I worked in a very specialized, perhaps unique hospital; from that experience emerges the view I present about research. The hospital, which I shall call the University Medical Research Center, was established with the sole aim of housing scientific studies in all branches of medicine. I worked on social scientific problems in the psychiatric program. As a regular staff member—a participant particularly in studies of adult mental patients—I was forced to the hypothesis that *the intimate social conditions in a research hospital significantly influence the procedures and results of its scientific research.* Although I shall not prove this hypothesis by the standard replicable techniques of precise demonstration in science, I can present the observations that led me to its formulation. These observations are sufficiently intensive and intimate to generate some ideas about how the influence might operate.

Whatever human problems the clinical researcher in psychiatry shares with other scientists, there is one continually nagging problem that he shares only with other clinicians: How can he combine his responsibility for the welfare of his patient with his responsibility for the advancement of his scientific field? There may be other, more important strains and social pressures in the work life of the research physician, but as Renée C. Fox has shown in her poignant *Experiment Perilous* (New York: The Free Press, 1959), this is a constant and inescapable conflict.

I have chosen to concentrate on this particular social and psychological problem in the work of the research psychiatrist because it exemplifies, as I believe nothing else can, the inextricable strands of value commitments that help constitute science in any field. True, this kind of conflict between clinical values and scientific values is particular to medical research, but I believe that it is merely a peculiarly visible illustration of the pull of social, psychological, and cultural commitments that enter into any piece of scientific work, arising out of the relations of scientists to each other and to the world they live in.

The research physician (I shall actually focus on events in the work of research psychiatrists only) may try to escape a commitment to the welfare of his patient, but he cannot, for it is a part of his training, his experience, his medical world, his larger world. Any other scientist may try to escape one or another nonscientific commitment—to home, to nation, to custom, to religion, to manners, to beauty—but in the end, his very attempt to escape redirects his work. And if one commitment may be eluded, temporarily or permanently, another is joined, for even the man who is occasionally a scientist is always a man.

No one is more than occasionally a scientist, while no matter what one does, one is always human. Scientific interests may permeate a man's life so that at times the mold on his bread interests the biologist in him or the sudden anger in his breast interests the psychologist in him; even so, he sleeps, eats, loves, shies away, hates—lives. And in so doing he carries with him the social and psychological values, influences, and urges that are part of sleeping, eating, loving, and so on. These same values weave in and out of his scientific work—sometimes more visible than at other times, but never wholly absent.

For the psychiatrist who engages in clinical research, there is always an interest competing with scientific advance, an interest in the patient's welfare. That is one of the inescapable concerns that shape his work. It involves one set of social forces that I shall particularly concentrate on in this book.

I shall focus on how the job requirement of concurrent research and treatment affected the scientific operations of the research psychiatrist at the Medical Center. How did the dual responsibility affect his research procedures and his research results? What happened to his ideas and to his experiments as he juggled the two kinds of responsibility? What social techniques did he use to carry out his work, and how did these techniques participate in the scientific product that emerges? These questions will be examined by means of the observations, interviews, and inquiries I made during my years at the Center.

I shall also look more briefly at two other aspects of the research process at the Center. One of the two briefer analyses will ask: "How are the ideas of the research psychiatrist about his scientific methods influenced by the propinquity of colleagues with different technical backgrounds?" In the other, I shall use a case study to examine the question: "How does the social organization of the psychiatric ward shape the psychiatric theories that emerge from that ward?" In this instance, I shall be recounting the influences that played upon an emerging theory for the care of certain schizophrenic patients.

The highly specialized situation that I shall be examining here becomes, on close scrutiny, simply understandable as the sort of behavior that any scientist engages in. In fact, I believe that this world of psychiatric research, as esoteric as it may seem on first glance, can be seen as a stage quite as simple as any upon which man must play his part. In short, I argue that howsoever different the scientific pursuits may be from other concerns of man—even in the example of scientific research in psychiatry—the tools of social and psychological and cultural analysis reveal them as having a common human nature.

Science in a Social Perspective

Aside from a certain satisfaction to be gained from putting the pieces of human activity together and aside from a certain curiosity perhaps, how can I justify a study like this? In science, presumably, there need be no justification save the desire to understand; but if I am to take the position I do, I must surely examine in my own instance the shaping of a study—this study. I shall do so in more personal terms in the final chapter, but here I shall set forth the general intellectual rationale for the study.

The most general reasons have to do with our understanding of the texture of knowledge in science itself, of which psychiatry is here viewed only as a case example. I shall explore, from the vantage point of social science, the very serious philosophical issues about the sense and significance of science that this sort of study can illuminate—such as the nature of scientific truth. And I shall answer possible objections that might be raised against the use of psychiatric research as a case illustration of the general process of science—for example, the objection that research in psychiatry cannot be scientific.

The study of the social order of science (or any social order) can be conveniently circumscribed as *macrosociology*—studying the broad institutional patterns and processes of society—or as *microsociology*—studying the intimate, constricted structures and processes of the primary group, people in frequent and continued face-to-face interaction. My study is in the *micro*sociology of science. I am concerned with what goes on within the small interacting group of researchers in a single research program. Of course, the effects of over-all patterns of the society as a whole reach down into any encounter of members of small groups, and so I shall have to occasionally give some consideration to the macrosociology of events in the scientific group I examined. Also, what happens in the small group can have implications for the society in which it works, so I shall have to deal briefly with such broader implications as well. However, my data bear almost exclusively upon the microcosm of the Center and especially upon conflicts in the research psychiatrist's role there.

There can be no doubt that conflicts of role expectations and values occur in all scientific research and in the collateral activities of the scientist. These conflicts can require difficult decisions for the working scientist, and it is often in the resolution of the dilemmas that creativity in science and in social process occurs.

C. P. Snow's writings have offered some insight for scientists and laymen alike into the human dilemmas of science. In *The Search*, for example, Snow presents an excellent account of the conflicts in the careers of natural scientists. However, in his book there is an implicit, if not explicit message that one is *either* human *or* scientist. For example, Snow's central character turns from a brilliant and established scientific career to journalism because he feels he does not hold enough allegiance to science to expose the scientific dishonesty of a close friend. By giving up science, Snow's protagonist resolves the conflict between the roles of friend and of scientist.

Snow's novel oversimplifies and distorts artistically the alternatives open to the working scientist. The observations that I shall present will indicate a greater complexity and richer set of choices in scientific role conflicts. The relatedness of the concerns of our Western culture provides extremely varied opportunities for choices, including creative solutions that can integrate otherwise conflicting values.[2] The data of my study will help to document and conceptualize the ways that integrate disparate values in the

---

2. Of course, Snow's own life is the best argument for that, for he has found a way to further science as an artist.

research psychiatrist's work life, as well as ways that fail to mesh conflicting values in his science and medicine.

The intellectual rationale for a study of this nature must be an illumination of the process of understanding per se. Science is only one way in which we encode our experiences of the world and of each other, but it is an especially important way. It is fundamental to its growth that the means by which its code is constructed and manipulated are examined as intimately as possible. This is especially true for fields, like psychiatry, in which there is least satisfaction with current answers. Science must turn its searchlight upon itself so as to remain science.

So I write this book not just to show that research in one particular discipline and in one particular setting was influenced by the social organization of the work, but to advance the idea that all science is subject to that influence.[3] I want to mount an attack with empirical materials, however crude they may be, against a view of science quite generally held by scientists, philosophers, and laymen alike that science can be essentially independent of its social setting. Their view often recognizes that the rate or direction of scientific development may at any point be influenced by the availability of funds, personnel, and so on, and that this availability is of course a social matter. But their view insists that this does not compromise the essential independence of the substance of science.

It is true that what might be called the social budget for science is an important influence, but I do not mean to treat of that influence. The significance of such an influence is already easily accepted. I will cite only two well-recognized examples of that influence, although the number is legion and well-documented in the scientific world. It is frequently pointed out that Russian studies in genetic science languished until Stalin's influ-

3. *Cf.* Talcott Parsons, Introduction to Part Four, "Culture and the Social System," pp. 963-93 in Parsons, *et al.*, eds., *Theories of Society*, Vol. II, New York: Free Press, 1961; Alfred de Grazia, "A Concept of Scientists and Their Organization," *Amer. Behav. Scientist* (1962) 6: 30-34; and an application to American sociology itself, Kurt H. Wolff, "Notes Toward a Sociocultural Interpretation of American Sociology," *Amer. Sociol. Rev.* (1946) 11: 545-53.

ence abated, simply because Stalin had decreed that Lysenko's theory of acquired traits was correct and only work within that theory would be supported.[4] Another example is found in the search for a polio vaccine, at the expense of other medical research, under the influence of President Roosevelt, the competitive pattern of the American drug industry, and so on.[5] Most people, including many philosophers of science, hold that social influences go no further than this allocation of resources. Thus a distinguished philosopher insists:

To be sure, scientific inquiries are often initiated and subsidized by those concerned with problems of commerce and technology, and the manner in which scientific discoveries are assimilated by a society depends on its economic and political organization. But once a department of inquiry establishes its traditions of workmanship, so the history of science seems to indicate, the course of subsequent developments in it is determined by the materials explored, by the talents and skills available, and by the logic of theoretical investigation.[6]

In this view, science, within its social budgetary restrictions, pursues the truth wherever it may lead, no matter what the topic, no matter who the scientist, no matter when or where the work takes place. I do not think this view is quite accurate. It may be indicted especially for the quite vulnerable notion that science not only pursues but achieves a full and unassailable truth, despite human failings. Thus, the content of scientific thought is held high above its human and social generators. That view, I believe, distorts the fundamental nature of science.

The very nature of science can be fundamentally understood only in its human, social context. Otherwise science is cast loose from the source of all that man does, from his social and cultural

---

4. See, for example, David Joravsky, "Soviet Scientists and the Great Break," and Leopold Labedz, "How Free is Soviet Science? Technology under Totalitarianism," Chapters 7 and 8, in Bernard Barber and Walter Hirsch, eds., *The Sociology of Science*, New York: Free Press, 1962.

5. John Rowan Wilson has written a remarkable, indeed brilliant book that shows the personal, social, and cultural determinants of the research that went into the development of the polio vaccines. See John Rowan Wilson, *Margin of Safety*, Garden City: Doubleday, 1963.

6. Ernest Nagel, "Malicious Philosophies of Science," Chap. 38, in Barber and Hirsch, *op. cit.*, esp. p. 623.

milieu. I must admit that sociological thought generally avoids the position that the content of science is also a social and human matter. Even those who otherwise emphasize the effect of socio-cultural reality as a source of forms of knowledge and thought seem to exempt science from this effect. Marx, for example, and his colleague Engels stressed the social, historical genesis of all knowledge, but they seemed to back away from the conclusion that science was also influenced in its content and truth. On the one hand, Marx and Engels firmly denied that any truth, even in natural science, was more than a historically limited event, a part of an ever-changing process in the ceaseless dialectic of conflicting social forces; on the other hand, they held that knowledge both of nature and of the social forces of history could advance progressively and in fact that "pure mathematics" and "all established facts in every science and indeed . . . all facts whatsoever" must be granted "a validity which is independent of the *particular* experience of each individual." [7]

Mannheim, who may be said to have originated the contemporary field of the sociology of knowledge, sharply criticized the Marxist formulations as not general enough, but he too felt that "to a large extent" the content of natural science could be excepted from social influence.[8] Contemporary sociologists of

7. Frederick Engels, *Herr Eugen Dühring's Revolution in Science* [*Anti-Dühring*], translated by Emile Burns and edited by C. P. Dutt, Moscow and Leningrad: Cooperative Publishing Society of Foreign Workers in the U.S.S.R., 1934, p. 47. Compare, however, the following: "Each mental image of the world system is and remains in actual fact limited, objectively through the historical stage and subjectively through the physical and mental constitution of its maker." Engels, *op. cit.*, p. 46. See also Karl Marx, *A Contribution to the Critique of Political Economy*, N. I. Stone, tr., New York: International Library Publishing Co., 1904, esp. pp. 11-13. Karl Marx and Friedrich Engels, *The German Ideology*, edited by R. Pascal, New York: International Publishers, 1947, esp. pp. 13-14 and p. 36. See also T. B. Bottomore and Maximilien Rubel, *Karl Marx: Selected Writings in Sociology and Social Philosophy*, London: Watts & Co., 1956, esp. p. 77. For a general discussion of this point in Marx and Engels, see Robert K. Merton, "The Sociology of Knowledge," Chap. 12, in Merton, *Social Theory and Social Structure* (revised and enlarged edition), New York: Free Press, 1957, esp. pp. 467-70.

8. Karl Mannheim, *Ideology and Utopia*, translated by Louis Wirth and Edward Shils and with an introduction by Wirth, New York: Harcourt, Brace & World, 1936; p. 243.

science seem even more decidedly to take the position that science is not at all influenced socially in its form and content—in short, in its truth. The man who is perhaps the leading sociologist of science today, Robert K. Merton, believes that sociology can examine science only to determine how social forces facilitate or retard it. He says: "The sociologist of science is specifically concerned with the *types* of influence involved (facilitative and obstructive), the *extent* to which these types prove effective in different social structures, and the *processes* through which they operate." [Italics in original.[9]] He suggests that the reluctance to see any influence whatsoever of society upon science comes from a fear that the autonomy and objectivity of science would be jeopardized. This explanation is probably especially true for the matter of considering social influence upon scientific thought itself.

Perhaps the view that scientific thought is somehow basically independent of its social setting has also grown out of the vast changes spurred by science in the social and personal lives of us all. No doubt this view was also implemented by the new and dazzling illuminations of the universe often presented by natural science in the logical and mathematical implications of but a few equations and a few experiments. Science seems to insist that cultural values, social conditions, and personal needs are fundamentally irrelevant to it, even if they are peripherally influential.

It is true that these "irrelevant" factors are not ordinarily a part of the internal, rational-empirical logic of any one science per se. What distinguishes all science from other human activities in relation to the so-called irrelevancies is that as a system of

---

9. See Merton, "Science and Economy of 17th Century England," Chap. 19, in Merton, *Social Theory and Social Structure, op. cit.;* p. 607.

See also in the same book his Introduction to "Part IV: Studies in the Sociology of Science," pp. 531*ff.* He insists upon the "interdependence" of science and the social order but apparently does not include in the interdependence any influence of the social order upon the form of scientific thought. See also Bernard Barber, *Science and the Social Order,* New York: Free Press, 1952. Merton has contributed a foreword that deals with this point.

thought and of activity it not only seeks to escape its social, personal, and cultural context but, more than any other system, it has managed in part to transcend the contextual influence, even when it does not escape it. It is this hope of transcending time and place that so excites the scientist and inspires his efforts towards "objectivity." That is what makes science so absorbing and so useful. As some philosophers have emphasized, in a continually developing science, even the most basic definitions become outmoded, so that the result of science cannot transcend time and place as much as the quest.[10]

Certainly we can and must idealize science as the pursuit of true knowledge without concern for other values and motives or the social ties of time and place. Yet the conditions of human life mean that science—just as poetry, politics, garbage collection, parlor games, pet-raising, or praying—is in part shaped and constituted by all other ways of thinking and feeling and all other social behavior occurring in its environment. I shall try to show how true this is in the case of psychiatry, by presenting what happened at the University Medical Research Center.

But first, is psychiatry itself significant enough in science to be studied as an example in the sociology of science? I shall have to deal briefly with some of the technical considerations about this question.

The Sociology of Psychiatry as a Science

For a sociologist to choose psychiatry as a science for investigation may call up objections from social scientists and others, for many do not cede a place to psychiatry in the realm of science. Partly this is a matter of definition. Certainly the general practice of caring for the mentally ill is not itself a science; it is the application of knowledge, including scientific knowledge. But I define psychiatry here, following Sullivan's classic formu-

10. See, for example, Mario Bunge, *Intuition and Science*, Englewood Cliffs, N. J.: Prentice-Hall, 1962.

lation, as the study of interpersonal relations.[11] Thus, while psychiatry as the study of interpersonal relations historically arises out of the care of the mentally ill, it is not limited to its historical origins.

Even with this definition, there are still some who could not accept psychiatry as science; they would allow the honorific label of science only to the biological in psychiatry. If, then, one demonstrates that psychiatric research of primarily psychological matters—as in psychoanalytic studies—is socially conditioned and defined, one has merely demonstrated to these critics that such psychiatry is not scientific.

The psychiatric research I observed was mainly though not exclusively concerned with psychological issues.[12] I intend to describe how, as scientific research, it was penetrated by social processes in its environment. Many contemporary critics would insist that such psychiatric investigations are not science and therefore are always susceptible to social influences, as contrasted to real science. Their view of science and psychiatry is, I believe, merely a part of the nineteenth-century idea of science that, like a stricken giant, speared by the changes of the twentieth century, dumbly stumbles on.

I will not review the hoary considerations that place the social sciences, including psychiatry, on the same level as the natural sciences, qua science,[13] but it does seem necessary to

---

11. See Harry Stack Sullivan, "Psychiatry: Introduction to the Study of Interpersonal Relations," *Psychiatry* (1938) 1:121-134. Reprinted as "The Data of Psychiatry" in Sullivan, *The Fusion of Psychiatry and Social Science, op. cit.,* pp. 32-55.

12. Actually, however, I shall present in most detail a case of research that was also concerned with biological issues. This may help to temper the psychological trend of the sample of research I studied.

13. For recent treatments of the scientific standing of the most suspect part of psychiatry, psychoanalysis, see Sidney Hook, ed., *Psychoanalysis: Scientific Method and Philosophy,* New York: Grove Press, Evergreen paperback edition, 1960. See also E. Pumpian-Mindlin, ed., *Psychoanalysis as Science,* New York: Basic Books, new ed., 1956; Jerome Richfield, "The Scientific Status of Psychoanalysis," in Philipp Frank, ed., *The Validation of Scientific Theories,* Boston: Beacon Press, 1957; C. G. Schoenfeld, "Three Fallacious Attacks Upon Psychoanalysis as Science," *Psychoan. and the Psa. Rev.* (1962) 49:35-47. Kenneth M. Colby, *An Introduction to Psy-*

point out several features of psychiatry that make it especially appropriate as a focus for the sociology of science. First, psychiatry is definitely a frontier field in which many scientific standards are in the process of developing. This means that it should be particularly easy to see *in vivo* the operation of social factors at decision points in the construction and application of its scientific standards—as suggested in Nagel's remarks quoted earlier. In more established fields so many of these decision points have already been met and at least temporarily standardized that much research can take place governed by pre-set decisions. The resolution of early difficulties in these fields has been traditionalized and rationalized into forms that now obscure the cruciality of the choices then made and that often make the resolution of later dilemmas cut and dried. Of course, even in the most established fields, such as physics, there are still frontiers of thought with no fully accepted standards for handling scientific problems. Psychiatry is simply very much less developed.

Second, psychiatry deals with materials and ideas of critical social import. Therefore the penetration of social considerations can be expected to be more clearly visible. For example, the coincidence of the social requirements of controlling deviant behavior and the aims of psychiatric treatment is necessarily close.

Third, psychiatry, as a social science, is close in subject matter and outlook to sociology itself; and this is a tactical advantage to the sociologist of science. He will sometimes have a headstart for sufficiently understanding. the scientific field he wants to scrutinize, as contrasted with the task of mastering some field totally unrelated to sociology.

Fourth, psychiatry, like psychology, is also closely related to the natural sciences through biology. Therefore, the sociologist will have opportunities to study at least peripherally the natural science implicit in psychiatry as a biological field.

---

choanalytic Research, New York: Basic Books, 1960. For a general statement on the science of human behavior, see the valuable book by Abraham Kaplan, *The Conduct of Inquiry*, San Francisco: Chandler, 1964. See also, William P. McEwen, *The Problem of Social Scientific Knowledge*, Totowa, N. J.: Bedminster Press, 1963.

Fifth, psychiatry as a relatively undeveloped science is not as technically forbidding for a social scientist as, say, physics.[14] Thus the sociological study of psychiatry actually fits a general trend in the sociology of knowledge. The early studies in the field of the sociology of knowledge examined ideas that could scarcely be called science at all—ideas of society that were part of the layman's common fund of social theory.[15] Much later, social scientists turned their searchlights upon their own special-ized disciplines and upon natural science.[16] When the sociologist first began to examine the natural sciences, he ordinarily restricted himself to fairly nontechnical matters. For example, in one of the earliest studies Merton reviewed merely the topics of the papers presented at the Royal Society meetings in seventeenth-century England; he demonstrated in this way that the scientists did not confine themselves to tasks that had immediate practical implications for England at that time—that is, he was able to show that the broad needs of society did not always choose the scientists' topics.[17] (Of course, his results did not demonstrate the absence of any social influences on the choice of topic.)

In summary, there are a number of features of psychiatry that make it especially useful as a field for the sociologist of science to study. By no means do I intend to suggest that the sociology of science must begin with studies of such disciplines as psy-chiatry; I only wish to have persuaded the reader that psychiatry is one scientific discipline that is worth studying in this context.

---

14. Of course the use of its propositions in the care and treatment of mental patients is another matter. Certainly a mere academic understand-ing, no matter how easily it may be attained, is no preparation for a psychiatric career—a fact which complicates psychiatric training no end.

15. For example, Karl Mannheim, *op. cit.*

16. For a study of psychologists' orientations, see Nicholas Pastore, *The Nature-Nurture Controversy*, New York: Columbia University Press, 1949. For sociology, see C. Wright Mills, "The Professional Ideology of the So-cial Pathologists," *Amer. J. Sociol.* (1943) 49: 165-80; Robert A. Nisbet, "The French Revolution and the Rise of Sociology," *Amer. J. Sociol.* (1943) 49: 156-64; and Nisbet, "Conservatism and Sociology," *Amer. J. Sociol.* (1952) 58: 167-75. See also Warren Bennis, "The Social Scientist as Re-search Entrepreneur: A Case Study," *Social Problems* (1955) 2: 44-49. Werner Stark, *The Fundamental Forms of Social Thought*, London: Rout-ledge and Kegan Paul, 1962. For a study of anthropology, see Alfred G. Smith, "The Dionysian Innovation," *Amer. Anthro.* (1964) 66: 251-65.

17. See Merton, "Science and Economy," *op. cit.*

Two

A RESEARCH HOSPITAL HOLDS
A BUILT-IN CONFLICT
FOR ITS STAFF

NOWHERE IN THE United States and probably throughout the world is there a more impressive architectural symbol of man's struggle against disease by the rational mastery techniques of twentieth-century science than the University Medical Research Center, the hospital and research complex that is the setting for this study. The great Y of the towering red-brick-and-pale-stone building rears up from a green and rolling plateau, its fourteen stories rising into the clean air of a small bright suburb of a vital metropolis and visible for miles around, like a fortress commanding the town. The long stem of the Y contains the wards for the patients who are studied in this setting. In over-all space, the Center is surely the size of a fifteen-hundred-bed hospital, but all this space is designed to house no more than three to five hundred patients. The rest of the enormous structure—especially the wings, one face of the stem, and even three basement levels— houses the equipment, libraries, animal kennels, laboratories, and offices of a staff for whose research efforts the building was constructed.

The psychiatric program is allocated approximately three floors, just above the main, ground floor. These provide an extensive area for six wards or nursing units of double and single rooms, enough for ten to twenty patients in each unit, depending upon how the staff wish to use it. In addition, there are the rows and corridors of offices and laboratory alcoves. Each room is flexibly transferable in function from a standard office for two or three people to a laboratory housing a ton or more of intricate equipment; or rooms can be opened into each other for more space. The walls of every room conceal pipes that make available anywhere such routine laboratory resources as oxygen, distilled water, ordinary hot and cold water, steam, and extra-heavy electric current. A panel can be removed from almost any wall to connect equipment to an outlet; or within a matter of an hour the outlets can be closed over and replaced with a fitted new panel. All the office areas in the whole building are constructed as modules with standardized, interchangeable parts. Thus, complete changes in research goals and programs are physically possible with minimal effort.

As the Center neared completion, men of national and international reputation in medicine or in the various sciences took up posts of leadership to gather a staff together, to organize technical equipment procurement and installation, to initiate the clinical operations and the research program, and so on, in order to begin a vast new push against medical disease and disorder. Among these men was a noted physician, who became the director of clinical research in psychiatry. He began to recruit the nucleus of a staff and to acquaint them with his philosophy of research and care of mentally ill patients.

The research director made it clear that he had no intention of directing anyone's research but his own. He sought competent workers simply on the basis of strong interest in any of the possible solutions to the mysteries of mental illness. For this purpose he recruited psychiatrists trained in biochemistry, or psychoanalysis, or neurology, and so on, who wanted an opportunity to test their ideas and develop new ones for the understanding and alleviation of mental illness. To these psychiatrists were added nonmedical specialists of every order. So far as the director was concerned, the specific allocation of the resources—supporting staff, bed space, office and laboratory space, and so on—for particular research projects was to be determined by the staff as a group, not just by him as director of the program. Furthermore, he recognized that the initial phases of the program for many months, perhaps even for a period stretching into a couple of years, would be limited primarily to the task of getting an organization going, getting a completely new hospital into full, smooth operation. He assured everyone who joined the staff that his expectations of their research productivity was conditioned by this fact and that his main goal—and, he hoped, theirs —was simply to get a good clinical operation going as a foundation for future research activity. Anything additional would be a special and unexpected dividend in the beginning period, so far as he was concerned.

The Medical Research Center as a social institution posed a special task for the director and his staff. After all, it was not organized merely to provide another clinical facility for people who were sick and needed help. It was not just another hospital in which, when the opportunity could be seized, a staff member might squeeze some time out for research. The Center was specifically established as a research facility, and part of its resources would be a clinical program so that the investigation of illness and health could proceed by observation and experimentation with patients who agreed to serve as research subjects. To make clear to everyone the ethical values guiding the Center, formal announcements, publications, and public speeches by the top staff emphasized that in any research conducted in the hospital, the patient's welfare would come first. Thus, explicit in the institutional charter was the priority of therapeutic values over research values insofar as any work on patients was concerned. Also explicit was the expectation that the hospital was not organized for service purposes but as a means of conducting research. The research director, his staff, and all the physicians in all the other programs had the task of somehow dovetailing the research goal and the treatment goal in their activity as clinical researchers. Accepting a post at the Center posed the task for each physician of how he was concurrently to conduct research and treatment— to combine the two functions which his role in the organization required him to perform. For the worker at the Center, as for any clinical researcher, the task of combining research and treatment and of resolving any conflict between them was crucial to the performance of the role of research physician.

As a staff member of the Center, I soon found myself discussing this problem with my colleagues. I was a social scientist, not a psychiatrist, but I had worked as a clinician, and I felt myself immediately responsive to what troubled the physicians as they talked. It is such an obvious problem and, of course, physicians in all specialties have struggled with it in years past. As a matter of fact, the conflict between the demands of scientific development and the responsibility to one's patients marked the great crisis in medicine in the nineteenth century when a modern scientific outlook invaded the rather hit-and-miss medical field. Especially in France, where modern medicine was born, the medical fraternity and the public at large railed at the innovating physicians who rejected tradition and prejudice and sought to give medicine a scientific underpinning through concentrated research. Nihilists they were called, because they did not believe in any of the current remedies for the sick, remedies that others were willing to use on faith, on authority, on prejudice, on whim, or whatever.

There is a striking short story written in the nineteenth century by the Frenchman, Villiers de L'Isle-Adam, in which a scientist-physician is savagely criticized because he preferred to sacrifice patients in the service of science.[1] Even earlier, in America, Nathaniel Hawthorne wrote several wonderful stories redolent of Faustian brimstone, linking the medical scientist with mysterious forces of evil. We have come a long way since then. In most of the world's societies, the research physician is encouraged as well as respected. We are more likely to think of Lewis's Arrowsmith than of Hawthorne's Rappacini. But great acceptance has not changed the research physician's task, how-

---

1. P. A. M. de Villiers de L'Isle-Adam, "The Heroism of Doctor Hallidonhill," E. O'Neil, tr., in Max Lieber and Blanche Colton Williams, eds., *Great Stories of All Nations*, New York: Tudor, 1933.

ever much easier it has made it. In his own research wards, with his own patients, he periodically faces the conflict between what he might do as a physician and what he might do as a scientist. He can only escape that conflict by slipping away from the bedside of the patient forever into the recesses of his laboratory, or by caring for patients only and foregoing the questioning, searching frame of mind that has brought medical care and treatment to its present height.

For each physician at the University Medical Research Center, taking a job meant taking on a set of anxieties and conflicts that were as surely built into the very structure of the Center as any of its pipes, steel beams, and conduits. As a participant observer, I soon gathered a considerable number of observations of this fact quite naturally in the course of my regular work. Later, however, I began to make a more systematic effort to see how the conflict appeared in the various research projects that were going on. I made rather intensive case studies of a number of projects, attending their meetings, interviewing the staff and patients involved, going through the records, both clinical and research, that were routinely kept at the hospital.

Most of these projects took place on the first psychiatric ward opened at the Center. From the beginning, this ward was designed to be a locked ward for psychotic patients who were to receive intensive therapy of a psychoanalytic orientation. The nursing unit in which these patients were to be housed was not really a ward in the usual sense, for it offered comfortable, almost luxurious single and double rooms for no more than ten or twelve patients. Other wards on the psychiatric service, as they came into operation, followed much the same pattern.

Perhaps the best introduction to the crucial conflict faced by the research psychiatrists is a sample from my notes of their conversations with each other at a group meeting several weeks before this first psychiatric ward opened, during the first year of the Center. Table 1 introduces the participants, all psychiatrists, in that meeting.

Table 1: Personae of Staff Meeting [2]

Dr. *Lowe* Director of all clinical research activities in psychiatry; also trained in psychoanalysis, and biology (Ph.D.); interested in intensive studies of psychotherapeutic interview; formal or informal consultant with The First LSD Research; generally laissez-faire in research attitude, but demanding high clinical standards.

Dr. *Bates* Ward administrator of initial psychiatric ward; psychoanalytic psychiatry; interested in content analysis of therapeutic interview; as ward administrator responsible for ward program for patients on The Trade-Off, Therapy Observation, and The First LSD Research, but especially figuring in the latter project; unanimously selected by the other psychiatrists to administer the first ward on which their patients would be lodged.

Dr. *Dirainey* Senior staff member; psychoanalysis, psychology; interested in psychotherapy with psychotics; assisted on observations for The First LSD Research, but later directed his own project, The Permissive Ward; more definite about own research plans and goals than most staff members.

Dr. *Hall* Administrative assistant to Dr. Lowe; eclectic training and experience in psychiatry; interested in studies of patient interaction; temporarily working on The Trade-Off project; no definite research plans, tended to shift interests.

Dr. *Kimball* Junior staff member; in psychoanalytic training; interested in family relations of patients; participant in The Trade-Off; initially saw this research experience primarily as a training opportunity to learn clinical care procedures.

Dr. *Navarre* Junior staff member; in psychoanalytic training, social science (Ph.D.); interested in conceptualization of the psychotherapy process; participant in The Trade-Off; sought after by other staff members as consultant on their projects.

Dr. *Oxford* Junior staff member; in psychoanalytic training, also biology and psychology; interested in psychosomatic studies; stayed at Center only a few months.

---

2. All names of these psychiatrists are, of course, fictional, and certain details of the professional background of staff members have been changed, interchanged, and so on, to maintain anonymity and still give a sense of the individuality of personnel and an impression of the range and variety of psychiatric staff. Information given includes, in this order, staff post; special training; special research interests; participation on projects to be described; and one special feature of professional career or background or attitude toward psychiatric research.

Dr. Richards Unit chief; neurophysiology, biochemistry; interested in pharmacological influences on behavior; co-director of The First LSD Research; received three special awards within the first two years.

Dr. Seldes Junior staff member; in psychoanalytic training; interested in conceptualization of psychotherapeutic process; participant in The Trade-Off; came into medicine and psychiatry after a successful career in city government.

Dr. Steiger Senior staff member; psychoanalysis, social work; interested in alcoholism and drug addiction rehabilitation; not connected with any specific projects to be described, but became the therapist for a patient on The First LSD Research; resisted efforts of colleagues to get him to assume various leadership functions.

Dr. Thorpe Unit chief; psychoanalysis; interested in psychotherapy with schizophrenics and in psychopharmacology; co-director of The First LSD Research; from time to time was offered a hospital or pavillion for his own research by one or another university.

The meeting was called by Dr. Lowe to discuss the development of the clinical and research policy for this first ward. At the point at which I excerpt from my notes, Dr. Richards had raised a question for group discussion: *Suppose someone else wanted to admit a new patient; would it ever happen that in order to make room, the first patient would be discharged or transferred against the wishes of his physician?*

DR. HALL: I wouldn't relinquish the right to keep a patient in therapy. I wouldn't like to have to decide to relinquish a patient in favor of substituting another one for a research project. Before taking on a patient for therapy, I would have to know ahead of time what the situation will be.

DR. KIMBALL (*who had just arrived on the staff*): Who decides?

DR. RICHARDS: I raised the question in order to definitely establish the rejection of it. I would suggest a general policy that no one can force the therapist to give up a patient—even a decision by the entire group.

DR. HALL: In general, I agree, but the case supervision might suggest otherwise [that is, that discharge would be best for the patient even if the therapist did not agree].

DR. RICHARDS: This is like academic freedom.

DR. NAVARRE: We have greater freedom financially and academically [than in most academic medical settings].

DR. DIRAINEY (*whose work eventually required an entire ward*): But you don't have bed freedom [that is, there are only a limited number of beds for patients].

DR. LOWE (*speaking as the director*): Even better ideas [for another research project] can't force the discarding of previous patients against the therapist's wishes.

DR. NAVARRE: But suppose a beginning project takes up a number of patient beds?

(*Dr. Navarre answers his own question almost in concert with Dr. Lowe, both of them laughing and causing general laughter, as they say*): The idea is to tie up beds early.

DR. HALL: A safety valve is that the other part of the floor will be open in about six months.

DR. OXFORD (*who later made it clear that he did not plan on staying in his job for more than a year*): A research coordinator is needed to decide on priorities.

DR. HALL: Well, the mechanism we have now is the group.

DR. OXFORD: This is unwieldy.

DR. DIRAINEY: It has its virtues though. I would be afraid of a research coordinator.

DR. LOWE: He might become a research dictator?

DR. RICHARDS: The individual should have the power of veto.

DR. OXFORD: We don't know what the demands [for bed space] would be, yet.

DR. SELDES: We are misplacing the emphasis on the nature of the patient as to whether he would be suitable for research. Any patient would be okay because the research focus is on the patient-doctor processes.

DR. NAVARRE: It does make a difference because there are different processes to different degrees in different patients.

DR. RICHARDS (*apparently satisfied with the results of the discussion*): There are no conflicts because we don't even know what projects there are. They'll work out as soon as we know what projects there will be.

It is clear that in this meeting staff members were working out questions about where decision-making power lay in the event of competing plans by different staff members. But for purposes of my study, it is important to note that the issue around which the discussion focused was the integration of

research goals and treatment goals.[3] Different points of view on
this issue are evident. Dr. Richards, for example, felt that treatment goals—as seen by the individual therapist—should take
precedence over research goals; he did not believe that there
would be any unresolvable conflict between the two sets of goals,
once all staff were clear about what research they were going
to do. Dr. Navarre anticipated conflicts between research goals
and therapeutic goals in which research perhaps should take
precedence, and he and others attempted to press the issue of
how such conflicts might be resolved. Drs. Richards, Hall, and
Lowe considered the issue settled by the notion of allowing the
individual therapist to decide in terms of his own patients. Again,
Dr. Seldes saw no possible issue because he viewed research as
synonymous with treatment.

In summary, there were three general positions taken on the
issue in this meeting: (a) there can be no conflict between
research and treatment; (b) therapy goals take precedence over
research goals; and (c) perhaps research goals should take
precedence over therapy goals in some situations. In this meeting,
planning the ward policy led to imagining future dilemmas,
which in turn led to the staff members' resolving in fantasy what
actions they might take to combine research and treatment. What
later happened to these staff members as they tried to find a
means of adjustment to the social demands of their jobs is the
burden of this study.

A meeting held a few days later gave the staff a further opportunity to face the problem of meshing research and treatment
goals and to see where each other's interests lay. Most of those
present indicated that their main interest was in doing psycho-

---

3. I have abstracted a single issue—how do social forces operate in science—out of all possible issues in the description of events at the Center.
And within the boundaries of that single issue, I have selected here only
one of the many social forces that might be analytically abstracted—the
conflict between treatment and research goals. The fact that I have made
these selections certainly means that I consider them very important in
what went on at the Center. It does not mean that my selections are the
only important ones that might be made in trying to explain those events.

therapy, mainly with schizophrenic patients, with the intention of studying the treatment process itself or the psychodynamics of the patient as they appeared in the course of therapy. Dr. Lowe (whose main work as a psychiatrist had been in the study and treatment of schizophrenics) presumably found no objections to these plans; he raised questions only in regard to plans presented on two projects in which the treatment itself was not the central aspect of the research. An extract from this meeting illustrates the kind of interchange that occurred around one of these actual clinical research proposals: [4]

DR. OXFORD: My interest depends upon the opening of a psychosomatic ward. I am interested in the interchangeability of psychosis and psychosomatic diseases: the possibility of inducing psychosis as a substitute for the psychosomatic trouble. Then you can treat the psychosis—because the psychosomatic problems are almost impossible to deal with. I will also be available to do therapy with [research] patients as the needs of the service might require.

DR. LOWE: I am opposed to this point of view in the precipitation of psychosis.

(Dr. Dirainey and Dr. Bates express their agreement with Dr. Lowe and their disagreement with Dr. Oxford's view.)

DR. RICHARDS (supporting Dr. Oxford): I think you have to accept the risk of this kind of approach.

DR. DIRAINEY: It depends upon whether you are confident to help afterwards.

DR. RICHARDS: One's confidence is often misplaced so that is no criterion.

DR. NAVARRE: It depends upon the illness. I did this once with an ulcerative colitis patient . . . (mentions similar work done by another psychiatrist).[5]

DR. BATES: Well, his work is to be followed up [as to whether the patients remained improved]. Maybe it wasn't so good.

---

4. The discussion of the other questioned proposal will be presented in a later context.

5. I use three dots to indicate that I have omitted words (less than one sentence) in quoted materials, and three asterisks to indicate an omission of one sentence or more. Occasionally other sorts of symbols, such as dashes at the end of a sentence, appear in the original material, and I have maintained these, even though I do not know whether they indicate a trailing off, a pause, or some other nonverbal communication. This occurs

Further direct discussion of the project and its problems was precluded by a suggestion by Dr. Hall that they continue to hear from the others what each wanted to do. Throughout the rest of the meeting there were occasional disapproving references to the idea of inducing psychosis, and it is interesting to note that after a general discussion on ways of studying the psychotherapeutic interview, Dr. Oxford told his colleagues, "I will be glad to be a guinea pig for the others to look at—for group discussions of the therapy without the therapist participating [as had been suggested to prevent undesirable feedback to the therapy]." Dr. Oxford, as it were, offered up himself as a sacrifice to the group as a means of indicating his solidarity with them, despite his unpopular research proposal. At any rate, it was clear that at this time most of those present were fairly definitely committed to a general preference for therapeutic values over any possible conflicting research values, although there was no unanimity.

I have presented these excerpts from the psychiatrists' meetings to illustrate the kind of concern about research versus treatment that they experienced—in this instance, before they actually began work with patients. If the hospital as a research center presented the staff member with a built-in job problem, then the staff member had to construct some sort of work adjustment to fit around this problem. This adjustment could not dissipate the troublesome situation; it could only provide the physician with a way to live nimbly with it. Since the hospital was so new, there were none of the traditional ways that institutions always construct, a little at a time, for their members to live by. The new staff members in the new building were just beginning, consciously and unconsciously, the process of creating those ways.

---

only in recordings made by others, such as physicians' treatment notes, nurses' charting notes, and so on. When these materials contain unexplained dots that I have not inserted, I have so indicated. I use brackets for my own, later insertions into quoted materials. Parentheses within quotations are in the original; or are punctuation supplied by me; or, in interviews or conferences, enclose my own italicized comments, added at a later date.

Analyzing the psychiatrist's dilemma and his adjustment to it in sociological terms requires conceptualizing the dilemma and its sequelae as a role conflict—that is, as a conflict between two competing obligations within the organized structure of his activity as a psychiatrist. The social solutions available to the person acting in the role of clinical research psychiatrist can be seen as varieties of activity that either integrate or quarantine the competing obligations in the context of a role definition constructed in relations with the patients. In the course of "The First LSD Research," a project at the Center, the doctors and their patients evolved ways of behaving that can be described by this conceptualization. The physicians adopted two styles of work. The first failed; it did not provide them with a way of doing their work and balancing the demands of treatment and of research; and so they had to work out another. Further studies of other projects showed me that (with the variable I looked at) there were in all probably only four possible work styles—four definitions of the role of the clinical research psychiatrist— that might be adopted or evolved in the course of a project. And yet even a choice among these over-all styles of adjustment to the dilemma was not enough to allow the physician to proceed without further trouble.

Whatever role definition the psychiatrist chooses as his basic solution to the chronic conflict, he still faces recurrent acute eruptions of the conflict in day-to-day relations with the patient —situations in which what the physician wants for research purposes competes with the patient's interests. That is, the styles of work adjustment offer a general solution but cannot provide for every contingency. The acute eruptions of conflict call out secondary social responses, directed toward a resolution of the immediate conflict but, by protecting the psychiatrist's chosen role style, also operating indirectly to assist the psychiatrist to continue on in his work. The protective or role-maintaining techniques comprise a rich range of interpersonal responses such as "temporizing," "extenuating," "invoking common values," "reconceptualizing the situation," and so on—all being ways to smooth out the conflict in the relationship with the patient.

The history of the LSD project offers a glimpse of some of these secondary maneuvers, but again, others were visible in the histories of the other projects. These techniques and the basic role-styles may be significant in themselves as sociological events, but what is especially important is their influence as a part of the context of the scientific work going on. I shall try to describe quite thoroughly the different role definitions or styles of the psychiatrists and the different role-maintaining techniques that they used, but I do so in order to see their possible effects as constituents of the human scientific process.

Three

THE FIRST LSD
PROJECT BEGINS

DURING THE TIME that the Medical Research Center was being completed, lysergic acid diethylamide (LSD-25) achieved widespread attention in and out of psychiatry as a drug that induced hallucinatory and other psychotic-like behavior. Discovered in 1943, LSD-25 did not come into prominence in the medical literature until some time after the close of World War II. Many investigators felt that it held a clue to schizophrenia, since the symptoms it induced looked like schizophrenic behavior. Some even felt that the body processes of schizophrenics must manufacture this substance, which then caused their odd behavior. Obviously, thinking about this drug was confused, and definitive studies had yet to be made.[1] It is not surprising then that one

---

1. Enough is now known to conclude that LSD-25 has no intrinsic relation to the biochemical antecedents of schizophrenia. Its current professional use as an adjunct to psychotherapy (to encourage verbalization by the patient) poses difficulties, since side effects are not well known and possibly dangerous, especially for suicide risks. Some psychiatrists have noted also that it can engender such high anxiety as to encourage reticence rather than talkativeness. See Charles Savage, "LSD: A Clinical-Psychological Study," *Amer. J. Psychiat.* (1952) 108: 896-900. Savage's early studies also suggested that "where any response at all to the LSD could be demonstrated, anxiety was present." Charles Savage, "Variations in Ego Feeling Induced by LSD," *Psychoan. Rev.* (1955) 42: 1-16. However, he, like most of those who continue to work with this substance, maintains that it can be useful. For a survey of this and other views, see David Solomon, ed.,

of the earliest projects to get underway at the Medical Research Center was a study of LSD in relation to schizophrenia.

Two of the original patients admitted to this first ward were each scheduled to receive a series of LSD infusions during the course of their psychotherapy. After a series of complicated events, the project was terminated with only one dose having been administered to only one of the patients. Thereafter both patients refused to take the drug, precipitating a crisis on the project. The therapists for each of the patients recognized that the drug was an extremely disturbing substance, but how could they do their research if the patients refused to cooperate?

I first learned about the dilemma of the two psychiatrists from a third psychiatrist who worked on the same ward as they. The issue was so clear that it was obvious that I should follow the course of events on this project to see how an acute conflict between research goals and therapy goals would be resolved and how the process of the research was affected in the resolution of the conflict. So that the reader can follow what happened

LSD: The Consciousness-Expanding Drug, New York: G. P. Putnam's Sons, 1964.

Use of the drug in the United States is now specifically confined to medical experimenters, except for illicit use "for kicks," or for "overcoming spiritual poverty," or for "transcendence and a new beginning." See Jane Dunlap, pseud., *Exploring Inner Space: Personal Experiences Under LSD-25,* New York: Harcourt, Brace and World, 1961. Constance A. Newland, *My Self and I,* New York: Coward-McCann, 1963. These reports describe the euphoric effects of the drug, and there is at least one journal (*The Psychedelic Review*) as well as various organizations, concerned with establishing and defining the positive effects of LSD and similar substances. However, the general medical and scientific opinion is cautious if not negative toward the so-called psychotomimetic drugs, the substances that induce schizophrenia-like states. See an editorial warning by Roy R. Grinker, "Lysergic Acid Diethylamide," *Arch. Gen. Psychiat.* (1963) 8: 425. This journal publishes many LSD research studies. Conclusions from a review of the literature are authoritatively summarized in Jonathan O. Cole and Martin M. Katz, "The Psychotomimetic Drugs: An Overview," *J.A.M.A.* (1964) 187: 758-761. (Reprinted in the Solomon compendium.) In considering my report on the first LSD research project at the University Medical Research Center, the reader should recognize that I am describing an exploratory project conducted some years before much of the research cited here.

with more sophistication than I could muster at the time, I will provide two guides before presenting my observations in detail. The first is an analysis of remarks recorded from an early meeting in which the LSD project in its initial outlines was briefly discussed and which foreshadowed much that was to come, as I viewed it later. The second is a quick overview of the entire history of the project. In the light of these two frames of reference, I will be better able to communicate the significance of the information provided me by the clinical records, the interviews I conducted, and the meetings I observed.

An Early Discussion of the Project

During the preliminary phases of organization of the psychiatric program of the Medical Research Center, occasional informal staff conferences were held to discuss the future structure of the research program. At one of these meetings, for each other's information all the staff members presented their provisional plans for their individual work.[2] Undoubtedly the LSD project had not been fully formulated by this time, but Drs. Thorpe and Richards, the principal investigators in the research (see Table 2), were definite about their interest in one of the effects of the drug, depersonalization.[3]

---

2. A part of this same meeting has been described in Chapter Two.

3. Depersonalization means that the person experiences himself as detached from his body or as otherwise in nonhuman form. An end-of-year report on the project, prepared a few months later, reads: "Depersonalization is a symptom complex characterized by confusion regarding the relation of the self to the outer world, and difficulty in determining where the self leaves off and the rest of the world begins. It may be observed at the beginning of almost any emotional disorder, and also in the course of such organic disturbances as epilepsy, temporal lobe dysfunction, toxic states, and rarely as a disease syndrome itself. Further study of this syndrome should lead to a better understanding of how the normal personality develops; how the individual establishes a clear boundary between himself and his environment; and of the stresses that interfere with this process. It is expected that an investigation of clinical and experimental depersonalization being carried on by Drs. Richards and Thorpe will throw light on mechanisms by which either emotional or biochemical disturbances can lead to identical psycho-

At the meeting they told their colleagues how they planned to conduct the research. It must be emphasized that what was at stake at this meeting was not actual events in the conduct of clinical research, but merely plans. Yet despite the fact that the group was reviewing ideas and not events in the conduct of research, the members can be observed to be struggling with the conflict that was built into their work roles. In discussing the project, staff members implictly took certain positions on the task they faced. Some of these positions constituted a general solution to the built-in work conflict; others seemed to be rather minor tactics in the solution of the research-therapy dilemma. It will be useful to view the major strategical solutions to the research-therapy conflict as definitions of the work role of the clinical researcher, while the variety of minor solutions seem better conceptualized as ways in which the work role definition was and can be defended.

Table 2: *Main Participants in the First LSD Research Project*

Co-directors
  Dr. Richards   Psychiatrist; special training and experience in physiological research; psychotherapist for Miss Burton.
  Dr. Thorpe   Psychiatrist; special training and experience in psychoanalysis; psychotherapist for Mr. Pickett.
Patients
  Miss Mary Burton   Formerly a department store employee; came to Center from out-patient treatment at a near-by family clinic; in therapy with Dr. Richards first, later with Dr. Steiger; one of the two patients originally admitted for The First LSD Project.

---

pathology. A patient [Mr. Pickett] whose illness is characterized mainly by depersonalization is being studied to determine how depersonalization develops, to what extent it serves as a protective mechanism, how such a mechanism is learned, and what types of stress produce it.

"It has already been demonstrated by the investigators and others that depersonalization can be induced by minute doses (ten one-millionths of a gram) of the synthetic ergot derivative lysergic acid diethylamide. Depersonalization thus induced lasts three to twelve hours and is free of harmful effects to the individual. Thus it is possible to study in great detail and in ideal circumstances a symptom complex which ordinarily takes a lifetime to develop."

Mr. Lawrence Pickett Former Navy enlisted man; came to Center from near-by state mental hospital; in therapy with Dr. Thorpe; one of the two patients originally admitted for The First LSD Project.

Others

Dr. Bates Psychiatrist; administrator for ward to which the two patients were admitted for research and treatment; responsible for all matters of ward life except specific psychotherapy.

Dr. Dirainey Psychiatrist; special training and experience in psychotherapy with psychotics; agreed as favor to the project investigators to make observations of the patients while they were under the influence of LSD.

Dr. Lowe Psychiatrist; director of the research psychiatry program at the Center; served The First LSD Project as an occasional consultant.

Dr. Steiger Psychiatrist; special training and experience in psychoanalytic psychotherapy; took Miss Burton as a patient, on transfer from Dr. Richards.

The following is extracted from notes made during a staff meeting on September 21, the first year.[4]

DR. THORPE (*co-director of LSD Project*): I am rounding up some people who are depersonalized. My original plan calls for four patients.

DR. OXFORD (*a psychiatrist studying psychosomatic problems*): You are not interested in using a whole ward for your project?

DR. THORPE: No, because there are not that many beds, and others might want beds.

DR. OXFORD: Are you going to do the therapy with the patients on the project?

DR. THORPE: I would with two only. I have discussed this with Lowe.

DR. LOWE (*director of the entire clinical research group*): Would you continue on with them in therapy after you got enough material on depersonalization?

DR. THORPE: I anticipate a longitudinal study, so yes.

---

4. All lengthy quotations from my data will hereafter be dated. "First Year" refers to the initial year in the development of the total research program of the Center; "Second Year" is of course the following year, and so on. Except where otherwise indicated, all quotations from records of meetings or interviews are made from my notes taken on the occasion and transcribed within a day or two.

I would expect to get turnover, bed-space for further patients, through discharge upon improvement, I hope.

DR. BATES (*later chosen by the group to run the first research ward*): Would you keep on with them as outpatients?

DR. DIRAINEY: Then the patient is here for therapy, and research is secondary?

DR. NAVARRE (*another research psychiatrist*): On what basis would you transfer the patient to outpatient status or to another hospital—cure or the end of the research?

DR. THORPE (*to Dr. Navarre*): I would entertain both considerations. It is hard to estimate cure.

DR. LOWE: Whether or not the patient stays in this hospital until he is cured depends upon the purposes of the ward—as all of you here want to set it up.

(*A short technical discussion follows about the relationship between depersonalization and degree of illness. Presumably this might enter into the question of discharge of the research patient who showed depersonalization.*)

DR. BATES (*impatiently*): This whole question revolves around doing research or doing therapy.

(*The group moves to the future interests of other staff members.*)

This short exchange among the staff around Dr. Thorpe's discussion of his plans provides a view of the general apprehension about the potential conflict between research and treatment. More importantly it illustrates one choice of a primary means of resolving the conflict and at least two minor ways of resolving that conflict. It also indicates the especially strong sensitivity of the staff to their obligations as therapists. The first indication of a problem occurs in Dr. Thorpe's response to Dr. Oxford's question, "Are you going to do the therapy with the patients on the project?" Dr. Thorpe replies that he will do so only for two patients and defends his plan by citing his discussion of this with Dr. Lowe, the program director. Superficially, it was simply a request from Dr. Oxford for information from Dr. Thorpe, but the latter's response indicates the touchiness of the subject, for he answers by referring to an authoritative standard—Dr. Lowe's opinions—which presumably would legitimize the plan for therapy. In other words, Dr. Thorpe resolves any implied conflict by invoking the judgment of a person who is present and whom everyone respects.⁵ The problem did not end there, however. A second implied conflict was presented to Dr. Thorpe when Dr. Lowe asked whether he would continue the therapy even after the research was completed. Dr. Thorpe's solution to this potential difficulty is to point out the congruence of his research aims and his therapeutic obligations in the very design of the project as "a longitudinal study."

There are illustrated, then, in Dr. Thorpe's response to his colleagues' questions two of the minor, transitory solutions to the research-therapy conflict. One (reference to the authority of Dr. Lowe) is a purely social technique, invoking a consensus of values in the staff, and the other (the longitudinal design) is the social use of a technical research tactic. These sorts of minor adjustments and solutions to the research-therapy problem can be utilized by a psychiatrist who has adopted any one of the possible general orientations to the problem of conducting clinical research. That is, different conceptions of how to operate on the job may be defended by the identical type of minor job adjustment.

In Dr. Thorpe's instance, the general adjustment to the potential conflict included the acceptance of both sets of obligations with the two patients and the expectation that both sets of obligations definitely would be integrated in his interactions with the patients. When his assumption of that general solution appeared to be challenged by the questions of his colleagues, he defended it with the two minor tactics, by reference to Lowe's authority and by specifying his research design. These tactics thus served double duty. They met the immediate eruption of an apparent conflict between Thorpe's research and his treatment obligations, and they also helped Dr. Thorpe maintain his choice

---

5. One is especially likely to interpret this response as somewhat defensive, in view of the fact that Dr. Lowe was present at this discussion. There is quite a difference between invoking authority when the authority is dead, like Freud, or at least absent from the encounter, and invoking authority when the authority is a witness to the encounter. The latter invocation is much stronger, for an issue is apt to reach resolution on the spot.

of a general posture on the conflict—that the two goals could and would be integrated in his relations with patients.

It seems clear that in the staff interchange with Dr. Thorpe it is not just Dr. Thorpe's personal solution to the role conflict that is being elicited; rather, all the staff members are galvanized by Dr. Lowe's question about whether Dr. Thorpe would continue to provide therapy after the research was completed. Dr. Thorpe's answer is a side-step, in a sense, as well as a reasonable solution, for he rejects the very possibility of a conflict between his research goals and his therapy obligations by showing that they are parallel, at least in time, according to his project plans. Dr. Thorpe's colleagues, however, are not reassured by his answer—not because it does not solve the potential conflict for Dr. Thorpe but because it cannot do service for any and all conflicts that they themselves might encounter. Three of the other psychiatrists (two of whom, incidentally, were to figure centrally in his research problems) pepper Dr. Thorpe with questions that reveal their recognition of a basic issue at stake. Dr. Dirainey generalizes the issue, feeling it necessary to get a clarification of policy. He asks: "Then the patient is here for therapy and research is secondary?" His aim to obtain a definite reassurance that patient welfare comes first (despite the clear statements to that effect in the public announcements of the Center, both written and spoken, and despite Dr. Lowe's often reiterated statement that he was first interested in a good, going clinical operation) indicates the uncertainty and confusion in the group and the lack of usable guides for action. Dr. Dirainey's question as well as the remark by Dr. Bates that closes this quotation from the meeting record ("This whole question revolves around doing research or doing therapy") establish the fact that the conflict is explicitly recognized by the group.

What the group was striving towards in this series of exchanges can be described as some sort of over-all or global solution to the potential conflict between research and treatment in a role definition. They appeared to be seeking a generalized pattern of the hierarchy of obligations that could constitute the definition of the professional role of research psychiatrist. Since they were dealing in anticipatory terms, in fantasy rather than actual work situations, it was particularly difficult for them to come to some conclusive definition. Without a standardized and institutionalized set of guides, each researcher, as a matter of fact, had to construct his own definition of his role in the course of the work he undertook. So it was that a variety of organized solutions—generalized role definitions—came to be constructed in practice as the psychiatric program developed. The major solutions and the minor adjustments that occurred in the course of the LSD project—and their effect upon the scientific process —can be described better once a short history of the project has been presented.

A Short Project History of the First LSD Research

The first LSD research in the new hospital was carried out collaboratively by Dr. Richards and Dr. Thorpe (see Table 2). The interests and experience of the one complemented that of the other; moreover each had a secondary interest in the other's major area of work. Dr. Richards had spent some years in physiological and neurological research subsequent to his basic clinical training in psychiatry. Although he was the younger of the two psychiatrists, he had had considerable experience before coming to the Center. He was curious about the physiological concomitants of depersonalization. Dr. Thorpe, somewhat older, had undergone psychoanalytic training over a period of years after his basic training in psychiatry, and this had stimulated a research interest in the process of depersonalization so often found in the schizophrenic patients he had treated. He had experimented with LSD in work carried out before he came to the Center. In fact, he had not only administered it to patients and to selected normal persons (as an experimental control), he had also taken some himself to see its effects.

The two psychiatrists, as might be expected, divided up the

tasks in the research according to their complementary interests. Dr. Thorpe took most of the responsibility for clinical problems and their evaluation, and Dr. Richards was most concerned with assuring the proper physiological assessments. Yet each shared in all aspects of the work. For example, while Dr. Thorpe selected the patients to be studied, Dr. Richards concurred in their suitability and accepted responsibility for psychotherapy with one of them.

Two patients were originally selected for this study. Miss Mary Burton, an attractive, twenty-six-year-old former department store clerk, had applied for help at a nearby outpatient clinic. She had a history of treatment by several psychiatrists but she was still plagued with fears and anxieties. Dr. Thorpe talked to her after having read in the case history at the clinic that she had symptoms of depersonalization, and she expressed her willingness to be hospitalized at the Center. Although she could have managed with outpatient care—which she had requested— she was sufficiently passive that she gladly accepted the suggestion that she go into a hospital and give up the idea of employment during her treatment. The other patient was Mr. Lawrence Pickett, a patient from a nearby state hospital. Mr. Pickett had been in several private and public institutions in a long bout with intermittent psychotic symptoms. He had had a term of service in the Navy but had been discharged after a psychotic breakdown and had not worked much thereafter. He was about the same age as Miss Burton but he was obviously more disturbed, more prone to symptoms of depersonalization, and more in need of hospital care.

Miss Burton was very shy and retiring. She posed no problem for routine nursing care, but Mr. Pickett was an enigma to the staff at the Center. The nurses described him as alternately personable, ingratiating, exasperating, sarcastic, openly hostile, and assaultive. They had a good deal of trouble with him. Mr. Pickett went into psychotherapy with Dr. Thorpe when he came to the Center, and Dr. Richards took Miss Burton for psychotherapy. Both patients were hospitalized on the first ward that opened on the psychiatric service. It is interesting to note that

Mr. Pickett, the sicker of the two, was told before coming to the Center that "there would be drugs for research—though not for treatment." Miss Burton, who had not been hospitalized before coming to the Center, was not told anything about the projected use of experimental drugs until a few days before she was to take the LSD, long after she came to the Center.

Essentially, the research plan that Drs. Thorpe and Richards worked out was as follows. There would be an initial period in which the patients could become accustomed to the new surroundings and the nursing staff could become sufficiently acquainted with them as persons and as patients. The first course of LSD doses would then begin. The patients would get the drug on different alternate weeks. Each patient would be scheduled for a minimum of three administrations, including one placebo. Direct observations would be made of the patients' social and ·psychological behavior under the influence of the drug; and certain physiological tests, such as EEG (electroencephalographic tracings) and urinalysis, would be made.

Dr. Thorpe was the senior member of the team in clinical experience, and it fell to him to try to foresee any possible clinical problems in the research plan. He anticipated that the patients would show quite extreme reactions to the drug, and he undertook to work out some means of handling the possible clinical and administrative difficulties that the reactions might imply. With Dr. Richards' agreement, he arranged a conference with Dr. Bates, the ward administrator, and Dr. Lowe, the program director. Dr. Richards did not attend this conference, having told Dr. Thorpe that he would go along with anything Thorpe worked out. The organization of the project that developed from this conference, then, should be seen as the result of the efforts of the most clinically experienced of the two project directors, in consultation with others who were especially concerned and, at least in the case of Dr. Lowe, highly experienced in clinical administration.

In the discussion between Drs. Bates, Lowe, and Thorpe, there was a tacit assumption that the administration of the drug could be looked upon best as a nontherapy procedure. According to a working principle accepted at the Center, the ward administrator dealt with patients on all topics except therapy. It would therefore fall in the province of Dr. Bates as the ward administrator to approach the two patients and schedule the administration of the drug; if any questions arose about the administration of the drug, it was agreed that the ward administrator would handle these questions as the ward authority in the eyes of the patient. This split between therapy and ward administration had been adopted for all mental patients at the Center; it was an organizational procedure developed at an intensive treatment hospital that had been used as a model for the Center's psychiatric program.[6] Clinical experience in hospitals had indicated the usefulness of putting all decisions on passes, sedatives, visitors, and so on, in the hands of a ward physician and thereby relieving the psychotherapist of any such responsibilities. Thus in this conference, the new research problem of who was to schedule the drug with the patient was handled by applying a general consensus about the utility of the division of labor between administration and therapy, with the LSD looked upon as an administrative matter.

In this same meeting, the three participants decided that another staff member, to be selected, should make the actual observations on the patients' behavior, schedule the taking of urine specimens during the observation period, and so on. Also at this meeting or possibly later, Dr. Thorpe also decided that the ward administrator would present the LSD observer to the patients as the person who had planned and was centrally responsible for the research. This was agreed upon by the three physicians before they selected and asked Dr. Dirainey to be an observer. The separation of research and treatment would exist, of course, only in arrangements with the patient; in other respects Dr. Thorpe and Dr. Richards would actually conduct the research. Thus, Dr. Thorpe and Dr. Richards would be simultaneously pursuing goals of research and therapy, as their work role

---

6. See Alfred H. Stanton and Morris S. Schwartz, *The Mental Hospital,* New York: Basic Books, 1954. A bibliography lists the early descriptions of the role of the ward administrator.

required, but the two patients would be relating to the two doctors as therapists only.

After this meeting, Dr. Richards and Dr. Thorpe asked Dr. Dirainey, who was not actively engaged in any work on the ward at that time, to be the research observer. Dr. Dirainey was conducting preliminary studies with LSD at another hospital until a second psychiatric ward would be opened at the Center for a project that he was planning. This work kept him away from the Center and he was not well known by staff or patients. In future months he came to be regarded by most of the staff as the psychiatrist who was most obviously concerned with the feelings of his patients, a man especially sensitive to the compassionate requirements of the therapeutic relationship. It is noteworthy that a man who was so identified with patients' needs was selected by Dr. Richards and Dr. Thorpe to take on the role of the researcher in the patients' eyes. He agreed to carry out the direct observations of the patients' behavior immediately after the administration of the drug.

The insulation of the researcher function from the therapeutic function in the psychiatrists' relations with their patients was not complete. One research procedure, an EEG test to be taken shortly after the administration of the drug, would be conducted by Dr. Richards—since he was the only staff member on hand who had the necessary technical knowledge. This, together with the fact that Dr. Thorpe had actually told Mr. Pickett (though not Miss Burton) that research drugs would be given in the Center, assuredly linked the two physicians to the LSD on some level in the patients' minds. However, Dr. Bates was to present the drug and the necessary data-gathering procedures as the work of Dr. Dirainey. Dr. Dirainey agreed to make observations each Monday, the day on which the drug or placebo was to be given each week, until the necessary data was collected.

Though Miss Burton had not been informed before hospitalization of the plan to try out some experimental drugs during her hospital stay and was presumably less prepared for it, she was selected to be the first to receive the LSD. Dr. Bates approached her to take the first dose a few days before it was scheduled to be given. According to therapy notes Dr. Richards made at the time, she mentioned this to him in the therapy session: "I guess you know that Dr. Bates asked me about a medicine. I didn't really understand. . . ." The therapist replied at the time: "Well, ask him more about it." And after a pause, the therapist asked the patient a question about something else. Thus even at the point of getting the drug, the patient received little or no preparation for the research—none from Dr. Thorpe or Dr. Richards and apparently nothing clear from Dr. Bates. However, Dr. Bates did present a short orienting lecture for the nursing staff to prepare them for what to expect in temporary behavior changes in the patients after they had been given the shot. Dr. Bates also introduced Dr. Dirainey to Miss Burton the week before as the person who would observe her.

The shot was to be administered at 8:00 in the morning of the day of the experiment. On that day, the nurses coming on duty for the morning shift at 7:30 were prepared to carry out their part, but they could not find a medical order for the drug. The ward administrator, Dr. Bates, had forgotten to write the order in the patient's chart. The chief nurse on duty remembered from the orienting lecture that the research required administration of the drug early in the morning, and she telephoned Dr. Bates at his home—for he was not due to arrive until 8:30. Over the telephone Dr. Bates gave the nursing staff the go-ahead to give the LSD, promising to write the necessary order in the chart when he arrived at the hospital.

Dr. Dirainey was supposed to go on the ward at 9:00 A.M. to begin the period of observation. Some minutes before, however, Dr. Richards hurried into Dr. Dirainey's office to ask him to go onto the ward right away since he had found out from the nurses that Miss Burton was already exhibiting the expected behavior sequelae.

Dr. Dirainey's report of his research observations included notes on the patient's behavior, what she said to him and to others, and his own interaction with her. Apparently Miss Burton's reaction to the LSD was very marked, and Dr. Dirainey became concerned. He reported in his notes the following episode that occurred about a half-hour after he began his observations:

At this time since we did want a urine specimen and she had not been able to void when I went out of the room to allow her to void, and [since] she seemed willing to make [another] attempt, [I started to go out of the room again]. However as I left the room she said, "I really can't void because I don't have any body." I was out of the room for probably five to ten minutes. During this time my anxieties were such that I went to Dr. Richards and asked him what he thought of giving her some barbiturates because we seemed to be having an extremely severe reaction. His calmness was reassuring to me, and as I thought it over I became more comfortable in the situation myself.

I came back into the room and from the look on her face I surmised that she had not been able to void. I said, "Couldn't void, could you?"

These notes do not fully communicate the extent of Dr. Dirainey's concern. About six weeks later, in a meeting in which the LSD research was discussed with the entire staff, Dr. Richards reported his own anxiety and recalled Dr. Dirainey's coming to him: Speaking to Dr. Dirainey at the meeting, he said, "Look at your own reaction!" Then speaking to the staff group, he said, "One half-hour after the dose, he ran in to me and said, 'God, stop this; I feel like a ghoul.'"

Although Dr. Richards did not see the patient at the very height of her reaction, he conducted an EEG test after Dr. Dirainey's observations were completed. And at 1:00 P.M. the patient had her usual therapy hour with Dr. Richards. The therapist's notes during this hour show that Miss Burton was still considerably upset, still under the influence of the drug, but at times calm and lucid, even somewhat insightful into her present experience and into the relationship between some of her present feelings and her past history.

The next day's therapy-hour record reports the patient mentioning that the ward administrator, Dr. Bates, said that she was supposed to take another dose, and she said that she would rather die than take it. She asked Dr. Richards, "Do you mean for me to have to take that again?" He replied, "It's up to you.

Dr. Dirainey is the one that's interested in it." She said, "He seemed like such a monster to me."

A month passed by, and then Dr. Bates asked the patient again. She refused to take more of the drug. The next week Mr. Pickett was approached by Dr. Bates and asked to take the drug. Mr. Pickett was angry. In an interview a few days later, Mr. Pickett's therapist, Dr. Thorpe, told me: "Buoyed up by Mary Burton's refusal, Pickett refused, though he had been advised about the drug-taking before he came. This poses an unresolved problem."

Perhaps the immediate problem for Dr. Thorpe was what to do about the two patients' refusal to take the drug. But the anxieties about the drug were not confined to Mr. Pickett and Miss Burton. In the meantime the other patients on the ward expressed their feelings about the affair. Some had been disturbed by Miss Burton's peculiar behavior while she was under the influence of the drug; they were angry at the hospital for this reason, as they reported to Miss Burton. Others, as one psychiatrist discovered in his therapy hour with a patient on the same ward, considered the LSD as a treatment, a medicine. The psychiatrist reported:

My patient wanted LSD too. She claimed that I was depriving her of possible treatment. . . . Earlier . . . she had charged that I cared for her only as a research subject, a guinea pig. In general the patients on the ward looked upon LSD as a treatment rather than a research experiment, despite Dr. Bates' announcement that it was a research procedure.

The patients' confusion around the drug might be easily interpreted as a product of their disordered thinking. But as it came out later, the charge nurse, in preparing Miss Burton and the other patients for her first LSD dose, had specifically told them all that the drug was an experimental medicine, designed to help her. The staff, then, was at least one source of conflicting conceptions of the LSD. As will be shown later, the confusion by no means stemmed merely from the charge nurse's orientation; the physicians were unclear too.

The impasse between the needs of Miss Burton and Mr. Pickett and those of their therapists, Drs. Richards and Thorpe, lengthened out into about six weeks. During this period, the project remained suspended—except that Dr. Richards took some LSD himself to see what it was like. Dr. Thorpe had already taken some a couple of years previously, and he felt that Dr. Richards' feelings toward Miss Burton's fears were more sympathetic after Dr. Richards had seen what it was like. But this did not solve the "unsolved problem." Finally, Dr. Thorpe arranged a conference to include himself and Drs. Lowe, Bates, and Richards. (Dr. Dirainey could not attend the meeting. I was permitted to come as an observer.) Dr. Thorpe opened the conference by stating: "We are here to discuss the difficulties which have come up in combining psychoanalysis and drug research. They seem to mix like oil and water." The conferees went on to review the situation, clarifying some points for each other, but came to no definite conclusion except to meet again in two days, when Dr. Dirainey would also be present.

In the course of the second meeting, Dr. Thorpe and Dr. Richards decided that they would tell their patients that they were indeed the principal investigators of the LSD research and that they were the ones who wanted the patients to take the drug. The patients were also to be told that their reactions to the LSD at the beginning of psychotherapy were to be compared with their reactions at the conclusion of treatment—in order to evaluate the effectiveness of the psychotherapy in providing ways for patients to deal with anxiety.

At this conference Dr. Richards indicated to his colleagues that he would not continue therapy with Miss Burton if she refused to take the experimental drugs he planned to use, but Dr. Thorpe told the group that in any case he would continue with Mr. Pickett and take over Miss Burton's treatment if Dr. Richards wanted to discharge her. Dr. Thorpe discussed his own possible resentment at spending time treating patients who did not cooperate in his research, and Dr. Lowe pointed out that it would be Dr. Thorpe's responsibility to decide if and when that resentment would interfere with his therapy. It was clearly recognized that if a doctor became too resentful, the relationship between that doctor and his patient should be terminated by transferring the patient to another therapist. However, it was not clearly determined that that possibility should be mentioned to the patient. Dr. Lowe had expressed his opinion "against the ventilation of counter-transference feelings unless the patient brings it up. Then you just admit your anger, but not discuss it. Just let him know you will transfer him to another doctor if it gets out of hand."

In a therapy session the next day Dr. Richards explained his research interests to Miss Burton, telling her that his main concern was psychopharmacology and not psychotherapy. He asked her cooperation, but he avoided saying at that time that if she did not take the drugs he planned on using, she would be transferred or discharged. However, a few days later, he did make it clear that he would not continue treating her if she did not want to take the drugs. At any rate, after two weeks, she decided that instead of leaving the hospital (which she was free to do) she would stay and take the drugs. She complained bitterly that Mr. Pickett was not required to take drugs as a condition of staying with his therapist the way she was and that he was "getting off scot-free—and he'll get the benefit if anything is discovered. I feel he is so much stronger physically. He could recuperate better [from the effects]."

During the next four months, Miss Burton took a number of different drugs. She also was given, on at least two occasions, placebos which she was led to believe might be any sort of drug, including LSD, but she actually never received LSD a second time. Then she was transferred for further therapy to Dr. Steiger, another physician in the unit. (Dr. Thorpe had decided that he did not want to take her as one of his own patients.) One month before her transfer, Dr. Richards told me during a luncheon interview that he was planning to use LSD on Miss Burton once more, as soon as he had a technician attached to his unit who could conduct the necessary tests. However, he did not administer the drug again, and the LSD research with Miss Burton was never finished. Dr. Richards transferred Miss Burton to Dr. Steiger because "I wasn't getting enough out of seeing her to justify spending the time. . . . With other subjects [normals and psychiatric patients], I might only have to spend a half-hour a week on things besides the work. But I had to see her for an hour a day [for psychotherapy]."

In an interview with Dr. Steiger, I learned that he accepted Miss Burton as a patient, on Dr. Bates' suggestion, because she exhibited certain "problems of orality" and alcoholism in which Dr. Steiger was interested.

Miss Burton told me a couple of months later that Dr. Steiger was doing "research with psychoanalysis" and that "it's just taking the recordings of therapy hours, comparing my history with others." She said, "I'm getting along better than with Dr. Richards. Of course, I'm not taking the medicine, which is nice. Dr. Richards did ask last week if I would take some again. I said, No, because it makes me too anxious." Miss Burton's final refusal to take LSD again marked the end of the First LSD Project.

Four

THE FIRST LSD
PROJECT EVOLVES

≈§

As the extracts from early meetings at the Center indicated, the guidelines for defining one's role as a research psychiatrist were insufficiently developed. In each project, then, the research psychiatrist had to evolve his own orientation to the problem of concurrently conducting research and treatment. Working out a job orientation—a role definition—is something like balancing on a high wire. First, one must determine on a general stance; then one has to work out the fine movements that will maintain the stance. I want now to discuss the over-all posture that the research psychiatrists, Drs. Thorpe and Richards, determined to use in their relations with their project patients. In the process, I will review some of the minor adjustments that they made— the role-maintaining techniques that they used.

Their role definition evolved over a period of several months. It will be convenient to divide this period into four phases. In the first, the original pattern of the doctor-patient relationship was set up to balance research and treatment; in the second, this balance was threatened after the first dose of the drug was administered; in the third, the investigators undertook to reassess their role definition and construct a new one; in the final phase, the new definition was shored up by a variety of maneuvers in the research plans or in the interaction of the patients and their physicians.

The Original Structure of the
Doctor-Patient Relationship

The relationship between the two physicians and their patients began under several handicaps. First, the patients were not told the same thing about coming to the Center. Dr. Thorpe held the initial interview with both patients, but he told only his own therapy patient, Mr. Pickett, that there would be drug research. He did not tell Miss Burton.

An extract from the interview with Dr. Thorpe, March 30, second year, is illustrative:

DR. THORPE: In response to Pickett's questions, I told him that he would get no drug for treatment purposes, but there would be some for research purposes. I told him this each of the four times that I saw him at the state hospital before he came here. And I told him the day that he came to the Center.

INTERVIEWER: Did you actually make this drug-taking a condition of his coming?

DR. THORPE: No, not precisely. But it was implied in what I said.

INTERVIEWER: What about Mary Burton's case?

DR. THORPE: No. She was so disturbed. I thought she would have to get in better shape.

In an earlier interview (March 25), Dr. Richards reported on his view of the same events:

DR. RICHARDS: I think Thorpe did not tell her a thing about the drugs; just told her she was coming for study and treatment.

INTERVIEWER: Is there anything about the research design that would mean that she should not be told?

DR. RICHARDS: No. Thorpe said he had intended to tell her but never got around to it. He just said "study" without saying what kind of study.

INTERVIEWER: How did it happen that he never got around to telling her?

DR. RICHARDS: I think it was because she was upset at the time of his interview. He was afraid that it might upset her. I am not sure.

It is worth noting that Dr. Thorpe considered Miss Burton, who was an outpatient, too disturbed to discuss the drug research; yet he did tell Mr. Pickett, who was diagnosed as psychotic, had been already hospitalized, and was therefore presumably more disturbed. Moreover, after the patients were admitted, no specific action was taken to orient them to their research obligations. Dr. Richards himself did not discuss the research when he began therapy with Miss Burton. In fact, she was not informed of the research until a few days before she took the LSD. By that time, further complications had arisen: Dr. Thorpe, with Dr. Richards' acquiescence, had worked out the plan by which Dr. Bates would handle all administrative contacts with the patients and Dr. Dirainey would conduct the research observations. Enlisting Dr. Bates and Dr. Dirainey to deal with the patients was a structural complication, introducing additional links into the chain of communication, although of course it was intended to simplify the work by de-emphasizing the research components in the doctor-patient relationship.[1]

While Dr. Richards and Dr. Thorpe sought to integrate their two duties, therapy and research, they tried to prevent the patients from recognizing this fact. Although it seems as if they were trying to insulate or shield the patient from what might be a disturbing piece of information, the precise reasons for this sort of role definition for the research psychiatrists was never completely clear. One reason must have been, of course, the anxiety of the physicians themselves. The lack of clarity in the rationale of the role definition was itself evidence, I think, of the anxiety in the role conflict. Nevertheless, the definition, as chosen, was at some level an effort to anticipate and plan for difficulties in combining research and treatment. The generalized solution, then, that Drs. Thorpe and Richards began with was built upon an integration of the two duties in their own activity but a segre-

---

1. Structural traps always hide in a division of labor that requires close coordination. All psychiatric hospitals, like all hospital settings, suffer from this problem. See Jules Henry, "The Formal Social Structure of a Psychiatric Hospital," *Psychiatry* (1954) 17: 139-51; and "Types of Institutional Structure," *Psychiatry* (1957) 20: 47-60. For special problems incurred by the role of ward administrator, see Stanton and Schwartz, *The Mental Hospital, op. cit.*

gation of them insofar as the perception of the patients was concerned.

The insulation of the patients from the idea that their doctors were conducting research on them was far from complete, and this was a further complication. Dr. Richards had to do the routine EEG tests after each dose of the drug. Mr. Pickett, of course, had been told that his therapist was interested in drug research. True, it had not been mentioned between them after the initial interviews, but it was sufficiently clear to Mr. Pickett so that he announced after seeing Miss Burton's reaction that he would never agree to taking "that drug." This naturally caused some stir among the nurses, for they knew he was scheduled to take it the next Monday, although he did not know it. Moreover, Miss Burton's insulation from her therapist's interest in the research was also problematical even before she took the first dose. It is a commonplace that patients assume rightly or wrongly that their therapists have something to do with just about everything that happens to them in the hospital. As is understandable—considering the psychological importance and the social role he assumes—the therapist is usually endowed by the patient with the most encompassing powers and concerns in the hospital. Thus, once Miss Burton was asked by Dr. Bates to cooperate in some research, she immediately assumed in her therapy hour later in the same day that Dr. Richards already knew about it: "I guess you know that Dr. Bates asked me about a medicine," she said. In accordance with the aim of insulation, Dr. Richards had responded at the time in a way that kept him uninvolved for that moment. His response was to ignore the implication that he was aware of Dr. Bates' communication to her; he evaded talking with her about it by referring her back to Dr. Bates; and when this apparently stemmed her flow of talk and left the topic hanging before them, he asked her a question about something else (from Dr. Richards' therapy notes for February 12, second year):

MISS BURTON: I guess you know that Dr. Bates asked me about a medicine. I didn't really understand. I can't understand what he means most of the time. He just talks kind of vaguely. I asked him if it was a barbiturate or a narcotic. I didn't understand him.

DR. RICHARDS: Well, ask him more about it . . .[2] How are things at the table? [*Patient has been nervous eating with the other patients.*]

The maneuver of evading potentially ticklish subjects and diverting attention to something else is of course frequent and useful in all sorts of social situations. Here it was primarily one of the minor ways by which the research psychiatrists sought to maintain the role definitions of themselves vis-à-vis the patients; it was in the service of the insulating aspect of the role relationship. Of course, in the days after Miss Burton had taken the drug, she naturally recurred to the topic again and again. In responding, Dr. Richards had to exercise a certain ingenuity in order to keep up an appearance of noninvolvement, and he was able to maintain that image of his own role for a period of time. The following occurred the day after Miss Burton received the drug (from Dr. Richards' therapy notes for February 16, second year):

MISS BURTON: I just can't go on . . . I've just got to figure out something . . . I know there's too much wrong with me. That really showed me what insanity can be . . . and I just cannot stand it. Everyone seemed like a horrible menace. I just had nightmares all night. Mad things of big shapes. It made me so confused . . . I can't think . . . I couldn't dress myself. I can't do much today. I can't coordinate. Now I'm so mixed up. I don't know what is real anymore. Dr. Bates had said I was supposed to take it again. I'd rather die. I really don't want to stay here anymore . . . the way I was yesterday . . . it lasted for hours . . . all last night . . . I just can't stand this.

DR. RICHARDS: What did you show everybody?

MISS BURTON: How I was infantile and crazy. They had to dress me . . . I couldn't function. It just tightened me up more . . . and made the confusion worse.

---

2. The dots here are in the original notes and apparently indicate a pause.

In this and all other extracts from Dr. Richards' notes, three asterisks (* * *) will indicate that considerably more than one sentence has been deleted within the quoted material. Dr. Richards used the ellipsis (. . .) in his original notes to indicate a trailing off or pause rather than omission of remarks. To avoid confusion I will not indicate ellipses by dots in editing his notes. As it happens, I have not deleted anything less than a sentence or more, so that I use asterisks only.

Do you mean for me to have to take that again?

DR. RICHARDS: It's up to you. Dr. Dirainey is the one that is interested in it.

MISS BURTON: He seemed like a monster to me . . .

In this interview Dr. Richards fended off Miss Burton's question and evaded his part in the project by citing Dr. Dirainey as the responsible researcher; but more important, he defined the situation as one in which Miss Burton had freedom of choice—so far as he was concerned. While it is true that Dr. Richards would never have forced Miss Burton to take a second dose of LSD, nevertheless his saying, "It's up to you," was not completely true, in that, of course, he would expect to take some sort of action with her if she did in fact refuse. However, there was no occasion at the time for any trouble of this sort. Miss Burton was satisfied with his leaving it up to her. She returned to the topic of the drug,. of course, on other grounds, in succeeding therapy hours. But her remarks always singled out Dr. Bates as the target of her dissatisfaction. This half-truth of Dr. Richards served its purpose of maintaining for the patient the segregation of his research duties from his therapy duties, as illustrated in the following extract from Dr. Richards' therapy notes for February 17, second year:

MISS BURTON: You know, I just can't get over that medicine being given without telling me what it was all about. It must have been that thing I read about that causes schizophrenic hallucinations.

DR. RICHARDS: How are you feeling today?

MISS BURTON: I have a feeling of anger about that medicine. I would never have taken it if I had known what I was going to feel. I've waked up last night and the night before with this terrible fear about it. It just scared me. People make me mad. They don't give me a straight answer. * * *

I keep going back to that medicine. Dr. Bates said it was for research. I don't think it's fair to give it to someone like me, who's so anxious anyway. I'm vulnerable, so I just . . . Lawrence [Pickett] is a schizophrenic—why didn't they give it to him. I'm mad with Dr. Bates.

Miss Burton expressed her anger at Dr. Bates only in interviews with Dr. Richards. She did not say anything to Dr. Bates himself. It was a situation that could remain stable, however, only because something else also helped to maintain it: Further administrations of the drug were being delayed. The moratorium on any action on the project permitted the doctors' role definition to remain in the form in which it had been communicated to the patients. The moratorium was the direct and indirect result of the investigators' own appreciation of the patients' point of view. As Dr. Thorpe said in a later interview, Dr. Richards did not want Miss Burton to take any more LSD at the time. Dr. Thorpe reported Dr. Richards' telling him, "[If Miss Burton was pressured into taking more LSD] she would be spoiled for research; she would be belligerent." Dr. Bates, therefore, was not asked to schedule another injection, either with Miss Burton or with Mr. Pickett—at that time. By this additional technique of temporizing, the research physicians, waiting for the excitement over the LSD to quiet down, avoided forcing the issue and thereby maintained their separation from the research, at least in the eyes of the patients. The role definition handled the chronic conflict, so long as the temporizing prevented any acute outbreak.

The situation changed one month later when Dr. Bates asked Miss Burton to take a second dose. This time, Miss Burton again returned to the idea that her therapist must know what was going on. In her therapy hour with him, she asked him if he knew she had been asked to take the drug again. This time, he simply admitted his knowledge and again said that it was up to her. He was more solicitous of her feelings and through his frequent inquiries during the therapy hour he encouraged her to talk more about it. Perhaps one of the reasons that he did not deflect her communications on this topic as much as in the earlier therapy sessions is the fact that he had in the meantime taken an injection of the LSD himself. Like a true scientist, he had agreed to being interviewed and observed by a psychologist on the staff while he was under the influence of the drug.[3] Perhaps this experience heightened his sympathy for Miss Burton

---

3. It is interesting to note the difference here between Dr. Richards and Dr. Dirainey. Dr. Dirainey also took LSD during this same general period,

about the unsettling psychological aspects of the LSD reaction,
as might be deduced from the following sequence in Dr. Richards' therapy notes for March 22, second year:

> DR. RICHARDS: How are you?
> MISS BURTON: Over the weekend I felt terrible. I was afraid to
> move. Over the weekend I didn't go to the patients' dining room.
> Did you know about them wanting to give me the medicine again?
> DR. RICHARDS: Yes.
> MISS BURTON: I don't understand why you want to give it to me.
> DR. RICHARDS: Do you have any idea?
> MISS BURTON: It doesn't seem fair to take someone who has so
> much fear anyway and bring it on.
> I really felt that I was dying, and no one would give me any-
> thing to relieve it or anything. I don't even understand how anyone
> could ask me to take it a second time. It just makes me lose faith.
> It makes me think you are interested in me technically—but not
> really in me. Lawrence is schizophrenic. Why can't he take it? But
> they know he'd refuse.
> DR. RICHARDS: How does it make you feel to refuse?
> MISS BURTON: It makes me mad—that you should ask me to take
> it again.
> DR. RICHARDS: How did you feel talking to Dr. Bates?
> MISS BURTON: It made me so angry that he asked me. I was
> rather abrupt about it. I told him I just wouldn't take it. He said,
> "All right, but I want to talk with you about it on Monday [that is,
> today]." I don't think anyone could conceivably have understood
> how I felt that day. If they had they couldn't have asked me to
> take it again, unless they were inhuman, or something.
> And he said, "Well, do you think it will affect you the same

---

but he refused to allow the psychologist to observe and interview him.
I assume that his refusal was due to his general psychiatric perspective,
which was so different from Dr. Richards'. Dr. Dirainey was more committed to a psychoanalytic orientation that suggested his behavior under
the drug might be excessively revelatory and therefore embarrassing; and
moreover, he was generally not as ready to value research over other
considerations. He was also aware that the nature of the LSD experience
was in part determined by the interpersonal situation in which the drug
was taken. For example, read the chilling description of the experience of a
professional person who took LSD in an interpersonally unprotected situation: Charles Savage, "The LSD Psychosis as a Transaction between the
Psychiatrist and Patient," pp. 35-43, in Louis Cholden, ed., *Lysergic Acid
Diethylamide and Mescalin in Experimental Psychiatry*, New York: Grune
and Stratton, 1956.

way this time?" I said, "Yes, why wouldn't it?" It's the same drug.
It might not affect someone else the same way.

DR. RICHARDS: Try to keep in mind that you are perfectly free
to refuse.

MISS BURTON: Well, I don't see why anyone asks me again. I think
you could die from it . . . And I don't see what possible help it can
be. I'm unable to explain my feelings—I'm just cut off [under the
drug's influence].

DR. RICHARDS: As I say, it's perfectly all right for you to take
this position. I think it is good to come out and express your
feelings. * * *

MISS BURTON: I just have the feeling that I was brought here
for experiment, and no one really cares what I feel.

DR. RICHARDS: We do care for you.

MISS BURTON: I just don't believe it; I just don't feel it. I don't
see any reason why you should care anyway. I mean, why should
you? * * *

DR. RICHARDS: Were you angry at me? I guess so.

MISS BURTON: Yes, I knew it must be part of your decision. The
thing that made me so upset was feeling so angry at Dr. Bates, and
not expressing it.

In spite of their discussion of the patient's feelings towards
her therapist concerning the request to take more LSD, Dr.
Richards' insistence that the decision was up to her kept the
matter pretty much between her and Dr. Bates, who was, of
course, the one directly asking her to take the drug. To this
extent, Dr. Richards managed to continue carrying out the split
between research and treatment that was called for in the role
definition he had taken over. The patient regarded the LSD
request as Dr. Bates' business and tried to understand him. The
next day, in detailing a different problem she was going through
with Dr. Bates, she linked it up to the LSD: "Now he completely
reverses himself [on the other matter]. I think he got angry
because I overstepped his authority and didn't take the medicine
[LSD] . . . One night in the recreation room he was so gentle
and understanding. I guess he's like everyone else. At times he
gets angry."

While I do not have therapy notes available on Mr. Pickett [4]

---

4. Dr. Thorpe told me he did not maintain very readable notes on their
sessions, and I did not press him for access to them.

to give more direct evidence of his point of view on the same matters, I do have Miss Burton's report on Mr. Pickett's reaction, which she told of in her own therapy shortly thereafter: "Lawrence [Pickett] was very angry. They asked him to take the medicine. He certainly doesn't mind saying no. He had the same feeling I did. He said that Dr. Thorpe knew he had been insane a couple of times. He had the feeling that it might make him insane again. He had the feeling that Dr. Thorpe didn't really care about the way he felt." Thus, Mr. Pickett too tended to associate his therapist with the request for the drug. But Dr. Thorpe also tried to maintain a clear separation between his research and his treatment of the patient. Dr. Thorpe reported to me a couple of days later: "I have not broached the subject of the drugs with Pickett. Nor have I said whether he should or should not. I have just explored feelings—to it, to me, to Bates." Dr. Thorpe apparently stayed removed from the drug matter by depending upon the avoidance inherent in the standardized noncommittal and reflective techniques used in psychoanalytic and nondirective psychotherapies. Dr. Richards, on the other hand, tended to maintain the insulation by means of a rather categorical technique—that is, by definitely saying that the decision was up to the patient.[5] These appeared, upon the basis of later group discussions, to be the primary role-maintaining techniques used by each physician when his patient brought up matters that called for the insulation of the therapist from his research interests. Dr. Thorpe temporized by means of the noncommittal and reflective maneuvers of psychoanalytic technique; Dr. Richards reconceptualized the situation for the patient by actively stating a competing point of view for her to take.

In summary, then, Dr. Richards and Dr. Thorpe worked out a role definition that was their initial posture, their initial generalized solution to the demands of doing clinical research. As a

---

5. Of course putting a decision up to the patient is a common psychotherapeutic move too; its utility, however, depends upon the degree to which the consequences can be foreseen and handled by the patient and others. In a hospital, this kind of offer to a patient often brings on the resistance of any number of personnel whose prerogatives would be disregarded. It is therefore an empty suggestion in many instances.

definition of the role relationship between research physician
and research patient, it depended upon two components: an integration of the two functions insofar as the physicians themselves
were concerned and a segregation (albeit incomplete) of the
two functions insofar as the patients were concerned. To keep
the definition in effect, various minor role-maintaining techniques
were used by both doctors in the process of their work.

The Original Role Definitions
Called into Question

Dr. Richards' and Dr. Thorpe's solution for balancing the
competing demands of research and treatment was threatened
when the research goals were blocked by the action of the
patients—when Miss Burton refused to take a second injection
and Mr. Pickett balked at even the first. Yet it should be made
clear that it was not just the actions themselves that provoked
the quandary. It was rather the physicians' own indecision—
their reluctance to pressure the patients to cooperate. That is,
the physicians were restrained from pressuring their patients by
their own conception of their therapeutic duties: Specifically
(1) the LSD was a severely disturbing experience for the patient;
(2) the physicians recognized that fact from the patient's experience and perhaps from their own; and (3) they felt that they
could not exert pressure for cooperation in taking the drugs if
the LSD was really therapeutically destructive for the patient.
The evidence for these three assessments follows.

Miss Burton's distress under the influence of the drug impressed anyone who saw her. An extract from Dr. Dirainey's
research report for February 15, second year, makes this clear:

> She [Miss Burton] was much too preoccupied with what was
> going on inside of her to be too aware of the environment, except
> to ask for surcease from whatever it was she was feeling * * *
> "Oh God," she said, "it's terrible, but not really terrible because
> I'm not here . . . Why did you do it?"
> . . . I answered, "It's a rough experience."

"Can't I take anything to get over it?"
I said, "You'll be over it; it'll wear off."

Despite his attempt at reassuring the patient, Dr. Dirainey shortly left the room to hurry to ask Dr. Richards "what he thought of giving her some barbiturates because we [sic] seemed to be having an extremely severe reaction." At that time, Dr. Richards did not consider Miss Burton's reaction very serious. Yet in her therapy hour that day, she was still affected by the LSD—five hours after the injection. She began her therapy hour by telling Dr. Richards how terrible she felt, but soon began to scream and shriek, with obvious hallucinations. Even when she had become calm again, she occasionally experienced further hallucinations, according to Dr. Richards' therapy notes:

DR. RICHARDS: Feelings like this before?
MISS BURTON: Yes, but not so big . . . I think I haven't realized . . . oh God . . . what am I saying . . . everything is a threat to me . . . I hadn't realized how I mistrust everyone . . . how I feel so completely transparent. * * *
As a child I had fears that were so distorted . . . That's the way the whole world is to me now. If I could just love someone, and show them, and they would return it . . . but they don't. * * *
Dr. Dirainey seemed like a great frightening ogre to me. I don't know what there was about that man. He just got bigger and bigger . . . his whole body was swelling up. I felt like he was going to choke me.
I certainly have a problem on my hands. And how on earth will I ever cope with it. I can't. * * *
Everyone looms up as a horrible threat . . . I never realized that . . . I thought, I really felt that people were trying to choke me.
DR. RICHARDS: How have people treated you?
MISS BURTON: I've just seen eyes staring at me (hallucinating). That doctor, he gave me such a funny look. He got angry . . . he looked like he was tired of it all . . . he didn't want to be bothered with me . . . I've felt that all my life . . . that I'm in the way.
I just saw that look (hallucinating) . . . My speech is cut off . . . my thinking . . .

When Dr. Thorpe called a meeting with Dr. Lowe to discuss the patients' refusal, he, Dr. Bates, and Dr. Richards varied somewhat in their evaluation of the seriousness of the LSD effects;

but they agreed on the fact that Miss Burton had been sorely distressed. They wondered about getting her to take more LSD and about Mr. Pickett's taking it as well. At this meeting on March 31, second year, the following interchange took place between Dr. Richards, Dr. Thorpe, and Dr. Bates, in the presence of Dr. Lowe, of course:

DR. THORPE (*after a short summary of the situation*): I have not entered into discussion of the drug with Pickett. However, he is afraid that he will become permanently crazy. I do not think so.

He feels because Mary [Burton] refused, he was approached. I might correct him on this; but probably it would not be helpful. This would in effect be putting pressure on him to take it. Or I could show that taking it is his $15 an hour [a conventional rate for private psychoanalytic therapy]. * * *

DR. RICHARDS: Mary does not raise the same objections against taking the drug. Throughout life she has been taken advantage of. She has taken LSD once and was agreeable to that. But now we know she is very uncomfortable; so she asks, how can she be asked to do it again? Mary says people are letting her down on this. In treatment, I have looked at it as at other things in her life which have been troublesome for others, yet needed for her.

DR. THORPE: I suppose she can make a case for not taking more. But as Bates says there would be trouble in changing the research design at this point; and we wanted her to take a placebo this time.

· DR. BATES: Two things they feel: One, it is harmful; two, it is an unfriendly act on our part.

DR. RICHARDS and DR. THORPE (*together*): Yes.

DR. BATES: I do not know if this *will* be a benign substance for Pickett, myself. . . . In Mary's case, just the second feeling is present —that it's unfriendly—but after all that's not the issue: whether it's unfriendly or not.

DR. RICHARDS: It is the issue in their minds.

DR. BATES: We do not accept all their issues as debatable; we can't.

DR. RICHARDS: Well, are we out to hurt them?

DR. THORPE: No, and yet—(*trails off*).

DR. BATES: Yes, but on the other hand—(*trails off*). If we back off, that proves it to them.

DR. RICHARDS: It does hurt them; they are miserable.

DR. THORPE: But Mary is always miserable.

DR. BATES: It hurts to draw blood, but you do order it. It's not permanent.

DR. RICHARDS: No, it's just momentary; just unpleasant for the time. * * *

Might it not be said to her that the research is her payment for the treatment she receives? What motivation does she now have to take it?

DR. BATES: That is a sidetrack. That is in her thinking. The question is: Is this an unfriendly act, as we see it? If not, then we can be confident, as we are with drawing blood.

DR. RICHARDS: I disagree that it is unnecessary to consider her motivation.

DR. BATES: Yes, it comes in, but the issue is, do we feel it is unfriendly. It is our uncertainty. We have accepted their view.

DR. THORPE: No, we have retreated, but we have not abandoned everything. * * *

DR. RICHARDS: It is not being unfriendly in my opinion.

DR. BATES: The only way I would think this would be unfriendly is if it would do real damage. My reservation is this: I doubt whether psychosis is a good thing for a patient to experience at any time, whether brought on temporarily by LSD or whatever.

In this extract of staff discussion each doctor seemed to talk on both sides of the issue. This in itself is a clue to the reality of the conflict as subjectively experienced by the physicians. But a more significant clue to the dilemma of all of the physicians was their fastening upon a certain word in their discussion.

"Friendly" or "unfriendly" people? The discussants used and reused the word *unfriendly* in trying to get to the basic issue that troubled them. Their choice of this term was significant on two counts. First, it enabled them to depart from a frame of reference in which the only consideration was therapy. Second, it cast the question into a more generalized frame of reference for evaluation. The term muffled the specific invocation of the therapy values. That is, it was a substitute for the more narrowly but precisely evocative terms, *anti-therapeutic, contra-indicated,* or other related medical terms, which would specifically require decision on therapeutic grounds. Yet Dr. Thorpe, for example, clearly considered that Miss Burton's history, as Dr. Richards formulated it, made it important for her to have the chance to refuse to undergo what she felt was personally destructive and disagreeable. This would be a purely therapeutic consideration,

which Dr. Thorpe (though not Miss Burton's therapist) did accept as valid. The issue, however, becomes formulated not in terms of therapy but in terms of unfriendliness.

Considering the use of the drug in terms of the question of friendliness called upon a broader, more flexible scheme of values. The physicians thereby ask themselves whether, as persons rather than as professionals, they are doing the right thing. This can be interpreted as a shift in their frame of reference, which occurred because things did not fit into their earlier frame of reference. In a sense, the doctors temporarily abandoned the troublesome view of the situation that limited discussion to issues of a doctor-patient relationship; and thereby they could review their dilemma in broader human terms.

Ordinarily the de-differentiation of an issue—that is, moving from a more specific formulation to a more general one—can make a decision on that issue open to a larger variety of considerations. Moreover, as the potential considerations increase, the freedom of the person in choosing a decision also increases. Thus, since the generalized cultural value choices inherent in considerations of "friendliness" are more varied and less precisely worked out than the choices in psychiatric administration,[6] one might expect that the physicians would experience a greater freedom in resolving the issue, including a freedom to resolve it exactly to their own needs. But in actuality, by this de-differentiation they also allowed themselves to sense other considerations that paradoxically forced them to forego some of their prerogatives as physicians and required them to accept the possible validity of evaluations made by the patients, even though "we don't accept all their issues as debatable."

Perhaps what was really most significant in the use of the word *unfriendly* was that in dealing with a professional problem, the doctors found the conflict so acute that they were forced to fall back upon the fundamental bases of all value choices in their

---

6. See, however, Stanton's discussion of the problem of slippery theoretical bases for administrative psychiatric decisions. Alfred H. Stanton, "Psychiatric Theory and Institutional Context," *Psychiatry* (1954) 17: 19-26.

personal relations—that is, upon part of the generalized scheme of the over-all Western culture that they shared. I shall have to return to this matter again at a later point. As of now, it is necessary only to conclude that this attempted shift in frame of reference for guiding values was one of the minor movements directed toward the maintenance of the initial role definition. That is, if the physicians' role definition could be ratified in the wider scheme of things, then it could be maintained.

In the course of this same meeting, on March 31, the professional frame of reference was reinvoked by Dr. Lowe, who had not yet spoken in the conference. After asking some questions about the aims and design of the research, he reaffirmed the issue in terms of therapy obligations.

DR. LOWE: How would it alter the research to say [something like] this to the patients: "The drug seems to cause a limited intense anxiety. Anxiety is a common experience; what is important is the way it is dealt with. The question is, Does psychotherapy help make a change in the situation, or does it merely provide better defenses. LSD is a constant stimulus—not changing like most socially-aroused anxiety situations—and would show the result of psychotherapy. This is what we are asking your cooperation for." Would this interfere with the research? You could also say, "It is important for psychiatry."

DR. RICHARDS: I see no objections.

DR. LOWE: From the therapeutic standpoint, it is necessary to say that. In therapy, you treat the patient as an equal who has a right to know such things. But even so, what if they still say they won't do it? After all, other patients on the ward do not have to take LSD. * * *

DR. THORPE: "I'll keep you on," I'd say, "but I'll be mad as hell about it." (He laughs.) I would consider keeping them on, but I wonder about my possible annoyance [and how it would affect therapy].

DR. RICHARDS: I'll send my patient on—or I'll hand her over to Thorpe. He and I have discussed this: He's interested in her symptoms. * * *

DR. LOWE: It might well be a legitimate decision to dump the patient, but what is the effect on him?*** What about a group discussion of this with all the patients—and include the nurses?

Dr. Lowe's questions and comments ended in clarifying the

issue in therapeutic terms. He did not say anything new that the participants had failed to consider; they undoubtedly had considered it; but he said it in a group setting where his leadership was sought. The result was certainly to begin a process of change in the relations between the doctors and their patients.

To recapitulate: In the period before the meeting, the role definition constructed by the physicians had been called into question—it was obviously not working—and the commitment of the physicians to the definition was weakened. This loosening of role commitment [7] prepared the participants for the meeting just described in which they re-examined the situation and began to entertain different possibilities for their relationship with the patients. Before this meeting took place, however, there were other signs of the loosening of commitment to the original role definition. One of these signs appeared in my interviews with some of the participants before the meeting just reported. In these interviews, Dr. Thorpe, Dr. Richards, and Dr. Bates [8] each appeared to deny any real investment in the role arrangement they had been instrumental in setting up. In the process, they tended to shift responsibility for it, like a game of "button, button, who's got the button." In my interview with Dr. Richards (March 25, second year) he indicated that he merely went along with the wishes of others:

INTERVIEWER: How did you happen to decide that the therapist would stay out of it all?

DR. RICHARDS: Thorpe more or less worked it out that the therapist would stay out of the research. He designed the project that way after talking with Lowe and Bates. I told him to work it out however he wanted to.

INTERVIEWER: Do you think this is satisfactory?

DR. RICHARDS: I think there are problems either way. If I were in on the research in the patient's eyes, I could get her to take the

7. For the relevant discussion of the concept of role commitment, see Erving Goffman, "Role Distance," in *Encounters: Two Studies in the Sociology of Interaction,* Indianapolis: Bobbs-Merrill, 1961, pp. 83-152.

8. I did not get to interview Dr. Dirainey until a week later, at which point a new solution had already been worked out. Also, I did not interview Dr. Lowe. Therefore, I do not have their reactions to the same situation.

drugs when she refused to—by bribing her, threatening her, or some other way. * * *

If this organization of the project ends up by allowing her to refuse the drugs, I am against it. This is why she was brought here.

INTERVIEWER: Do you think this organization will result in her refusal?

DR. RICHARDS: I don't know. She might well refuse under any design.

INTERVIEWER: Who talks with Miss Burton about taking the drug?

DR. RICHARDS: Bates is the only one concerned with whether she takes the drug. The nurses administer it, but like other medication, on the ward administrator's orders.

In an earlier interview (March 20, second year), Dr. Bates noted his own participation but communicated a sense of disaffection for the arrangements he helped to make.

INTERVIEWER: How did you happen to be the one to deal with the patients?

DR. BATES: Thorpe, Richards, Dirainey, and I discussed it. The therapists did not want to; Dirainey was a stranger to the patients. I had the contact with them and so I agreed to do it. We discussed what we should say and what we would hedge on. It was not clear then and is not now what was the meaning of my saying it—that it was my role. But I did not see any objections. Anyway the patients would know that it had my participation as ward administrator.

Thorpe reported a different perspective in an interview on March 30.

DR. THORPE: I guess I let Lowe and Bates really make the decision. They felt the roles of researcher and therapist should be split. I myself felt that anything could have been worked out in the treatment relationship, but we left it at separation.

Two comments must be made on these interview materials in order to prevent misinterpretation. First, Dr. Richards' offhand remark about bribing or threatening the patient to get her to take the LSD has to be recognized as the defense of toughness-where-toughness-is-not-meant. On one level, it was his initial floundering toward reaching full communication with the patient. His remark should also be interpreted in the light of the fact that although Miss Burton later agreed to take further doses, he never asked her to take LSD again while she was his patient.[9] Dr. Richards was talking tougher than he was prepared to act.

This sort of reaction—or overreaction—that seems to deny the physician's allegiance to respectful relations with his patient was not limited to Dr. Richards. It was used by other physicians at the Center,[10] and it must be recognized as, in effect, a means by which a staff member tried to salvage a tiny corner for research against overweening obligations that he actually felt for therapy with the patient. It was as if therapy obligations pressed so strongly that research could only be conducted if it were strenuously defended. Here, the maneuver can be viewed as one of the minor role-maintaining moves of the research psychiatrist, a move by which he works to maintain a teetering balance between the demands of research and those of treatment. As a matter of fact the toughness defense has often been commented upon in the social science literature. Its function in medical institutions has generally been described as reinforcing the actor's obligation to conduct (or witness) technical procedures that violate the common taboos and general notions of personal privileges, of privacy, and so on. In other words, the physician assumes an overtough manner in order to emphasize and maintain the definition of himself as someone who must do things that he would not do were he not a doctor. Conflicts between general social roles and the role of the physician are minimized in this way. The same technique was used by Dr. Richards when he dealt with the conflict between his research obligations and his concern for the patient, as he discussed the LSD research with me.

Another potentially misleading aspect of this interview ma-

9. In later research, Miss Burton took another experimental drug which momentarily gave her very severe, asthma-like symptoms. She complained, and Dr. Richards told her that he would never again give her that drug. Thus, with this drug as with LSD, Dr. Richards was loath to subject Miss Burton to extreme discomfort if she took a strong stand on it.

10. For example, I have already quoted Dr. Lowe's words that it might be legitimate "to dump" the patient (Conference, March 31, second year). In unquoted material Dr. Thorpe talks about "firing" the patient, as if the doctor is the hiring one in the relationship. Dr. Lowe also used the term *fire* (Conference, April 2, second year).

terial needs interpretation. The interviews may erroneously seem
to indicate that Dr. Lowe had urged the original definition of
the physicians' relations with the two patients. In fact, he had
really stressed only the usefulness of having a special research
observer make the direct observations of the patients, and of
separating that task from therapeutic interviewing. However, he
had not made his position clear enough, as will be evident from
extracts to be presented from a later meeting held by Drs.
Dirainey, Lowe, Bates, Thorpe, and Richards.

The Reassessment and Redefinition
of the Role Relationship

Dr. Lowe recognized the central significance of the dilemma
that the LSD project workers had gotten into, and he hoped to
use the situation as a general corrective example by suggesting
a meeting of all the doctors, nurses, and patients to talk about
the project. Dr. Lowe's suggestion was never acted upon.[11] It
was, however, a logical extension of the general point he tried
to make—that the patients had to be clear on the research interests of their therapists and should not remain deceived and misled.

Essentially, Dr. Lowe was calling for a generalized reorganization of the manner in which Drs. Thorpe and Richards had
chosen to handle the research-treatment conflict. In general, he
seemed to appreciate their attempt to integrate the two functions
in their study of their therapy patients—which was, after all, an
attempt to perform the task of the group that Dr. Lowe headed.
What he urged would, as a matter of fact, merely carry out that
integration to its logical conclusion by apprising the patients of
what their relationship to their therapists called for in terms of
both research and therapy. As Dr. Lowe seemed to formulate the
problem, the solution was merely what was called for by the

---

11. One of the routine general staff meetings did discuss the problem,
but, of course, no patients were present. This meeting will be reported on
in the succeeding chapter.

nature of a therapeutic relationship. But, in fact, the problem was somewhat more complicated than that. For example, the physicians could not merely think in terms of the welfare of the patients; there had to be some payoff in terms of research as well. Dr. Lowe himself did not perhaps actually ignore the necessity of responding to the research values involved so much as he emphasized the preliminary requirement of adhering to basic procedures and obligations inherent in the purely therapeutic type of relationship. It is important to recall here Dr. Lowe's consistently voiced policy: Begin by getting a good clinical operation going, even if it takes a year or more; then there will be a foundation for good research.

As the program director and the person concerned with the long-term view of things, Dr. Lowe no doubt was not as vulnerable to the need to show research results as the staff members, who had no better gauge of their work than the completion of a particular project. Indeed, since it is so difficult to assess therapeutic progress—especially with severely ill, hospitalized patients—it is not hard to understand that research progress (as shown by reports, papers, and so on) would have a great attraction for the research psychiatrist for purposes of professional self-assessment. Aside from the difficulty of assessing progress with patients, any progress at all with severely ill or psychotic patients is apt to be a long drawn-out affair. For example, among therapists with the greatest reputation for success in the treatment of psychotics was the late Frieda Fromm-Reichmann and the group at Chestnut Lodge, where it was not uncommon to work with a discouraged and discouraging patient for twelve or fifteen years. This long-term view was a tradition congenial to a senior person like Dr. Lowe, but it was more difficult for the younger psychiatrists to sustain. They had yet to achieve assured professional standing, and they had joined a new organization that did not have a guiding tradition of long-term treatment.[12]

---

12. In pure research of any kind the time perspective of the senior man will be longer than that of those junior to him. He is willing to be more patient about getting results, more willing to undertake long-term projects, and so on. The younger man tends to select for his own personal work

Moreover, the Center was so bureaucratically organized that promotion and advancement depended upon indices of performance that could be relatively easily assessed (such as number and importance of research reports and papers, and so on). Dr. Lowe could exert minimal influence on behalf of a younger man who chose to take a slower pace in developing research results so as to deal with a long-term therapy problem. These difficulties, of course, were recognized to a greater or lesser extent by most of the staff. But recognizing them is not the same as accepting them wholeheartedly. Certainly these influences tended to eclipse considerations of therapy and clinical management from time to time, but they could also handicap good research. It would naturally be one of Dr. Lowe's duties to prevent the freezing-in of any such handicaps. Yet he could not take a very active part in the individual projects without violating his precepts of individual freedom for the staff members. It is significant, then, that he always attended the LSD conferences at the insistence of the staff involved.

There were two additional conferences on the LSD project that should be mentioned. In the second of these (a general conference attended by about sixteen staff members), Dr. Lowe restricted his own participation to generalized comments on the nature of the Center as a setting for psychiatric research without much specific reference to the LSD project under discussion. But in the first conference on April 2, second year, the group was small, and Dr. Lowe was quite specific about what he thought ought to be done about the LSD project.

DR. LOWE: I think the difficulty, as I see it, is that the patients are in intensive therapy. Thus the negotiations about taking the drug

---

project one of shorter duration in which he will confirm himself more quickly. Of course, this is a general difference of perspective that goes along with age. See W. I. B. Beveridge, *The Art of Scientific Investigation,* New York: Random House, 1961. See also David L. Watson, *Scientists Are Human,* London: Watts and Company, 1938. Glaser reports on the difference in pace of work in senior and junior staff in a medical research institution. Barney G. Glaser, "Recognition in Scientists' Careers," *Social Problems* (1962-63) 10: 268-76. See also Glaser, *Organizational Scientists,* Indianapolis: Bobbs-Merrill, 1964.

cannot be reasonably carried out by someone else. It would be the acme of indirection to have someone else do it.

DR. THORPE: If this is so, why did we have the research observations done by someone else [which Lowe had originally approved]?

DR. RICHARDS: Yes, is there any reason for that?

DR. LOWE: Well, I think having another observer is a different matter. But this is not someone else's experiment in which you are willing to go along. If it were, then the researcher would discuss it with the patient and negotiate with him—not the therapist.

DR. BATES (*nodding vigorously in approval*): Yes.

DR. THORPE (*to Bates*): You don't have to be so goddamned pleased.

DR. BATES: I am not pleased. It's just a different situation—to have the observer to do observations for you is different from not negotiating with the patient yourself.

(*At this point Dr. Richards is called out of the conference; he is absent for the rest of the discussion.*)

DR. LOWE: I would present it fairly directly. The problem is if you decide you would not work with the patient if he said, No. Then Bates is involved, for this brings up something among all the patients which would have to be brought out into the open. If you fired the patient, this would have to be discussed with all the patients—and Bates would be involved in that.

Does this point to the fact that we have not dealt directly with this problem—that all the patients are here for experiments also? We have tended to ignore this.

My impulse is to assume that the refusal to cooperate is partly negative transference, and over time this could be dealt with probably, and the patients' cooperation reached. Also, there are other reasons in reality for their balking, for example, a therapist undoubtedly [has shown in other ways] . . . that he cannot be counted upon all the time, and this intensifies the patient's feelings. In therapy, though, you enter into a contract. This is different from research in which there is no such contract. * * *

Where you are involved, you have to take it up with the patient. The patient otherwise experiences your refusal to admit your involvement as a trick, a manipulation. My experience is that these schizophrenic patients look upon this as dishonesty and duplicity, rather than as reasonable separation of administration and therapy.

DR. THORPE (*and others*): Okay.

DR. LOWE: This is not a pronouncement—it's my opinion.

The first time Dr. Richards saw his patient after this meeting, he began to put into effect Dr. Lowe's suggestions. Even though he had not been present for much of what Dr. Lowe had said, he was swift to follow the leadership that Dr. Lowe had reluctantly provided. The new definition of the relationship between doctor and patient began to take shape, as evidenced in a portion of Dr. Richards' therapy notes for April 5, second year:

DR. RICHARDS (*opening the hour*): How are you feeling?

MISS BURTON: Not too badly . . .

DR. RICHARDS: Tell me more.

MISS BURTON: I still have that feeling of not being able to talk. I just have the feeling that I don't want to bring things into my mind to talk about.

[*Dr. Richards' notes only summarize at this crucial point*:] Patient then given explanation à la Dr. Lowe. Patient seems pleased at being told, but says, "I'm sorry at not being able to cooperate, but the feeling is just too horrible." Patient asked what it would mean if she did not cooperate. I told her that I couldn't say at present, that we would have to talk it over.

MISS BURTON: I have the feeling that this [request to take the drugs] is just an excuse [to make her leave the hospital, where she feels no one wants her].

DR. RICHARDS: You just don't feel that under any circumstances you would take it?

MISS BURTON: I don't think so. I feel badly about saying no when you want me to. If I felt that I'd have to take it again, I don't know what I would do. I'm just terrified about it. . . . If you feel that I should leave the hospital because of this I can understand; but I can't take it.

DR. RICHARDS: What was the worst thing about the reaction?

MISS BURTON: I know it was torture. I felt like I was choking to death—I kept seeing my head off—my neck was being choked. It was horrible. I couldn't breathe that night. I thought I was dying. I felt no one could reach me in time. I had the feeling that no one understood. It was such a feeling of being trapped. I had such a headache.

Anyway I can never get well through analysis: I can't trust a doctor well enough to let go. I can't feel that trust, so how can I ever get well? I feel so badly about refusing to take the medicine when I know it's something that would be of benefit—and help you. But I just can't do it.

Dr. Richards' proposal on the drug met an immediate refusal, and he did not press the matter directly at the time or in the succeeding therapy hours. Miss Burton, nevertheless, guessed that she was expected to take the drug or leave the hospital. She worried the decision over and over again in her therapy hours, often trying to get Dr. Richards to say that he really liked her and wanted to keep her in the hospital. The following extracts from Dr. Richards' therapy notes, beginning with these for April 6, second year, tell the story:

MISS BURTON: Well, have you talked to the doctors—about—me.
DR. RICHARDS: We haven't really decided anything yet.
MISS BURTON: Actually I'd like to leave. * * * I feel so guilty about not taking the medicine. I have a feeling that I'm not cooperating—and that I'll continue to be pressured about it. * * * I just feel like—like I'm not really wanted.
DR. RICHARDS: How do you mean?
MISS BURTON: I just feel that since I won't take the medicine—and since I'm so tense about talking to people—and make people so uncomfortable— * * * It's making me have this feeling of guilt and anxiety about not taking it. I have the feeling that if I don't take it, the doctors won't like my not taking it. At the same time, I can understand that it's part of your work. But Lawrence has only been asked once. They don't keep after him the way they do after me. I guess it's because he's so firm. * * *
Do you think I could leave the hospital?
DR. RICHARDS: You might ask Dr. Bates about that.

Dr. Richards tended to be inactive during the therapy in this period, but there were times when he had to respond, at least minimally, as in the following extract from the notes for April 7:

MISS BURTON: Would you like me to leave the hospital? I have the feeling that you would like me to leave—trying to do it in a subtle way so that I wouldn't be hurt. The way you brought up that medicine again—after you had seen me suffering so much.
DR. RICHARDS: Do you know why?
MISS BURTON: Yes, I know it's for research—I keep telling myself that. When I said something about wanting to leave, you said to ask Dr. Bates. That made me feel as if you wouldn't care at all.

On the next day, April 8, an extract from Dr. Richards' therapy notes indicates that the patient continued to pursue her aim to find out Dr. Richards' position:

MISS BURTON: . . . I talked to Lawrence yesterday. He said Dr. Thorpe hasn't said anything to him. . . . It all makes me think that it's just an excuse for getting me out. * * * It just makes me so mad. I suppose Lawrence can definitely stay. I don't know—you didn't say anything about this before, when I didn't take it. It's just the last few days that you've said it. . . .

DR. RICHARDS: Tell me about your talk with Dr. Bates [in which patient planned to ask to leave the hospital].

MISS BURTON: I didn't say much to him after all: I asked if I could go home and see my sister. I felt so self-conscious and embarrassed.

Well, I think maybe I better just leave. I don't want to stay where I'm not wanted. * * * I feel that this is just an excuse, because this was just talked about suddenly. It's not being given to any other patients, you're not insisting that Lawrence take it. Oh, I know, you're not insisting that I take it, but—

DR. RICHARDS: What have you been thinking about other than this?

The notes for April 9 show that again Miss Burton tried to get some reassurance from Dr. Richards, this time with some success:

MISS BURTON: . . . Are you going to let me know what happens in regard to—

DR. RICHARDS: To what?

MISS BURTON: Well, in regard to me.

DR. RICHARDS: Sure.

On April 12, Miss Burton came into her therapy hour crying. Someone had found out that it was her birthday and she was panicky at the thought of being sung to, stared at, and so on. She again asked if she could leave the hospital, and Dr. Richards told her again to talk with Dr. Bates.. On April 14, she reported to her therapist that she was still thinking about the possibility of taking the drug and staying in the hospital. She told him, "I thought, 'What am I doing! Thinking I am going to take that drug again!'" On April 15, she wondered whether she might go insane taking the drug again, since the effects had seemed to last so long. "And yet, when I think about leaving, I could just as easily go insane that way." On April 16, Miss Burton came ten minutes late to her therapy hour. She had been lying down and did not realize the time. She began by saying, "Well, I've just about decided that I'll take the medicine. I might as well take a chance." She was irritated that Mr. Pickett was "getting off scot free—and he'll get the benefit if anything is discovered." But she was ready to go ahead with her treatment under the new conditions of her research obligations. On April 20, Dr. Richards explained his interests in more detail and outlined the specific procedures which he intended to use, such as taking her blood pressure, and so on. He told her that he would never identify any of the drugs to be used, and he specifically did not reassure her that he would omit LSD from the series. On April 21, the patient received her first in the new series of injections. It was a placebo —merely salt water—but it represented the beginning of the new relationship between the research patient and her research psychiatrist.

The new relationship between Dr. Richards and Miss Burton explicitly called for their combined efforts in carrying out both treatment and research in the course of their contacts with each other. The insulation of the research from the therapy that had marked the original structure of the role relations of doctor and patient did not completely disappear—as will be discussed later— but at least it was clear to both doctor and patient that the relationship was based upon both research and treatment. The basis of the relationship was complemented by mutual understandings between Miss Burton and Dr. Richards as to certain obligations of each in the situation.

Dr. Richards reported to me his discussions with Miss Burton that set up the new relationship. He reported that he had told Miss Burton that he was "only" interested in his research, not in treatment. He also reported that he was using "the dodge" of getting her interested in the research so that she was motivated to cooperate. He seemed to deny that he was in fact concerned with the patient as anything other than material for study. This is again the toughness defense of the physician who finds it necessary to go counter to a strongly held value in his relations with a patient.[13] Nevertheless, he had earlier experienced a good deal of difficulty in the relationship because he had not, by plan, been able to take the patient fully into his confidence. Now he had the opportunity to do so, and he made rather full use of it—with one exception. He had not been able to bring himself to tell the patient right away that she would be transferred if she did not agree to taking the drugs. As his therapy notes on April 5 recorded, "Patient asked what it would mean if she did not cooperate. I told her that I couldn't say at present—that we would have to talk it over." It was over lunch on April 20, two weeks later, that Dr. Richards reviewed the latest developments with me informally, as evidenced in my notes made immediately afterwards:

. . . Richards then said that Miss Burton was now quite agreeable to taking the drug. He had had a long talk with her. In this first talk with her, just a short one, he had only said that he was interested in the research; that in fact his interest in her was only in terms of the physiological research and not the psychotherapy. He did not then tell her what the alternative was—that is, of [her] being fired. He later told her that he wanted her to take a series of drugs of various kinds, which he would never identify. He had informed her that these drugs would not be of any therapeutic value to her, though there was a chance that if things worked out well, in a couple of years they might have something that would be helpful. He explained the research problem to her and what they were trying to find. She was upset about it at first, but later decided that it was fine with her.

He had told her that he might give a drug like benzedrine. (Benzedrine makes her feel better temporarily.) Now she is more worried about getting benzedrine because she would feel guilty about feeling better, than she is about getting LSD which she would in fact now prefer. The next dose is scheduled for tomorrow, and Richards is going to have a discussion with the nurses about LSD again, this afternoon. . . . However, the injection will actually be a placebo, saline solution.

Richards said that he was now using the "dodge" of getting the

13. It is necessary to point out that this does not mean that, over-all, Dr. Richards was more interested in patient care than in research. Quite the contrary was true. But once having placed himself in the position of therapist (as well as researcher) he had to accept and react to the demands of the therapeutic aspects of his relationship with the patient.

patient interested in the research, getting her motivated to cooperate. I said that it was not necessarily a "dodge." And he replied that that was what he called it, and he discussed it [with me] in that tenor.

He told me about Miss Burton's special sensitivity to drugs of all kinds, and how that makes her a good subject for screening various kinds of drugs; and he discussed the nature of his research in general. * * *

I asked him why he felt that the project was better structured the way it was now than the way it had been. He said that it was definitely better and that was why he was doing it this way. What was better was that the situation was clearer for the patient, who had previously been unable to get information from Bates—who really did not have it and with whom she did not have a good relationship anyway. In the previous setup, if she had tried to get information from him [Richards], he would refer her to Bates. Now it is all centered in Richards, and he can deal with it. This he feels is quite a factor in the patient's being more happy with the whole situation. Another thing: it is simpler operationally as far as he is concerned; he does not have to try to round up other people to do things, talk to them, arrange procedures and so on. He just does it himself.

Maintaining the New Role Definition

When it became clear to all participants that the LSD research would require a change in the role relations of doctor and patient, Dr. Thorpe, over time, elected not to conduct the research with his own patient, Mr. Pickett. Even though he had specified to Mr. Pickett before admission that research drugs were to be used, he did not remind the patient of this subsequently; nor did anyone else do that for Dr. Thorpe. That part of the patient's obligations in his relationship to his therapist was allowed to lapse. In a sense, then, Dr. Thorpe implicitly began a new relationship with Mr. Pickett in which, as researcher, he gave up the possibility of conducting the LSD studies. In another sense, this might be considered merely a continuation of the previous doctor-patient relationship they had been enacting. However, the covert or implicit research requirements of that relationship (even though not communicated to the patient) had, as has been

demonstrated, wide consequences. It is therefore equally important to assay the covert or implict changes in that relationship,
once the drug research obligations of the patient were renounced
by the therapist. This, too, had its consequences, which will be
discussed later. For the time being, it is merely necessary to point
out that Dr. Thorpe, in the course of the new definition of his
relationship to the patient, had to engage in role-maintaining
adjustments for this new definition. One of these was his recognition of the increased importance of continuing treatment with
Mr. Pickett as a source of data for his psychological analysis of
depersonalization. For additional information about depersonalization—including the depersonalizing effects of LSD—he had
to look elsewhere. Of course, one source of information was the
behavior of Miss Burton.[14] Dr. Thorpe conducted some psychological perception tests with her, and he later selected and admitted another patient to substitute for Mr. Pickett and Miss Burton.
He conducted LSD studies with the third patient—a woman—
as will be discussed later. It is necessary to point out that in his
work with this third patient, Dr. Thorpe changed his research
design from a longitudinal study, as originally planned, to a cross-
sectional one. This and other changes in the research activities
and plans of Dr. Thorpe illustrate the main technique he used
to maintain his redefined role as a clinical researcher, even though
he would not carry out the original LSD research with Mr.
Pickett. That is, Dr. Thorpe made technical modifications in his

---

14. Dr. Richards' therapy notes were intended to be available to Dr.
Thorpe for such analyses as the latter felt were useful. This is one of the
reasons why the therapy notes were as full (and as clearly handwritten)
as they were. They were, therefore, incidentally available to me, through
Dr. Richards' kindness and his willingness to open his experience to scientific investigation. I asked Dr. Thorpe for the use of his notes on one
period in his therapy with Mr. Pickett. He demurred at the time, and I
did not press my request, since he had never thought that his notes might
be read by anyone else. I was then and am now convinced that therapy
notes in a research center ought to be routinely available for study by
others but, also, a therapist must have some choice as to who those others
will be. To organize research on treatment otherwise is to be blind to the
stagnation or deterioration of both the research and the therapy that would
ensue.

research activities that enabled him to continue as both researcher and therapist in the clinical research program. He dropped the LSD work with Mr. Pickett; he emphasized more heavily his investment in the clinical management and treatment of Mr. Pickett as a patient showing particular symptoms that might be studied during therapy; he gathered information on Miss Burton; and he chose another patient whom he admitted for a differently designed LSD study. All these actions helped him to sustain the new role relationship with Mr. Pickett.

Several other techniques for maintaining the new role definition can be illustrated in the ensuing relationship between Dr. Richards and Miss Burton. While the main technique involved in Dr. Thorpe's role-maintenance operations was technical modification in the research activities, the role-maintenance techniques used in the relationship between Miss Burton and Dr. Richards were directed toward a different goal. Since Dr. Richards had obtained Miss Burton's permission to continue LSD studies, he did not have to deal with the problem that Dr. Thorpe had— how to maintain the research sector of his role. Instead, the role-maintaining operations in the Burton-Richards relationship were primarily directed towards the task of reinforcing the therapy aspects of the relationship. The main threat of conflict of research with therapy occurred in terms of Miss Burton's apprehension that she was "just a guinea pig." In general terms, the threat is that posed for any research patient who recognizes himself as object rather than subject, in the context of the research activity. Since Miss Burton's sense of self and of security, as with any patient with a serious and long-term emotional illness, was very limited anyway, she did not have many resources to utilize in order to affirm her personal worth in the potentially devaluing situation. The day after the placebo, she obtained what crumbs of comfort she could by ascertaining that at least she would not have to be interviewed by another physician the way two other patients on the ward were. On this point, Dr. Richards spelled out a limitation on his behavior in this respect; he assured her that he would not subject her to that procedure, as reported in the following extract from Dr. Richards' therapy notes for April 22:

MISS BURTON: . . . I was thinking about the fact that Phoebe sees Mamie's doctor and Mamie sees Phoebe's doctor.[15] I hope you don't have plans like that.
DR. RICHARDS: No, I don't. How do you feel about it?
MISS BURTON: I wouldn't like it. I don't think they do either.
DR. RICHARDS: What is it that you wouldn't like?
MISS BURTON: I don't like to talk with people—it's difficult enough to talk to someone I know. I don't want to have to talk to someone I don't know.

Reassurance on specific points of her research obligations could counter Miss Burton's anxiety about what might be in store for her. Her generalized concern about her status as a research patient remained. General reassurance rarely dissolves a general anxiety that is situationally determined. Yet, Dr. Richards attempted to use this means also—to emphasize that he too had basic obligations in the relationship that he intended to observe for her welfare—as indicated in his therapy notes for April 26:

MISS BURTON: I guess I'll be taking some medicine this week.
DR. RICHARDS: Yes, probably on Thursday.
MISS BURTON: I don't—seem to have much to say today.
DR. RICHARDS: Why not?
MISS BURTON: I don't know—I just feel—it's all so pointless anyway. * * *
This weekend I've had that awful feeling of not being liked. Everything that people say seems to . . . I thought I'd forgotten . . . When I thought you wanted me to leave—that the only reason I'm here is because I'm taking the drug. That doesn't happen to anyone else. Every other doctor wants his patients.
[Dr. Richards' notes summarize:] Research and therapeutic program again formulated—that patient is to receive both research *and* rx [treatment].

The italics appear in the notes, reporting Dr. Richards' emphasis to the patient that he wanted to treat her.

---

15. This is a reference to the "Trade-Off," a project to be discussed in a later chapter.

Dr. Richards' attempt to get the patient interested in the research has already been mentioned. This kind of operation is perhaps the best cement for binding research patient and research physician in a common cause—if the physician considers it not as an instrument to achieve research cooperation from the patient, but as an affirmation of the worth and status of the patient. Such a partnership growing up between research patients and their physicians has been described by Renée Fox.[16] Although she does not specify the connections between the research versus treatment conflict and the partnership between doctor and patient, she concludes that the "patient-colleague" role for the research patient is one of the means by which the patients and physicians handle the stress of the conflict and several other stresses on the research ward she studied.[17]

In Dr. Richards' case, the partnership of patient and doctor was rather abortive, for he only partially subscribed to it himself. Nevertheless, such a relationship seems to appear in embryonic form in the remarks of Miss Burton during an interview I had with her on July 23, second year, from which I made notes immediately afterward:

[She reported that] she had told Bates and Richards that she would leave the hospital rather than take more LSD. Then Richards said that "he couldn't keep me as a patient unless I took it, so I agreed." Four times since then there have been "medicines" but no more LSD.

"Several times the medicine did not do anything to me." When it did, it was only for a few seconds, but then it was "rough." "They make me anxious, but Dr. Richards says that they do make people anxious. . . . He says I have a more marked reaction. That's why he likes to use me, because I have such a sensitivity to them."

Miss Burton is able in this interview with me to take the role of the clinical observer, the researcher, in looking at the activity in which she is engaged with Dr. Richards. She even

---

16. Renée C. Fox, *op. cit.*, see esp. pp. 89*ff.*

17. Fox rightly emphasizes another stress on the ward she studied—the stress involved in the fact that the patients were often terminally ill with the disorders about which the physicians knew too little to treat successfully. *Ibid.*, Chapter II.

takes a certain wry pride in her "sensitivity" to the experimental drugs, which makes her an especially good research subject. These evidences of an incipient partnership between Dr. Richards and Miss Burton are, however, accompanied by signs that Miss Burton did not fully accept the partner relation any more than did Dr. Richards. In the interview, she not unnaturally clung to the conception of herself as a patient in the hands of a doctor who was giving her "medicines." That is, she tended to reject the full implications of the research-subject component of her role—implications that she would have had to look at if she had considered herself in research partnership with Dr. Richards. Dr. Richards, on his part, sought only to engage the interest of his patient in the research, not to establish a partnership with her. As a technique for cementing their relationship it was perhaps useful but it was not as strongly binding as if the patient's interest had been that of a patient-colleague.

I have described in this chapter several techniques used by Dr. Thorpe and Dr. Richards in the service of their new defini- tion of their role as clinical researchers, especially vis-à-vis the patients. These were technical modifications in research practice; engaging the interest of the patient in the research; specifying the limits of the research obligations of the patient; and reaffirm- ing the therapeutic obligations of the physician. Other techniques were used by both doctors, but these illustrations underline the fact that the redefined role, although it was more easily per- formed, still required continued attention to maintain it in the face of the research-treatment conflict. Whatever role definition the research physician uses, he must continue to use minor adjustive techniques that will permit him to maintain his pre- ferred stance in balancing the conflicting demands of therapy and science. Dr. Thorpe and Dr. Richards evolved their role definitions under the constant stimuli of research-treatment conflicts; but they were not the only ones affected by the dilemmas of their project. In the next chapter I will conclude my review of their project by exploring some of its wider implications for the Center and its staff.

Five

THE LSD RESEARCH
SHOWS THE EFFECT
OF THE CONFLICT

❧

THE SPECIAL AIM of my study is to describe the ways in which science—even in its innermost parts—can be influenced by the social context that gives birth to it. Yet, up to this point, I have described only in general terms the way in which the LSD project was interrupted and changed by the therapy values in the research milieu. Now, in the first part of this chapter, I shall look at the specific scientific derivatives of the social conflict. In the last part of the chapter, I suggest two general reasons why it was inevitable that the research would be so influenced: first, because all of the staff, not just the project directors, were affected by the LSD conflict; and, second, because a variety of general social and cultural circumstances at the Center coalesced to make therapy values preferred over research values.

Influence on Research Design

The broadest effects upon the content and form of the research that the research-treatment conflict caused can be seen in changes made in the design of the project as it progressed. During the period in which Dr. Thorpe and Dr. Richards still contemplated using Mr. Pickett and Miss Burton as subjects for the study of LSD and depersonalization, the investigators made several changes in the plan of their research. All these were contingencies brought about by the apparent conflict between the patients' welfare and the doctors' research goals. The changes affected matters of research design such as the timing and number of drug administrations. It will be remembered that the psychiatrists planned to give one patient an injection every other week for about eight weeks, and the other patient an injection on the alternate weeks during the same period. After the strong feeling arose about the first administration of the drug, the psychiatrists waited for a number of weeks before trying to put their plan in operation again. The postponement, however, did not solve anything, so further changes in plans had to be considered. In the first conference (March 31, second year) after both patients had refused to cooperate, Dr. Thorpe reported changes in the number and scheduling of the doses.

DR. LOWE: What is the research plan for the LSD doses?
DR. THORPE: One or two times, with a control dose [placebo] during the illness and one more time after they are more or less cured. * * *
We abandoned many administrations [of the drug] for the patients. One or two administrations would highlight the disorder, as in Mary's case it did. Then one more for psychological testing during the period of influence. Then after cure, one more time. That would be two more doses and one placebo for Miss Burton. The control dose is not really necessary.
DR. RICHARDS: Oh, you need that.
DR. LOWE: Then it will be six, including the couple of duds?
DR. THORPE: Yes.

Even during this meeting, Dr. Thorpe expressed some indefiniteness about the new research design and considered cutting out the placebo, to decrease the number of times the patients would have to face the anxiety of another dose. Dr. Richards held fast to the necessity of a control dose (and in fact actually had Miss Burton take a saline injection, allowing her to think that she might be getting LSD), but he was agreeable to a decrease in the number of experimental doses. This extract also shows that the exact number of doses remained unclear in Dr. Thorpe's remarks until Dr. Lowe specified the minimum of six (rather than the apparent maximum of eight) that Dr. Thorpe wanted for both patients.

As Dr. Thorpe mentioned, they intended to give the patients psychological and physiological tests while under the LSD influence. The central one so far as Dr. Richards was concerned was the flicker-fusion test, which requires the subject to report at what point a light is flickering so fast that it seems to have fused into a single, steady beam. Dr. Richards expected, up to the last month that Miss Burton was his patient, to give her this test, telling me in an interview that he was waiting until he had a technician available. Yet in the end, even though the necessary technical assistance finally was available, he never determined her flicker-fusion threshold. I am not clear today why this test was scientifically important in the plans, but the point is that, while other tests (including equilibrium and certain perceptual tests) were administered to Miss Burton by Dr. Thorpe, Dr. Richards never determined one of the parameters that he had felt was significant for evaluating his own technical research questions. There is, of course, no reason not to make changes in one's research design as events suggest their necessity. In fact, one must often do so to take advantage of information gained as one works along. The crucial question here is whether those changes are made according to the logic of the research itself or whether other kinds of considerations suggest the changes. Since the logic of the research did not itself suggest changes, it seems clear that in the alterations of the research plans of the LSD project, scientifically irrelevant but socially potent influences in the environment of the work were operating to redesign the research.

Another change in the research plans was in the composition of the sample to be studied. It is, of course, standard procedure to select a new sample if, for one reason or another, the initial sample has been spoiled. This is true whether the sample is supposed to be white mice, soil plots, or college freshmen. So it is only to be expected that after the deadlock with Miss Burton and Mr. Pickett, Dr. Thorpe and Dr. Richards would have discussed the substitution of other patients—as in fact they did in the conferences reported. The use of other subjects theoretically would have permitted the research plans to be carried out as intended. It is significant therefore that the substitution of other subjects in the LSD research, with the elimination of Mr. Pickett and Miss Burton as research subjects, coincided with the period in which the most far-reaching changes in the research design came about. Both Dr. Thorpe and Dr. Richards sought out other persons for the LSD research—and at the same time each one changed his research focus. The coincidence of the new sample and new design within the same general period is noteworthy here.

For example, after Mr. Pickett and Miss Burton were eliminated as the research subjects, Dr. Richards replanned some of his work so as to use volunteer subjects; these subjects were conscientious objectors to military service who had volunteered to do any kind of hospital work as a substitute for military duty. Presumably they were normal young people and therefore would not show the depersonalization symptoms of severe mental illness. Yet the original research subjects—the patients—had been selected on the basis of having depersonalization symptoms, so that the use of normal volunteers did not constitute a repetition of the original research design. (Nor were they carefully selected as control subjects to be contrasted with mental patients.) Yet these normal subjects were the only group studied by Dr. Richards who ever received a full course of LSD doses.

At a later period, Dr. Richards was again able to obtain research access to a group of schizophrenic patients.[1] These patients, like the normal volunteers, were studied in a way different from the original plans for Mr. Pickett and Miss Burton: There was no plan to give any LSD to these new schizophrenic patients, and naturally, they never received any. In brief, then, Dr. Richards gave LSD to his normal subjects and no LSD to his schizophrenic subjects, after the elimination of Mr. Pickett

---

1. Note that for these patients, as of course for the normal volunteers, Dr. Richards assumed no psychotherapeutic obligations. All subjects were under the care and supervision of a cooperating physician.

and Miss Burton. These changes were not dictated by simple scientific considerations of a new research sample. As Dr. Richards told me, a month or so after he transferred Miss Burton to Dr. Steiger, he never finished his LSD work; he simply went on to other studies.

In discussing next the changes made by Dr. Thorpe in the research design after the elimination of Miss Burton and Mr. Pickett, it seems pertinent to review Dr. Thorpe's original plan, put forth before any patients had been admitted to the Center. In essence, Dr. Thorpe saw at that time no conflict between his research and his therapy. He planned a "longitudinal study," which would make it possible for him to make a long-term therapeutic commitment to the research patients without jeopardizing his research design. This longitudinal study would include a study of both the drug and progress of the therapy itself. As to the question of how he could make a long-term therapy commitment and also acquire new subjects for extending the research, Dr. Thorpe felt that additional subjects could be admitted by virtue of "turnover upon improvement, I hope." That is, he expected to get new patients to replace patients who had therapeutically improved enough to be discharged.

Soon after Miss Burton was transferred to Dr. Steiger, Dr. Thorpe actually admitted another patient who showed depersonalization; and she later received a series of LSD injections. But coincidentally with bringing in this patient he made two changes in his research plans. First, he decided to study the facilitating effect that the LSD would have on the patient's communications in the therapy hour; he planned the drug as a means of increasing the patient's communicative behavior with him. In other words, the LSD was to be tested as a therapeutic adjunct.[2] The other change was that Dr. Thorpe abandoned the idea of longitudinal study of depersonalization with this patient and abandoned any idea of a long-term therapeutic commitment to the patient. The

---

2. As has been mentioned earlier, LSD came to be used in many parts of the country as a therapeutic adjunct to facilitate therapist-patient interchange. Dr. Thorpe himself had used the drug with that purpose in research before he came to the Center.

patient was specifically admitted for the period of the LSD experiment only; upon completion of the observations, Dr. Thorpe intended to send her to another hospital.[3] In short, Dr. Thorpe, like Dr. Richards, accompanied his change of research subjects with a change in his research goals and procedures. Neither researcher carried out his part of the research as originally planned. In fact, they did not even continue their collaboration with each other.[4]

Influence on the Research Process

As I have just indicated, the anxieties inherent in the general and the acute conflict between research and therapy in the work of Dr. Thorpe and Dr. Richards ultimately refashioned their study of LSD and depersonalization. However, there were also evidences of the deflective and shaping power of that conflict on a lesser level—on the actual process of the original research as it was carried out, aside from changes in design. I refer here to minor interferences with good research procedure. Two of these have been mentioned in another context: Dr. Bates forgot to write the order for the first dose for Miss Burton, and Dr. Dirainey left his observation post to ask Dr. Richards to stop the effect of the drug by giving Miss Burton a barbiturate. That is, the conflict interfered with the execution of the researchers' directives to their colleagues, Drs. Bates and Dirainey. The meaning of these two events is not merely my interpretation, for they were discussed by the participants themselves in a full staff conference on April 7, second year:

DR. RICHARDS: . . . we were not alone in being unclear and feeling anxious. It was communicated to the patients by all of us.

---

3. The patient actually stayed somewhat longer, at the request of the nursing staff, as will be discussed later on.

4. Of course, I do not intend to suggest that the project ended simply because of the stress of the research-therapy conflict. Also important were the researchers' different interests, different conceptions of significant psychiatric processes, personality needs, and so on, combined with the usual stresses of an early stage in the development of a program.

DR. LOWE: Yes, the nurses were very concerned, for example.

DR. RICHARDS: There were some guilt feelings transmitted by the group.

DR. DIRAINEY: If we all felt that this was a *research* hospital, there would be less of this uncertainty. * * * The mixed motivations give us problems.

DR. RICHARDS (*speaking to Dr. Dirainey*): Look at your own reaction. (*Speaking to the staff group*:) One-half hour after the dose, he ran in to me and said, "God, stop this; I feel like a ghoul."

DR. DIRAINEY: Yes, I wonder if it is really worth while to upset the patients and the nurses—not to speak of me—with this research!

DR. RICHARDS: Even before that, Bates forgot to write the order, even though everything was scheduled for the first dose. * * *

DR. LOWE: What we have come to is that it is a group reaction.

In neither of these two instances of interference with the research was there, in all likelihood, any ultimately bad effect upon the research. But other evidence indicates more definitely adverse influences upon good research procedure.

A review of the formal hospital records indicates, for instance, that, except for sleeping pills, aspirin, and the like, Miss Burton's medication chart carries only one drug entry—the first LSD dose. None of the succeeding experimental drugs was recorded on her chart. Also, an unsigned entry on the patient's summary sheet records "experimental ampoule"—the LSD—as being administered ten months later than it was actually given according to all other records. The date was obviously incorrectly entered at the time the drug was given. These errors of recording subvert the normal requirements of research. They appear to be mainly the outcome of the conflict as experienced by the nurses; but the physicians were also responsible for maintaining an adequate record for future research.

Similar lapses are difficult to establish for the therapy notes kept by Dr. Richards, the only other regularly kept (if more informal) record available to me for research purposes. Yet, even here, there is some indication of such a lapse. The sign is the increasing sparseness of the therapy notes after the crisis that ended with Miss Burton's agreement to take the drug again. These notes, taken by Dr. Richards during the therapy hour, get shorter and shorter, until he actually transfers the patient to

Dr. Steiger. Keeping an adequate longitudinal research record of the progress of therapy was important for Dr. Thorpe's part of the research, and Dr. Richards as an experienced and conscientious researcher knew that; yet this crucial record simply diminished to the point that it was scarcely useful.

To summarize, I have reviewed explicit illustrations of the way in which the research efforts of Drs. Thorpe and Richards were shaped by the conflict they experienced. The research was actually changed in content and process. In the research process of the project, the influence of the conflict caused changes that were clearly handicapping of good research. As to the effects of changes in research design, aims, and objectives—changes in content—it would be difficult to judge the changed quality of the research. There is no reason to suppose that socially aroused anxieties in a researcher's work might not actually cause him to do better work just as easily as it might cause him to do worse.[5] Perhaps the inquiry into depersonalization and into the psychological effects of LSD in the later work of Dr. Thorpe and Dr. Richards became more refined in research not examined here, but it is not my aim to maintain that the social influences in the research laboratory are good—or bad. I have examined the LSD project in such detail mainly to demonstrate that scientific research need not be considered as an activity that proceeds only on its own logic. I want now to inquire into some of the reasons

---

5. On the other hand, unrecognized anxiety and its sources will undoubtedly plague a research project with technical and other difficulties that can result in a poorer research product than the same persons with more awareness, might produce. It is in the nature of anxiety that it reduces the effectiveness of goal-directed behavior if only because much of one's energy must be devoted to handling the anxiety aroused by that very behavior. However, when anxiety signals are recognized and their sources searched for, discovered, and dealt with, the researcher may be in a better position to construct creative solutions to the technical problems he handles. Anxiety, according to Sullivan, is one of the most educative experiences one can undergo. Compare his vector analysis of the effects of anxiety: Harry Stack Sullivan, *The Interpersonal Theory of Psychiatry* (edited by Helen Swick Perry and Mary Ladd Gawel); New York: Norton, 1953, esp. pp. 94-98. See also, Jurgen Ruesch and A. Rodney Prestwood, "Anxiety: Its Initiation, Communication, and Interpersonal Management," *Arch. Neurol. & Psychiat.* (1949) 62: 527-50.

why it seems, on hindsight, that the project investigators could not have easily escaped the influences upon their research.

The LSD Conflict as Shared by the Group

To expect that Dr. Thorpe and Dr. Richards could have somehow managed to evade the effect of the research-therapy conflict upon their scientific work is to expect that they could have freed themselves from experiencing the same general reaction to the LSD research that everyone else in the entire group had, including persons not connected with the project. The LSD conflict was not peculiar to the principal investigators; it was a general experience, a socially shared phenomenon. The evidence that others besides Dr. Thorpe and Dr. Richards experienced an anxious conflict between research and treatment in the course of the LSD research is fairly straightforward. I will begin with the conflict as experienced by those closest to the project but not conducting the research, Drs. Bates and Dirainey, and then move on to the nursing staff, patients other than the original two subjects, other psychiatrists in the Center, and nonmedical research personnel.

It will be useful to recall, first, some of the evidence already presented. For example, in the initial exchanges about the project in a group meeting (as reported in Chapter 3), Dr. Thorpe's presentation of his depersonalization study aroused general anxiety in the group participants. In other words, before the project even began, staff members were sensitized and vulnerable to signs of any serious conflict. It will be recalled further that one of the other physicians (Dr. Oxford) was rebuked by his colleagues at that same meeting for suggesting that inducing psychosis might be a good way to treat psychosomatic patients. LSD, of course, is a psychosis-inducing substance. Moreover, the drug was not to be used as an adjunct to treatment, but merely for research. Thus the stage was set for general staff reaction to the slightest difficulty in the LSD research, despite the support the research received from Dr. Lowe.

I have already reported the reactions of those who dealt immediately with Miss Burton on the first drug dose. Dr. Dirainey tried to get Dr. Richards to give Miss Burton a sedative. Even before that, Dr. Bates had forgotten to write his order for the drug—a slip that fed into the nurses' upset. Dr. Bates had tried to give the nurses an orientation lecture but, as they complained later, it had not prepared them for the patient's reaction.

Actually, the nurses were so upset and concerned about the patient that they felt helpless to do anything for her while she was feeling the worst of the effects. What especially handicapped them was their concern lest they interfere with the research observations of Miss Burton's psychotic behavior; that is, they thought that if they tried and succeeded in calming her down, the full effect of the drug might be minimized and therefore inaccurate for the purposes of research. Thus Dr. Bates found to his consternation, late in the afternoon of the day that Miss Burton took the LSD, that the nurses had not even seen to it that the patient had had lunch.

The other patients were also affected. For instance, Miss Burton's roommates were frightened and resentful of the hospital for the way in which Miss Burton had been treated. In an interview with me on July 23, second year, Miss Burton herself summed up well the reaction of everyone who had any significant contact with the event. My interview report reads:

What do the other patients feel about her research procedures, I asked. [She answered:] "Everyone was upset—no one thought it would affect me so strongly. Even the nurses were unprepared for it." The patients were pretty anxious, she said, and of course she felt bad too, and anxiety is contagious.

Even though Miss Burton said that the anxiety was contagious, she probably did not realize how much it spread. It gathered the clinical research unit into a common camp, although each person had his own particular way of handling the anxiety.

In fact, the LSD research loomed as an acute heightening of

a problem built into the purpose and structure of the Center.
It set off a rolling current of uneasy feeling that spurted out at
a general staff meeting.[6] This was the one meeting, mentioned
earlier, that arose from Dr. Lowe's suggestion that everyone
might benefit from a general discussion. Limitations of space do
not permit the quotation of the record I made of that meeting—
which, in any case, simply recapitulates much of what I have
already reported. However, a feeling for what happened in the
group can be communicated by noting the various techniques
that different staff members called up to dissipate their anxiety.
One psychologist cracked jokes—at which only a few even
tittered.[7] One psychiatrist tried to wall himself off from it all by
reiterating again and again that whatever decisions were made
about getting the patients to cooperate with the LSD research,
he wanted to be sure that no policy was being established that
would bind him in his relations with his patients. (His repeated
truculence on this exasperated the director and the chairman of
the meeting, who apparently got tired of repeating that the
meeting was not intended to set policy.) Another psychiatrist
participated only briefly but impugned the honesty of one of the
LSD researchers. Others, including myself, withdrew into silence,
and so on and so forth.

---

6. The phenomenon of emotional contagion in a small group has been
described by Fritz Redl and others, and systematic research has been
undertaken by a number of workers. See, for example, Norman Polansky,
Ronald Lippitt, and Fritz Redl, "An Investigation of Behavioral Contagion
in Groups," *Hum. Relat.* (1950) 3: 319-48. See also Jurgen Ruesch and A.
Rodney Prestwood, *op. cit.* The constriction of trust as a concomitant of
spreading anxiety suggests analogues in economic deflation and in the
downward spiral of political trust as in witch hunts. See Talcott Parsons,
"On the Concept of Political Power," *Proc. Amer. Philos. Soc.* (1963) 107:
232-62. On the collective disturbance in the mental hospital, see Stanton and
Schwartz, *op. cit.,* Chap. 17.

7. Of course, humor is recognized as an effective dissipator of anxiety.
For a review of the literature with special reference to the medical setting,
see Renée C. Fox, *op. cit.,* esp. p. 110. Since group consensus can give
birth to good jokes that are well appreciated, the failure of the psychologist's humor may indicate the lack of consensus in the group on means of
regarding and handling the research-therapy conflict. See Rose Laub Coser,
Life in the Ward, East Lansing, Mich.: Michigan State University Press,
1962, esp. pp. 84*ff.*

Without dwelling upon my own experience, it is perhaps useful to comment here that not only in the course of conducting
the data-gathering operations but months or years later in the
analysis of this project, I have recurrently undergone a good
deal of anxiety about the rights and wrongs of the situation, and
I assume that the reader too will have vicariously undergone the
conflict-anxiety that this case invoked. The intellectualization
and sociological conceptualization in this study serve not only
intellectual functions but also the function of dealing with the
conflict itself.[8]

There are then a variety of ways in which the research-
therapy conflict becomes visible as a socially shared phenomenon,
even in this single case history. While there were no common or
nearly common ways of handling the conflict that the LSD
project aroused, there were nevertheless common standards that
the clinical research unit shared among themselves and with
professionals and nonprofessionals beyond the walls of the hospital. This degree of consensus appears in the choices made
during the course of the LSD project that point to the preponderance of therapy values over research values—a preponderance that could only mean that the research would be heavily
affected.

The Preference for Therapy Values
and the Good-Bad Dilemma

Now I would like to argue the proposition that when therapy
values are socially invoked they will be preferred over research
values. This, like other generalizations I have made about clinical
research, is of course based primarily on the operation of one
research center—in which the director was a committed clinician
as well as a competent researcher. I have anecdotal reports on

---

8. Fox emphasizes the intellectual commitment to research as one of the
ways of coming to terms with the clinical researcher's problems. Renée C.
Fox, *ibid.*

another research center in which the director is not considered as proficient a clinician and in which research was apparently given preference over treatment a good deal more frequently. I hope sometime to do comparative studies that presumably would indicate the influence of such things as unit leadership. Whatever the immediate leadership, however, the social-cultural environment will probably be more important. Without the kind of generalized social support that existed in Nazi Germany,[9] for example, I do not think that the most determined research director can insulate his unit from the influence of the medical tradition of service and the Judaic-Christian emphases on "duty" and "love" that pervade Western civilization and its professions today. These values, I shall argue, will tend to supersede those of knowledge and science in the clinical setting.[10] Specifically, I want to point out here the circumstances in which Drs. Thorpe and Richards rejected their own research interests in favor of carrying out actions presumed to favor the patients' welfare. My contention is that if the research psychiatrist is faced in group interactions with a choice between research and treatment—as they are defined in his group—he will find it virtually impossible in our culture to resist a choice in favor of therapeutic considerations.

The practical issue for Dr. Thorpe and Dr. Richards was whether or not to insist that their patients take LSD. Dr. Thorpe chose to give up the idea of giving LSD to Mr. Pickett, even

---

9. See Alexander Mitscherlich and Fred Mielke, *Doctors of Infamy* (Heinz Norden, tr.), New York: Henry Schuman, 1949.

10. The significance of this weighting of therapy over research is not to be seen simply in the extreme cases in which it is clear that the patient's life or continued health is threatened by research; of course, it would be only a truism to say that science ordinarily backs off from situations like that. The critical points for decision are those in which the patient's welfare cannot be so clearly distinguished. These are the situations that tax philosopher, scientist, and practitioner alike. Illustrations of the complicated technical problems that can be involved in clinical trials of new drugs in psychiatry are found in Jonathan O. Cole and Ralph W. Gerard, eds., *Psychopharmacology: Problems in Evaluation,* Washington: National Academy of Sciences-National Research Council, 1959; see esp. pp. 394ff., for a consideration of toxicity as a criterion for terminating use of a drug or reducing dosage during an experiment.

though he had Mr. Pickett's preliminary agreement before admitting him to the hospital. Dr. Richards chose to insist that Miss Burton take the drug, but he never required her to take the drug, even though he got her to accept his ultimatum. Each physician, in his own way, came to define the drug requirement as simply not feasible. Giving up the research meant a considerable sacrifice for the investigators, but they did it, almost in spite of themselves. There were certain secondary adjustments (which have already been described in the first section of this chapter) that eased the renunciation for the two researchers, so that I do not imply that their investment in research was completely jettisoned. Nevertheless, this simple fact remains: Of all the LSD doses planned for Mr. Pickett and Miss Burton, only one was ever given.

Despite this fact, another student of the same situation might be disposed to argue that, for example, Dr. Richards' discharge of his patient—that is, her transfer to Dr. Steiger, the doctor who was interested in problems of alcoholism and orality—adds up to an abdication of therapeutic responsibilities that quite overweighs his discontinuing the LSD research. To my mind, the evidence will not unequivocally support that view. Looking at the total history of Miss Burton's relationship to the Center and the specific functions of her transfer, one can recognize the importance of therapy values in her Center experience. Two specific actions of Dr. Richards will illustrate this: the initial false impression he gave Miss Burton that the decision to take the LSD was up to her; and his transfer of her to Dr. Steiger. Each of these events looked at merely in and of itself assuredly bespeaks a certain devaluation of the therapy aspects of his relationship to the patient. Yet, in neither of these actions was Dr. Richards simply acting in terms of research values, and in both instances certain very important therapeutic aims were achieved.

In the matter of the formulation to Miss Burton "it's up to you," the following circumstances should be recalled: (1) Dr. Richards was thereby trying to carry out arrangements that had been made by Dr. Thorpe, the more clinically sophisticated of the two, on whom Dr. Richards depended for clinical administration. (2) The arrangements had apparently received ratification from Dr. Lowe, whose interest in establishing a good clinical operation ahead of any early research results was often stressed. (3) Restricting the patients' knowledge of their therapists' research plans was planned to make things less complicated for the patients—with the patients' welfare in mind. (4) Dr. Richards' remark that it was up to her rested upon what was considered by all the physicians one of Miss Burton's primary needs—that is, to assert herself.

None of these circumstances can disguise the fact that Dr. Richards was engaged in a complex interpersonal operation that threatened the therapy relationship. As Dr. Lowe pointed out, when a therapist denies responsibility for administrative decisions, the patient is apt to consider this as "a trick, a manipulation." [11] At the same time, it must be admitted that when Dr. Richards' remark to Miss Burton is viewed in the context of the four cited circumstances, it cannot be considered as a univocal devaluation of therapeutic values. Therapeutic considerations surely were involved.

The transfer of the patient to Dr. Steiger also must be viewed in the context of the larger social system of the psychiatric program; then it too can be recognized as furthering therapeutic values. The transfer of Miss Burton from Dr. Richards to Dr. Steiger was an event within the unit that, while it freed Dr. Richards from obligations to his therapy patient and gave him time for other duties, honored an implicit commitment by the entire staff to Miss Burton's therapeutic needs. The action set her up in treatment with a therapist who outranked everyone except the director in seniority of experience and training, a psychiatrist defined by himself and most others as a good therapist (and an unlikely researcher). Some data from interviews and records, not heretofore presented, is necessary to support these assertions. Particularly revealing are notes

---

11. Further, other staff often recognize that arrangements touted as "for the patient's benefit" are clearly motivated by the need to solve certain staff problems. Stanton and Schwartz (*op. cit.*, Chap. 7) have discussed a decision to discharge certain patients as an example of this.

made by one of the nurses in the patient's chart, on August 17, second year:

Suddenly Mary sat up and said to me, "Did you know I'm getting a new doctor?" Quite spontaneously I replied, "Who?" and she said. "Dr. Steiger." Again I was real pleased and gave forth with "Oh, Mary, I'm so happy—I think it is wonderful."

The reaction of the nurse indicates the relative personifications of Dr. Richards and Dr. Steiger as therapists, by the nursing staff. Miss Burton herself saw the situation in the same way in an interview I had with her, a couple of months after the transfer, on November 15:

MISS BURTON: I'm getting along better than with Dr. Richards. Of course, I'm not taking the medicine—which is nice. Dr. Richards did ask me last week if I would take some again. I said, No, because it makes me too anxious.
INTERVIEWER: Is Dr. Steiger doing any research? .
MISS BURTON: Yes, research with psychoanalysis—not like Richards . . . Apparently Dr. Steiger is interested in alcoholism, and I used to have—guess I still do have a problem there. The therapy sessions are recorded.
INTERVIEWER: Is that for research purposes?
MISS BURTON: It's for both.
I like him as a person and as a doctor. * * *
I guess there was some conflict in me with Richards. I think I found it a little confusing to have him as an analyst while he was doing the research. If he was going to do that, I would have liked to have had someone else as an analyst. It was a little confusing.
INTERVIEWER: How was it confusing?
MISS BURTON: I wondered, Is he a really good analyst if he is so interested in the other side—research. I wondered, How could I get well if he is not [a good analyst]. I felt that Richards was more interested in the scientific side. He probably will not continue with providing psychoanalysis for other patients. He told me that he was more interested from the physiological standpoint. It was basically this that he was interested in. [He was] more cut out to be that. I'm glad that it came about this way—that he did not have enough time to continue seeing me for psychoanalysis.

Thus Miss Burton felt satisfied with the outcome. The choice of Dr. Steiger was the result of consultations held by Dr. Bates with a number of colleagues; the transfer was a group decision;

it was not suggested by Dr. Richards. The unit as a group, through Dr. Bates' leadership, participated in placing Miss Burton with one of its senior therapists.

In sum, the transfer can easily be interpreted as a general decision with direct benefit to the patient. True, Dr. Richards' discharge of Miss Burton also had the meaning of his giving up therapeutic obligations for the patient. But the matter is more complicated than that, and even the events that seem most apparently ranged against the therapeutic values turn out, upon inspection, to have clear therapeutic advantages. In assessing the significance of the action of a group member, one has to see the manner in which it is handled by the group processes. In this respect, the transfer of Miss Burton to Dr. Steiger highlights the generalized therapeutic value preferences of the group.

It is on the basis of such considerations, in conjunction with the explicit weight given to therapeutic obligations in the therapists' discussions and decisions, that one can conclude that once the clinical research issue has been defined in terms of either research or therapy, therapy would be preferred.[12] Once the whole problem of getting the patients to take LSD was defined in this way, there was little room for the principal investigators to maneuver. They were situationally induced to accept and to further their therapeutic goals as most important and to downgrade their research goals.

Three circumstances serve to channel decisions in the direction of preferring therapeutic values: (1) the social dynamics of a moral dispute in which no one wants to be on the side of

12. The leverage of therapeutic values against research considerations is also illustrated in Dr. Thorpe's retention of the third patient he selected for the LSD research. As mentioned before, he had intended to discharge the patient as soon as the experimental period of drug injections was concluded, but the nurses objected to the discharge a few days before it was to take place. The nursing staff felt that they could do something useful for the patient and wanted the chance to help her. Dr. Thorpe acceded to their request though he was not completely agreeable to it. This shows how subordinates can prevail against a higher status person when the issue can be defined as the patient's welfare. How long the nurses could have prevailed in this case is an unanswered question, for the patient very shortly committed suicide.

evil; (2) the general scheme of values of Western society from which medicine as treatment rather than medicine as science is more easily deduced, so to speak; and (3) the absence of clear criteria of empirical evidence for value choices in psychiatry, an absence which makes nonempirical standards of values—broadly speaking, standards unrelated to science—relevant and applicable.

The LSD project revisions involved the invocation of a moral basis for action, for the scientist as a clinical researcher does not discard his allegiance to the basic moral commitments of his culture. It was to this effect that I earlier discussed the physicians' formulation of the LSD problem as the issue of "unfriendliness." When the conferees asked themselves whether they were "unfriendly" or not, they were harking back to broader and more fundamental standards for judgment than those explicit in the medical subculture. They were in fact not only wondering if they were being good doctors, they were asking themselves if they were good people.

The formulation of a clinical issue in psychiatry (whether or not research is involved) has a special resonance with questions of morality. One is, after all, dealing with matters of personal behavior, most of which have a loading of moral evaluations dating back for each participant to eras in his life long before he assumed the role of medical scientist. This is a problem which of course has often been recognized and analyzed acutely. I mean here only to note its relevance to any conflict between science and medical care in a clinical research operation. Essentially, what happens is that in the absence of a consensus on empirical standards of psychiatric knowledge, disputants are forced to fall back upon latent standards of moral evaluation. On these terms there often arise vivid jockeyings for position as "the good guys" and attempts to define matters so that the others are "the bad guys" who do not want what is beneficial for the patient.

In the good-bad dilemma there is only room for one side to be good. It is the old zero-sum game. One has to lose what the other has won. What loads the dice against research considerations in a clinical program is the fact that the good guy's role is already preempted by representatives of therapy. Obviously, then, science is represented by the bad guys. The medical traditions of service are articulated much more closely with the basic moral grounds for action in the Judaic-Christian culture than are the scientific aims of wisdom and knowledge. I need only mention the Faust motif in the arts and literature, in order to call up the issue from our cultural past. Many intimate relations can exist between the administrative, scientific decisions on a psychiatric research project and the broad, basic cultural heritage shared by a research group, and I have only suggested one possible aspect of these relations here.[13]

In summary, I have argued that in any conflict between therapy and research in a clinical research operation, the chances are that therapeutic values will supersede research values, if the conflict can be explicitly defined and accepted by the main participants as research pitted against treatment values—rather than defined by them as, say, "interpersonal difficulties," and so on. The circumstances that lead to an outcome in favor of the patient include such features of the clinical research milieu as the absence of clearly applicable empirical standards for psychiatric judgments; the social dynamics of deciding moral issues, which often force people into black-white choices; and the close relationship of medicine-as-service to the fundamental moral values of Western civilization.

---

13. Hans Selye grapples with another interesting moral-cultural problem for the medical scientist that arises out of different evaluations of the responsibility of the moral person in society: How much time should the researcher take from his studies, in order to deal with public issues, such as good government, war and peace, and so on? Selye defends his own relative disavowal of any such public responsibilities by citing the service of science. Note, however, that Selye can defend his choice only by invoking the value of knowledge for its moral uses, not knowledge for its own value. See *From Dream to Discovery: On Being a Scientist*, New York: McGraw-Hill, 1964.

Six

OTHER PSYCHIATRISTS
TRY TO SOLVE
THE CONFLICT

❦

To DEMONSTRATE that the medical scientist often undergoes a conflict between his scientific aspirations and his treatment goals in clinical research leads easily enough to the conjecture that he will try to minimize the conflict as much as possible. The first crucial question then becomes, How does he do it? I approach this question by considering that each psychiatrist must develop an over-all work style and that having done so, he will engage in various minor social techniques that enable him to maintain that style. The second crucial question is, How do these standard styles and techniques affect the content and procedures of his scientific research?

Types of Work Styles

Work styles (or so-called role definitions) may be examined by using two foci for determining the structural arrangements designed to avert or handle conflict. First, there are the technical maneuvers for integrating research and treatment procedures. Second, there are social maneuvers between the patient and the physician, by which each sorts out and handles the different obligations and privileges of each.

The technical problems of dovetailing research and treatment are those of determining the precise timing, methods, places, and personnel that will be utilized for achieving one or both goals. But given the limitations imposed by the technical considerations, the choices that may be made tend to be governed by the particular social values and their priorities, as held by the actors. The conflict, thus, is a conflict of social values, not of techniques. At the same time, some combination of the factors that constitute the technical situation are more conflict-inducing than others. For example, the application of standard diagnostic and therapeutic techniques as a research method will arouse less conflict than the application of untried techniques. Similarly, the experimental therapies will arouse less conflict than the use of a drug merely for the purpose of obtaining information unrelated to any medical regimen or treatment. It has seemed to me that technical decisions are related to the basic choices in the social style of relationship between the research physician and his research patient. Consequently I shall take some time now to go into detail about the modes of relating to the patient that the physician may choose. These provide the framework within which he makes his technical decisions—decisions that, however, seem to solve social problems as well.

The psychiatrist as a research physician has an especially complicated task. His work depends upon a capacity for psychological introspection, unless he happens to be only somatically oriented. He must be particularly aware of his own and others' motivations and feelings. He must be alert to the evaluation of any point of choice in his relationship with the patient. This becomes particularly complicated when the same act by the psychiatrist can have (and most often does have) multiple meanings, especially conflicting meanings. The event that especially poses the issue for the research psychiatrist is the action that can be defined as either research or treatment; and having been defined as one or the other, the event can imply and justify quite different further actions.

A good example of this complication is illustrated by "The Permissive Ward," a project organized by Dr. Dirainey. The

Permissive Ward was organized so that the nursing staff had the widest latitude to respond to patients as they thought necessary; the patients themselves were permitted the widest latitude in behavior; and the psychiatrist assumed mainly a consultative role, rather than a directive one. The patients, chronic, almost mute schizophrenics who had been hospitalized for many years, were expected to respond best to the situation in which they determined all decisions taken as to their life on the ward. In order to rouse patients out of old patterns so that they could take advantage of the opportunity for self-determination, LSD was prescribed for half the patients, randomly chosen. The main research question was whether LSD was useful for this purpose.

Other research questions had to do with the social expectations of behavior on the ward, for they were somewhat unusual. The general pattern of nursing behavior throughout the psychiatric service was definitely permissive rather than restrictive, but on Dr. Dirainey's ward, the expectation of permissiveness was carried a step further. For example, if a quite withdrawn and inactive patient had not bathed for several weeks, the idea that it would be good for him to bathe could not be used as a rationale to force him into the shower. If the patient's body odor became so offensive that the nurses complained to Dr. Dirainey about it and suggested that they bathe the patient, Dr. Dirainey would say only that the nurses should recognize that they were bathing the patient for themselves, not for the patient's sake. He neither granted nor withheld permission for the nurses to bathe such a patient. Each staff member accepted the reality that another staff member might at times require the patient to do something that the patient did not want, but it was presumably clear to all concerned that this requirement should not be rationalized as for the patient's good.

Dr. Dirainey himself faced this accentuated social expectation, in carrying out his research. His study required that the patients undergo one standard interview before several weeks of intermittently administered drugs and one interview afterwards. The patients came to an interview room where their interaction with a psychologist-interviewer was photographed.

Some of the patients were very loathe to enter the room, and they had to be cajoled and even physically pushed into it by the nursing staff on Dr. Dirainey's request. This was by no means an easy task for the nurses, but it was actually fairly disturbing to Dr. Dirainey who could be observed in another room, quite agitated and exclaiming that his own demands on the patients were going to set them back from the improved state that they had reached after some months of care at the Center.

The Permissive Ward project can be compared to the First LSD Research for a further illustration of the difficulty faced by the psychiatrist in trying to sort out his interactions with the patient. Both these projects used LSD, but with different intent.

In the First LSD Research, the drug was defined as purely a research tool for the study of anxiety responses and depersonalization. In the Permissive Ward, LSD was used as a means of upsetting the chronic schizophrenic equilibrium of long-term patients in order to provide an entry for psychotherapeutic intervention. In the research on the permissive ward, the drug was considered a therapeutic adjunct, and the research was geared to determining whether or not the LSD was helpful for treatment. Although the researchers on the First LSD Research were aware that they could define the LSD as treatment and thus presumably could prescribe it for the patients without the same difficulty as when it was defined as research,[1] an examination of their own motives at the time did not permit them to do this. One of the principal investigators in the First LSD Research, Dr. Thorpe, complained in a staff meeting on the project, "This shows the difficulty of being honest."

Indeed, that difficulty is built into the psychiatrist's job, for to do his work properly he must try to be as clear as he can about his own motives, actions, emotions—his own participation in general—in any relationship with a patient. If he then recognizes that some particular act is planned for research purposes, he must engage in adjustive processes in order to complete the

---

1. Dr. Thorpe had administered LSD as a therapy in the initial research he conducted before coming to the Center; he did so again with the third patient he admitted at the Center.

act—or even to contemplate the act further. The psychiatrist's operations with a patient are supposed to be in the patient's interests.[2] In any instance in which the psychiatrist comes to the realization that he is not so acting or planning to act on some level, he must have a means of dealing with that recognition in his relationship with the patient.

Various adjustive movements in the therapy relationship grow out of the full or partial recognition by the participants of some deviation from the conventional relations of doctor and patient. These adjustments help to sustain both doctor and patient in their conception of the relationship and of each other's part in it.[3] The constant concurrent presence of other goals in the therapist's mind (so to speak) for his interaction with the patient requires constant concurrent use of these adjustive techniques. The chronic problem for the research psychiatrist requires, for instance, that he sort out the prerogatives that go with doing research for himself and those that go with doing

2. For the sake of simplicity I have not distinguished between a general concern for the patient's well-being and the specific concern about his particular disease or disorder. The physician often balances the advantages of therapeutically correcting a specific malcondition with the disadvantages that the therapy may have for the over-all well-being of the patient. This and other potential conflicts inhere in the physician's multiple responsibilities—even when he does not conduct clinical research. Stanton and Schwartz (*op. cit.*) note the conflict between responsibility to the community and to the patient in the care of the mentally ill. Rapoport has studied in detail the disparity between "rehabilitation and treatment" as psychiatric techniques. Robert N. Rapoport, *Community as Doctor: New Perspectives on a Therapeutic Community*, Springfield, Ill.: Charles C Thomas, 1961, especially Chap. 3, "Unit Ideology."

3. The sustaining techniques of interpersonal interaction have been variously described by theorists of self as "defense mechanisms" (Anna Freud), "security operations" (H. S. Sullivan), and so on. Contemporary formulations in terms of role theory [for example, Erving Goffman, *The Presentation of Self in Everyday Life* (monograph No. 2), Edinburgh: University of Edinburgh Social Sciences Research Centre, 1956 and New York: Anchor ed., 1959] have widened and elaborated conceptions of sustaining techniques by continuing the melding of social theory and psychodynamic theory. See Theodore R. Sarbin, "Role Theory," Chap. 6, in Gardner Lindzey, ed., *Handbook of Social Psychology*, Vol. I, Cambridge, Mass.: Addison-Wesley Press, 1954. For a consideration of psychiatric theories themselves as sustaining techniques, see Alfred H. Stanton. "Psychiatric Theory and Institutional Context," *op. cit.*

therapy for someone else. The adjustive techniques available to him deal somehow with the conflicts between research and treatment, to dissipate, neutralize, or otherwise dispose of them permanently or temporarily, successfully or unsuccessfully, clearly or vaguely. These techniques evolve a work style and can be conceptualized as either role-defining operations or role-maintaining operations. The role-defining operations make up the generalized postures with which the physicians meet the conflict in its chronic or inherent form. The role-maintaining operations are the lesser adjustments to each acute signal of the over-all conflict; they serve not only to meet the acute conflict but to sustain the generalized posture—the role definition—that the physician has chosen as his over-all solution to the conflict.

Concepts of Role Conflict and Its Resolution

Role conflict as it has been conceived in social psychology and sociology is the competition of two or more roles that simultaneously imply mutually exclusive actions.[4] For example, a psychiatrist in his role as a citizen will feel the obligation to report some serious illegal action on the part of his patient, but in his role as a psychiatrist he will feel a competing obligation to respect the patient's confidences about the illegal behavior, to consider it part of the mental illness, and to refrain from reporting it.[5] This conception of role conflict differs slightly from the one that I have been using. I am talking about the case of two conflicting roles, scientist and doctor, that are united in one hybrid role, clinical researcher. The result is that the conflicts occur between two sets of expectations that have been

---

4. A very good recent discussion of role conflict theory is in Neal Gross, *et al.*, *Explorations in Role Analysis*, New York: Wiley, 1957, esp. Chap. 17. See also Sarbin, *op. cit.* Work in this specific concept was begun in Samuel A. Stouffer, "An Analysis of Conflicting Social Norms," *Amer. Sociol. Rev.* (1949) 14: 707-17.

5. See the study by Ralph B. Little and Edward A. Strecker, "Moot Questions in Psychiatric Ethics," *Amer. J. Psychiat.* (1956) 113: 455-60.

only incompletely fitted together within the single new role.[6] The latter sort of role conflict is more difficult to avoid; because it is built in, certain resolution mechanisms are ruled out. For example, if the person is under pressure because of *two competing roles* he may use the technique of playing off the social group pertinent to the one role against the group pertinent to the other. This is illustrated in the behavior of elected officials who also have another occupational identification. For example, a conservative businessman will and generally must cite his responsibilities to the wider community when he is elected to Congress and can no longer be as conservative as he once was.[7] The psychiatrist as clinical researcher, however, is faced with the conflict within the bounds of *a single role*, and he cannot resolve conflicts between treatment and research obligations by pitting a research group against a treatment group. The conflicts cannot be externalized in that way.[8] They are internal to his particular role and to its reference group of other research psychiatrists. The competing obligations derive from the two different sets of values: therapeutic medicine and medical science. The two sets of values, and the corresponding social systems, are partially identical and overlapping, and yet easily distinguished; they are quite distinct in some instances. The deliberate merging of the

---

6. At the other extreme is the definition of role conflict as any social conflict experienced by an actor while performing any role. See John P. Spiegel, "The Resolution of Role Conflict Within the Family," *Psychiatry* (1957) 20: 1-16. Also as Chap. 32, in Milton Greenblatt, *et al.*, eds., *The Patient and the Mental Hospital*, New York: Free Press, 1957. For a general discussion of different conceptions, see Neal Gross, *et al.*, *op. cit.*

7. For a study of the liberalizing influence of leadership roles that must mediate between conflicting reference groups, see Samuel A. Stouffer, *Communism, Conformity, and Civil Liberties*, New York: Doubleday, 1955.

8. Of course, others in the hospital can be representative of either fairly pure research values or therapy values. For example, in the Medical Research Center, the nursing staff no doubt represented therapy values almost exclusively, while certain nonmedical staff, such as sociologists and experimental psychologists, represented a rather pure breed of research values. But primarily the reference group for the clinical researcher was not the nurses or the nonphysicians, but other research psychiatrists who also faced the internal, competing demands of both duties. In other words, the conflict for the psychiatrist was not between his obligations to different groups playing different roles complementary to his own.

two systems in clinical research institutions means that the central actor, the research therapist, has to make certain value choices among those of each system. On one level the research-treatment conflict can be viewed as a conflict among these values, but as analyzed here it is primarily seen as a conflict of role obligations or role expectations.

The research psychiatrist carries within the bosom of his own role the gnawing fox of opposing obligations. Yet the competing obligations are activated at least in part by other persons. For example, in the case of Dr. Richards and Dr. Thorpe, the potentially conflicting obligations were revealed by actions of the patients—through their refusal to take the LSD. Resolution of the conflict then had to include the patients. Because persons other than the psychiatrist are involved, any resolutions of the research-therapy conflict will be embodied in social action—that is, in the relations of the research psychiatrist with those in the reciprocal roles of patients, nurse, colleague, and so on. While the conflict is internal to the role, the mechanisms for its resolution will have external embodiments and will in fact be realized only through social action, as contrasted with psychological processes that hypothetically occur "in the person's mind."

I am not aware of any theoretically exhaustive classification and description of the possible maneuvers for the social resolution of role conflict. However, a suggestive line for inquiry and some examples are given in a provocative paper by Jackson Toby.[9] While this is not the place to provide a general analysis of role conflict-resolving maneuvers, it will be necessary to make some theoretical distinctions as suggested by Toby's work. I begin here with the notion, outlined by Toby, of two main mechanisms by which role conflict is avoided in all societies. One is the *segregation of roles* or of selected role obligations—that is, the specifi-

---

9. Jackson Toby, "Some Variables in Role Conflict Analysis," *Social Forces* (1952) 30: 323-27. Toby poses but does not try to answer the question of what induces the choice of one maneuver rather than another. Cf. also John P. Spiegel, "The Resolution of Role Conflict Within the Family," *op. cit.*

cation of the conditions under which one role or a selected sector of it is activated so that another potentially conflicting role could not be simultaneously activated. For example, persons in federal government employ are restricted from doing business with the government. If the role of government employee can be filled only by someone who does not do business with the government, then no one in that role will experience certain conflicts between what a government employee role demands and what a business role demands.[10] The other mechanism by which role conflict is avoided is the institutionalization of *a hierarchy of roles* or of role obligations. For example, in America a woman customarily pleases her husband rather than his mother, when the two relationships seem to compete. Her role obligations as daughter-in-law are clearly subordinated to her role obligations as wife; in fact, the two roles are closely intertwined on that very basis. Yet in another culture, for example, China, the reverse is supposed to be true. In either case, the interdigitation of these two roles in the role-set [11] of the married woman is made as free as possible of role conflicts through an institutionalized hierarchy of preferred actions for situations in which the married woman must make choices.

Two roles having no particular relationship to each other may also be governed by institutionalized standards for giving precedence to the one over the other. For example, the role of national ordinarily takes precedence over any other role.[12] A wife is not supposed to protect her husband when he violates his obligations of national loyalty. On the one hand, she is not required to testify against him in a court of law; on the other hand, she is expected to put her obligations to her country above

---

10. Of course this would not prevent the employee from violating the expectation of his role; it merely makes clear what constitutes a violation. The clarity is buttressed by conflict-of-interest laws, but the role is not defined by them. Even though an alleged violator may be found legally innocent, others are usually sure that the person has not behaved properly.

11. See Robert K. Merton, "The Role-Set: Problems in Sociological Theory," *Brit. J. Sociology* (1957) 8: 106-20.

12. See Stewart E. Perry, "Notes on the Role of the National," *Conflict Resolution* (1957) 1: 346-63.

those to her husband. The mechanism of a shared scale of preferences among roles avoids the necessity of unguided choice when two or more roles are simultaneously activated.[13]

Either mechanism—role segregation or the shared scale of preferences among roles and role expectations—can prevent role conflict. The two mechanisms embody the two fundamental processes that are also visible in all other conflict-resolving maneuvers, a quarantining process and an integrating process.[14] That is, in the simplest terms, the solution of a problem in contradictions is either to keep the contradictory items apart or somehow to fit them together.

Both quarantining and integrating, as analytical processes, can be present in a single empirical act directed towards the resolution of a role conflict. To take an example of role segregation, the government employee in his private business can refrain

---

13. Of course, societal standards sometimes run aground on the shoals of human feeling, so that what everyone agrees is proper is really respected by no one. For the classic description of this sort of situation (in the Trobriand culture, in which a father's concern for his own children commonly competes with his obligations as an uncle for his sister's children), see Bronislaw Malinowski, *Crime and Custom in Savage Society*, New York: Harcourt, Brace, 1926.

14. In relation to the anthropological concept of the integration of culture, there are certain problems in the concept of quarantining. That is, quarantining can be viewed as a means of integrating. I cannot properly deal with this problem here, but I have chosen the term *quarantining* so as to allude to a special aspect of the matter of dominant and variant value schemes within a single cultural system. (See Florence R. Kluckhohn and Fred L. Strodtbeck, *Variations in Value Orientations*, New York: Harper & Row, 1961.) That is, there is an over-all organizing theme (or set of themes) against which one or more competing themes are pitted. The quarantining process, on the cultural level, compartmentalizes the foreign body, so to speak, so that the major theme is less influenced by it. Compare here Lasswell's notion of "restriction by partial incorporation." See, for example, Harold D. Lasswell and Dorothy Blumenstock, *World Revolutionary Propaganda*, New York: Knopf, 1939, esp. p. 14.

In terms of the specific conflict dealt with in this study, I have already pointed out the preponderance of therapy values over research values (in Chapter Five). In the clinical research situation, research and science are late-comers, so to say, and must compete with the more strongly held and more strongly entrenched values of medicine and therapy. That is, on the level of the cultural system of clinical research, therapy is ground and research is figure.

from bidding on any government contract; thereby he may be able to maintain an outside business firm without any conflict of interest. In this example, the same person can perform both roles; they are integrated in his behavior by means of the same quarantining process that keeps them separate. Any specific resolution technique for role conflict may then manifest both processes, quarantining and integrating.

Techniques for resolving role conflict can also be viewed as preventive measures or corrective measures. Preventive measures tend to be broadly institutionalized, like the two main mechanisms that Toby isolated. They are long-term watchdogs against a chronic threat of conflict. Corrective measures, while they will often have institutional sanction, are directed against acute eruptions of conflict; they are more temporary and are set aside as soon as the acute conflict is over. An example of a quarantining corrective measure is the real or feigned illness of a congressman, who is enabled thereby to miss a crucial vote. Once the vote is taken, the congressman can quickly recover. But he cannot remain in office and continuously use this means of handling conflict. Corrective measures are good only in a pinch. They can only tide the person over a critical period until he can correct his balance and work out a more long-term solution. Since any corrective measure is in a sense preventive, the distinction between the two is difficult to sustain. However, corrective actions are quite clearly directed against very specific events that are occurring or have occurred, while preventive measures are directed against a class of events that have not yet occurred.

I have suggested that the role-defining activity of the research psychiatrist is his major preliminary move for handling the research-therapy conflict. Clearly, this is a preventive measure directed against an anticipated chronic threat of conflict. The role-maintaining maneuvers are quite as definitely corrective measures aimed at the acute eruptions of conflict that the research psychiatrist experiences. Whether the role definition or the role-maintenance operation manifests primarily integrating or quarantining qualities depends upon the level of analysis. Since the very existence of the Medical Research Center required concurrent research and treatment, the question is not whether the two were fitted together or separated, but rather, how closely they were fitted together and by what means. Assuming on a higher level of analysis that all role-defining and role-maintaining activity was integrative for the clinical research system at the Center, one can still recognize quarantining processes in the role behavior of the research psychiatrist. Of the varieties of role definitions that were logically and empirically called for in the work at the Center, some appear to have quarantining features; others are primarily integrating.

Varieties of Clinical Research Role Definitions

Probably because the Medical Research Center was a new organization, the task of defining one's role in it was a much more overt problem than it is likely to be in an older organization in which roles are more traditionalized. In the older organization, the new staff member is likely to have a clearer idea of what he is letting himself in for; he has ordinarily been prepared in a number of different ways for assuming his work role. Only in circumstances in which it is expected that the person will learn on the job—as in medical residencies and other apprenticeships—does the person enter an organization with the same lack of consensus about his job as the research psychiatrist faced when he joined the Center staff. No one could tell him much more than that he was to conduct clinical research independently or in collaboration with other staff members. In most instances, the new staff member had had previous experience primarily as a clinical psychiatrist with at best only a small amount of sporadic experience with basic research; and this kind of experience offered him incomplete guides for taking up the full-time occupation of clinical research psychiatrist.[15] He had no prior answer for the

_____

15. Some staff members, like Dr. Richards, had previously had full-time research appointments of one sort or another, but this earlier experience had not required concomitant responsibility for patient care.

question, "Who am I or what am I in this organization?" He had to work out that answer, and his answer can be understood as one of a variety of role definitions visible in the course of the different research projects that I shall briefly describe later in this chapter.

Although medicine as science and medicine as treatment are overlapping social and cultural systems, the staff member of a psychiatric research organization can make in practice, by emphasis on one or the other, a choice between the two; or he can try to take advantage of the overlapping of the systems and enter into a deliberate attempt to combine the two more closely. He can choose to be a therapist, or a researcher, or a research therapist.[16] All these choices were made by one or another of the Research Center staff psychiatrists during the period of my study. In some instances, a psychiatrist at the Center would experiment with all three definitions during his career. It is clear, for example, that Dr. Richards began by choosing the research therapist role but later changed to the role of researcher with no therapeutic obligations. Such changes in role definitions were apt to occur with changes in research activity or plans.[17] The choice of either the pure therapist or pure researcher definition is less instructive for the purpose of my study than is the staff member's attempt to be both a therapist and a researcher.[18] The

---

16. The staff could of course make other choices that would extricate them from the research-therapy situation, such as resignation from the job, transfer to administrative duties, and so on. These can be considered role defections rather than role definitions, a distinction for which I am indebted to Robert N. Rapoport.

17. If I had focused on the natural career of the staff psychiatrist at the Center, I could comment more fully on this. However, my unit for study was the project, and within a project design the role choice was likely to remain stable.

18. One instructive point can be gained by looking at the matter of staff choices of either the pure research or the pure therapy role: If all staff had chosen one of these two alternatives, the clinical research organization would have ceased to exist, or at least its form would have been so changed as to be unrecognizable. If everyone had done therapy and no research, or if everyone had done research and no treatment, the organization would no longer have been a research hospital. However, the organizational structure of a research hospital is apt to include interstices within

psychiatrists on the projects that I studied tried in various ways to combine the two duties, and their individual solutions can be conveniently examined as either *disjoining* or *unifying* the two duties in relations with patients. Not everyone working with the psychiatrist, including the patient, was necessarily aware of his choice. But since the crucial person in relation to the psychiatrist is his patient, the psychiatrist's role definition may be said to be *overt* or *covert*, according to whether or not the patient is aware of the disjoining or unifying.

The First LSD Research. In presenting the First LSD Research, I pointed out that the two principal investigators accepted both sorts of duties in their staff role as research psychiatrists. These duties were unified in the definitions that Drs. Thorpe and Richards constructed of their work responsibilities at the Center. For themselves and for all staff, it was clear that they intended to conduct both research and treatment with the project patients. Yet the patients themselves were not fully apprised of this fact at first; indeed, many actions were taken to keep them from recognizing it. The central element of this definition was keeping the unification secret from the patients, while permitting full knowledge to nurses, colleagues, supervisors, and so on—the persons in all the other reciprocal roles. Because the patient— of all persons, the most important in the role relations of the research psychiatrist—was not informed of the psychiatrist's definition of their relationship, it seems appropriate to label this work style a *covert unifying definition* of the work role.

---

which a few staff members can (at least temporarily) disallow the one or the other of the two main organizational goals. Thus, in the Center, for example, someone like Dr. Richards could find an opportunity to give up all therapeutic responsibilities for patients and to concentrate on studying other physicians' patients, normal volunteers, or laboratory animals. Similarly, there were, at times, other staff members who simply treated their patients and conducted no research whatsoever with them or with other subjects. The resolution of conflict is in both instances achieved by a temporary repudiation of the one or the other duty. The moratorium can be indefinitely extended for some staff members but certainly not for all. In sum, a clinical research organization does not require the continual marrying of both duties in the work of each staff member, but it does require that somehow both duties be simultaneously carried on within the organization.

The Therapy Observation Project. In another case I studied, the Therapy Observation Project, the research psychiatrist conducted psychotherapy with a patient in a room with a one-way window and microphone, permitting a psychologist in the adjoining room to see and hear everything that occurred during the therapy hour. One object of this project was to study changes in the patient's values as verbalized during treatment. Essentially, the project was designed to find out (through "Q-sort tests," in which one sorts a number of statements into the same number of possible categories according to some scheme of questions) whether the patient in the course of therapy moved closer to the therapist's system of values, whether the therapist moved closer to the patient's values, or whether no changes occurred. The project was designed by the psychologist who obtained the collaboration of the psychiatrist for a pilot study on the two patients admitted by the psychiatrist for intensive long-term treatment and research.

In the beginning of the project, the psychiatrist was a full collaborator in the research, although the research was certainly not principally his own and his main duties were as a therapist. Later on, the psychiatrist had to drop some of his participation in the research actions because he and his collaborators came to feel that it would interfere with the patient's responses to the research tests. He reported this to me in an interview:

PSYCHIATRIST: At first I was in on the research interviewing and testing, but I dropped out because we felt that it might change his responses for me to do it. It was mixing up the roles of therapist and experimenter.
INTERVIEWER: What was the problem in "mixing up the roles?"
PSYCHIATRIST: That it would change his responses to the test questions.
I'm not kidding myself about this. This is not the ideal way for therapy anyway. It has its limitations because of the observer in the next room. But either you have to do therapy and let the other things go, or you have to reduce some of the efficacy of the therapy and do some research along with it. I do not think, after all, that it has been shown that actually the efficacy is reduced. . . .
This observation procedure and everything was sort of new to all of us. . . . So we knew we would have to figure out how we

would do it as we went along, according to how it worked out. Anyway, we switched, and now the psychologist does all the research procedures.

The psychiatrist had informed his patients before they were admitted that they would be expected to cooperate in research. Thus the psychiatrist had prepared the patients for the general fact that they would be studied, even though he was not then making the plans for what later became the Therapy Observation Project. He told me:

I had told the first patient [before he came] that I was interested in treating his illness, but in addition [that] this was a research hospital and there would be some research. I was not sure that the particular [biochemical] project I had in mind at the time would be possible because of problems in obtaining some special laboratory equipment that was quite expensive. So I did not mention the exact nature of the research to him.

By the time that my first patient was actually admitted, I had already agreed to work with the psychologist, and so I told the patient of that research plan and that he had three days to think about it and decide if he would cooperate. We also did some psychological tests during that time. I showed him the observation room, the one-way mirror, and the mike. Before the first therapy hour he had met the psychologist, and we told him that he would be observing and after each [psychotherapy] hour there would be an interview and questions and psychological testing. * * *

We tried to match the second patient as much as possible with the first one. In both cases, we made clear that we would take them in for three months for observation and working on the emotional aspects of the illness. Then after that time, if they felt like it, they were free to leave the Center and go elsewhere; and I too would have the option of discharging them then if I felt they did not work out.

The psychiatrist here reports very explicit arrangements with the patients on this project. He informed the patients in great detail of the research plan and specified the obligations and rights that each side had in the situation. Because the merging of research and treatment in the relationship of doctor and patient was made fully known to the patient, the psychiatrist's definition of his role here can be considered the *overt unifying* type. Indeed, everyone, including nurses, other physicians, and other patients, knew what the psychiatrist was doing. What is particularly noteworthy in this type of role definition is the specification of obligations and privileges, which in effect sets up a hierarchy of preferences for conflict situations that might arise.

When conflict situations arise in the case of this type of role definition, the expectations of behavior on the part of either participant are a matter of consensus. The resolution of the role conflict is provided for in the arrangement of agreed preferences in case of a forced choice. The socially shared standards for such choices are the main means by which, in any culture, role conflict is avoided: Everyone knows beforehand more or less what he should do. In the absense of such socially shared standards at the Medical Research Center, the psychiatrist on the Therapy Observation Project was forced to work out standards explicitly for himself and for the patient.

The central element, then, of the role definition in this project was a clear, shared hierarchy of role expectations. This is theoretically distinct from the role definitions initially used in the First LSD Research in which the central element was an insulation of the two role functions, so far as the patient was concerned. In an overt definition of role relations between research patient and research doctor, the main mechanism for handling potential conflict must be a shared scale of preferences and understandings about invoking obligations. That is, an overt unifying definition cannot depend mainly upon a form of quarantining, but the covert unifying definition is bound to depend upon quarantining. The open embracing of both duties in relations with patients requires the establishment of consensus between the patient and the physician. The concealment of obligations to perform certain duties within the compass of a particular relationship implies blurred understandings on all sides that are maintained by compartmentalization—that is, by a form of quarantining.

In the First LSD Project, the complete segregation of role of researcher and therapist was not attempted; the two were unified even though covertly. A closer approach to complete segregation is illustrated in the next project to be described.

The Trade-Off Project. In the Trade-Off Project, the research psychiatrists studied each other's patients but not their own. Concomitantly, each psychiatrist on the project provided treatment for his own patient who was studied by the other psychiatrist. In a way, this unusual research arrangement can be considered a project only dubiously, for the work was not particularly well thought out and the arrangement lasted only a short time. Yet it served as a pilot stage for a project that later developed into a significant piece of work. Moreover, short as it was, the Trade-Off Project beautifully illustrates a role definition that can logically be contrasted with the unifying definitions. It therefore deserves some serious attention.

Most research really begins with a little tinkering around, an exploratory foray, a bit of trying here, a little testing of something there, until an idea starts to jell and the necessary procedures fall into place. This was the history of the Trade-Off.[19] In the course of the project there were perhaps as many as four psychiatrists involved at one time, although eventually one dropped out and often only two would be working systematically at the same time. The focus of the project was personality theory as it might arise from and illuminate the treatment of schizophrenia. Each of the psychiatrists had at least one schizophrenic patient in intensive psychoanalytic treatment; but anticipating difficulties in combining research with psychoanalysis, they had developed the novel approach of doing research with each other's patients but not with their own. In a staff meeting, about two months after the first ward opened, one psychiatrist reported to the staff group that his entry into the trade-off relationship was specifically a means for handling the potential research-therapy conflict. He noted that the research tool he used was the psychiatric interview but by "using subjects who are patients of some other therapist . . . [the psychiatrist] tries to avoid being a therapist. That is one way of handling the conflict."

The Trade-Off psychiatrists' concern with the means of

---

19. Most of the materials on this case were gathered by Charlotte Green Schwartz, to whom I am much indebted.

avoiding the urge to be a therapist for research subjects was coupled with a concern over avoiding research interference with therapy. Their elaborate attempt to avoid any conflict between research and treatment indicates a special sensitivity to the problem, which requires examination here.

Their sensitivity was probably due in part to the participants' commitment to psychoanalytic theory and technique. As compared to the LSD Project, the Trade-Off Project was strictly concerned with psychological—that is, psychoanalytic—matters; and it must be remembered that there is a general tradition in psychoanalysis that the therapeutic process in analysis is so delicately structured that the slightest thing can disturb it, particularly any action by the analyst himself.[20] Thus, as psychoanalytically oriented psychiatrists, the Trade-Off investigators were especially concerned with what might upset the therapeutic process. In orientation they differed considerably from Dr. Richards who had had no analytic training, and they differed from Dr. Thorpe who, though as thoroughly trained as they in psychoanalysis, had long pursued an interest in drug research. (The Trade-Off psychiatrists viewed this interest of Dr. Thorpe's in drug research with some suspicion.)

However, the Trade-Off psychiatrists by no means believed that nonpsychoanalytic research was the only source of difficulty in the research-treatment conflict, or that such conflict occurred only in a research hospital. They felt that any kind of research interest in the patient anywhere might interfere with therapy. Their concern was nicely illustrated in the report of one of their consultants, well known for his own psychoanalytic research, who agreed with their need to exercise caution. This consultant

---

20. Freud advised, for example, that the analyst foreswear any research until the treatment relationship was terminated! "[In psychoanalysis] . . . research and treatment proceed hand in hand but still the technical requirement for one begins at a certain point to diverge from that for the other. It is not a good thing to formulate a case scientifically while treatment is proceeding. . . . Cases which are thus destined at the start for scientific purposes and treated accordingly suffer in consequence. . . ." Sigmund Freud, "Recommendations for Physicians on the Psychoanalytic Method of Treatment (1912)," in *Collected Papers*, Vol. II, London: Hogarth Press, 1933.

had worked almost exclusively at a private hospital as a psycho-analyst with no formal research obligations; yet he had occasion-ally found his intellectual and research interests interfering with his treatment of patients there. He told me, during work with the Trade-Off psychiatrists:

> I recently noted an instance in which research entered into my therapy relationship with a certain very sick patient. At the time I was interested in writing a paper on early ego development, and I was keenly interested in the fragmentation of the ego which this patient's behavior indicated.
>
> After a time the patient remarked, "I can't keep down forever," and I realized that I had been interested in her remaining sick and exhibiting the ego fragmentation so that I could observe it and learn about it. I gathered from this remark that the patient was saying that she could not stay sick forever while I learned about early ego development. I did not say anything to her about it, but I changed my behavior after that.

The competent psychoanalyst accepts the fact that he may participate in this sort of situation, and he tries to keep aware enough to catch himself in the process of any inappropriate interaction with the patient. The Trade-Off psychiatrists knew this pitfall and they hoped to forestall some of the problems by the trade-off arrangement.

In the Trade-Off, full segregation of research activities from therapeutic activities allowed each doctor to pursue his own research interests without having to worry about whether therapy was being adversely influenced. The therapist of each patient held and kept the responsibility for determining whether or not the research interviews were interfering. The researcher could depend upon him for that, and the therapist could depend upon the researcher to do the same for him with a different patient.

Note that it was the activities that were segregated. This was not an instance of role segregation; the two activities of research and treatment were combined in the role definition of the research psychiatrist. His activities remained within the research-psychiatry role-set, but the role relations were differen-tiated. Also, there was no real division of labor among the psychiatrists; there was merely an exchange of identical services. The trade-off arrangement here can be understood as constructing the *disjoining role definition* for the research psychiatrist in which both duties are accepted and are kept carefully separated. The arrangement was known to all the patients, as may be recalled by the statement of Miss Burton that she was glad at least that she did not have to be interviewed by someone besides her own therapist, the way "Phoebe sees Mamie's doctor and Mamie sees Phoebe's doctor." Thus the definition was overt.

I have mentioned that this project was both rather vague and short-lived. Yet it developed into an original piece of work, one of the earliest attempts to look on schizophrenia as a phenomenon of family-group dynamics. An examination of some of the early processes leading to the evolution of this project will afford a further insight into the role-defining activity of a research psychiatrist. This evolution involved changes in the psychiatrists' role definition, primarily as a natural result of ordinary clinical practice, in an atmosphere of research interest. In line with standard clinical practice, the Trade-Off psychiatrists had tried to have some contact with the relatives of their hospitalized patients. The necessity of dealing with these relatives was a clinical practice that turned into a research procedure.

Initially the Trade-Off psychiatrists, as I have noted, had very little in mind in the way of research aims. This is reflected in a report to the staff by one of the physicians, during a general staff conference in which progress reports were being made on all projects, September 22, second year:

We wanted to simply study a couple of cases. We have no particular hypotheses about what the interactions were like, but our original intention was to study the patient, the mother and father, and have some contact with the siblings. We have studied the mother-daughter relationships for the most part and have taken two schizophrenic patients with acute psychotic episodes. We are simply going about this by engaging people in a psychotherapeutic relationship. We have seen two patients five times a week and one mother twice weekly.

But with increasing contact with more family members as well as with the patients, the staff members' interests became more focused. Actually, by the time of the informal report that I have quoted from, the pure segregation of research activities had already begun to break down.[21] It was perhaps inevitable that the switching of patients would lead to mutual interests and common discussions about the progress of treatment and the dynamics of the patients. Each psychiatrist expanded his scope of research attention to include his own patient, although the practice of interviewing each other's patients for research purposes continued for some time. Further attention came to be focused on recordings of the interviews, which were routinely made, at first without much idea of what uses they would be put to aside from clinical inquiry. In the process, the psychiatrists became less worried about the possibility that their therapy efforts would suffer from the research, nor did their patients seem to be worried. In an interview on October 5, second year, one of the psychiatrists noted his own development:

I think I've had to make quite an effort to grasp the research orientation; essentially, it's what I've been trying to do for the last year:
. . . Somehow the notion of research seemed to me originally to conflict with the question of therapy. The attempt to quite consciously investigate particular hypotheses with a patient—somehow that seemed at variance with the freedom to be perfectly intuitive and sensitive and whatnot, with the patient. It's as if there was an ethical conflict too, which at first made me acutely uncomfortable. . . . I've succeeded in resolving that.
I think I can honestly say: Recently in the last few months I'm beginning to not only get a feeling of what it might be like but even to get some enthusiasm aroused. . . .

Although this psychiatrist, for example, found himself in the course of his work changing somewhat in his attitudes toward the possibility of research being conducted by a psychiatrist with a patient he had in therapy, he still would not consider doing

_____

21. In addition, in the course of time one of the psychiatrists left the project for another study and three others joined the project. Some of the evolutionary changes in the project were undoubtedly due to changes in the personnel involved in the work, but the core workers stayed together for the period on which I report.

anything really different in his therapeutic relationship with a patient. Speaking of the "Permissive Ward" project, this psychiatrist said in the interview on October 5:

I think I was a little bit shocked that anybody would conceive of setting up an experiment in which you would be doing anything less than making your utmost effort to be sensitive to the patient's needs and to do whatever was essential, [rather than leave things completely up to a patient to decide]. In other words, any notion of getting away from my conception of a therapeutic approach I found a little disturbing. And I think now that I've gotten away from that.

I can't say that I've moved a hell of a lot. . . . I think that the only way my attitude has been modified is that within the framework of my idea of doing therapy, I've gotten some interest in trying to develop a hypothesis about the patient—about therapy—and to use the therapy hour material to validate that.

That doesn't mean that there's been any great shift. . . . I still probably will always go on this way. But I think that now that my approach is somewhat less a matter of prejudice and more a matter of conviction.

By this time the disjoining definition of the clinical researcher role had evolved for this psychiatrist into a unified definition. While in the beginning he had studied someone else's patient, now he also studied his own. The conflict is still recognizable in his remarks, and he recognized it himself, but it was being dealt with by a different technique. What had happened was that in conjunction with a general change in role definition from the disjoined to the unified, a technical change occurred as an aid to the maintenance of the new definition. Instead of segregating research from therapy, the psychiatrist had designed his research in such a way that it was hardly distinguishable from his therapeutic activities, especially in his relationship with the patient. When the specific research interviews of each other's patients were dropped, all the psychiatrists began to rely upon the group's general clinical discussions of their recorded interviews for insights that normally would have been developed in the regular course of therapy.

The patients' reaction to all this more or less followed the changes in the attitudes of their therapists. In the beginning there were many troubles around the recording; later these dissipated. A second psychiatrist on the project reported in an interview on September 27, second year:

The primary use of these recordings was in more of a treatment pattern; in fact for most of the first year, the group meetings were run like a case seminar in which the recordings were presented, mainly with the idea of sort of assisting the therapy, and so on.***

. . . It would look as if I was terribly against recording. Psychologically, I didn't want to do it. For the first week and a half, somehow or other all recordings got destroyed [22] by my re-recording on the same tape. * * *

I mean, I never got away from the feeling, you know, that somebody is going to be listening to this. *   * *

The kinds of [research vs. therapy] problems that I got into with the patient in terms of these recordings . . . [are illustrated in] her feelings like, "Well, I can't tell you certain things because I know so many people are going to be listening." The keynote, as far as I can see, is entirely in that area.

However, this one area of difficulty apparently was not serious for the patients. Their attitude is exemplified in the remarks of the same patient just quoted by the psychiatrist. The patient, was interviewed a few days after the interview with her therapist, on October 1, second year, and she appeared to be rather uninterested in the whole matter of research, as the interview report indicates.

The interviewer explained the purpose of the interview to the patient and told her we were interested in finding out about patients' reactions to being in a hospital in which both research and therapy was going on. Her first response was, "I can't tell you much from the research angle. Most patients rarely think about research. I was resentful when I first came here when I thought that they were keeping me here for research, but I got over that." [Upon transfer to

---

22. Apparently this sort of mechanical ineptitude often dogs psychotherapy research. See L. J. Roose, "The Influence of Psychosomatic Research on the Psychoanalytic Process," *J. Amer. Psa. Assoc.* (1960) 8: 317-34. For further comments on the problems of conducting research on psychotherapy by recordings and other means, see Merton Gill, *et al., The Initial Interview in Psychiatric Practice,* New York: International Universities Press, 1954. See also Clyde H. Ward, "Psychotherapy Research: Dilemmas and Directions," *Arch. Gen. Psychiat.* (1964) 10: 596-622.

the Center from another hospital, most of this patient's early interaction with staff revolved around her insistence that she was not
sick and should be discharged.]

The patient went on to state that she didn't have much to say
about research but she had a lot of feelings about what went on
on the ward. . . .

"Is there anything that you can tell me about the research that
is going on?" the interviewer asked. Patient replied: "The patients
are pretty satisfied with the research. We don't have an active part
in research. Their part is just that they are here. In the rest of the
hospital, the patients have tests and things like that. On this ward,
there is nothing the patients have to do. They are just supposed to
cooperate with their doctor, which we would do in any hospital."

. . . The interviewer brought patient back to the question of
research, and she said, "The patients rarely mention it, except in
a joke." Interviewer asked if she knew about any specific research
that was going on. "The only research was Mary Burton's taking
lysergic acid. I was her roommate and I was very resentful because
they didn't tell me that she was going to get it. . . . She was suffering
very much, and I don't like to see her suffer. Then there are controls
[normal volunteers on another ward] taking lysergic acid too. And
five months ago, one doctor wanted a urine specimen. He thought
there was some connection between mental attitude and urine."

Patient changed the subject to talk about therapy. ". . . The
only thing you are sure about is that they [the doctors] won't spread
your confidence. There's no way of knowing whether you can trust
them on other things though."

Interviewer changed the subject back to research and asked
whether she was participating in any research here. At first she said
no, and then she said yes, that there were recordings of her therapy
hours which were listened to by a group of doctors. I asked her
how she felt about this. "It was hard to get used to the recorder. I
didn't want to say anything at first." Interviewer asked: "Did you
know what it was about?" [Patient replied] "No, just research."

In this interview, while the patient was willing to be quite
candid in her criticisms (not quoted here) of the ward and the
doctors on other topics, on the matter of research she indicated
little difficulty. Like Miss Burton with Dr. Steiger, the patients
on the Trade-Off Project did not quite know what the research
on the interviews was about, but regarded it as a general sort of
case conference in which their symptoms and history were compared with others. Indeed, this was a fairly accurate view of the

project. The consensus between doctors and patients was rather complete in the trade-off procedures.

In summary, this project offers insight into two sorts of role definitions as solutions to the research-therapy conflict. Initially, the project permitted the psychiatrists to do both research and therapy by segregating the two activities in relations with different patients. This was the disjoining definition. It was overt so far as the patients were concerned; and it was an understanding that was general among all staff. As the project developed and coalesced toward a more systematic research effort, not described here, the participants began to shift into a unifying definition of their roles, also on an overt basis.

The resolution of potential conflict between treatment and research in the new, unifying definition depended upon the research design. Instead of specific research interviews as in the beginning, the routine data of therapy interviews were studied. The research procedures were scarcely distinguishable from therapeutic procedures, and thus the psychiatrists found it possible to sustain a unified definition of themselves as both researchers and therapists with the same patients. The merging of research design with the therapy procedures was basically effective as a role-maintaining technique. However, other role-maintaining techniques were also necessary. These will be discussed in the next chapter.

The disjoining role definition in other forms. Since I have reported on both an overt and a covert form of the unifying type of definition, one might expect that there would be a covert form of the disjoining definition to match its overt form. However I have no recorded materials that permit me to describe such a form. Reflection suggests certain possibilities, but none of them seems quite right. One has to answer the question, Why would a psychiatrist keep hidden from his patients the fact that he is treating them but not studying them?

I can imagine a hypothetical situation: Since among research patients there is a certain prestige in being studied,[23] perhaps a

---

23. This is documented in Renée C. Fox, *op. cit.*

psychiatrist might not wish to take away that small bit of status from a patient whom he is actually only treating. This seems unlikely because a psychiatrist is not likely to admit onto a research ward a patient whom he has no intention of studying.

There are certain circumstances in which a psychiatrist might indeed delay studying the patient he admitted and was treating. He may be tooling up in various ways, reading the literature, discussing potential problems with colleagues, and so on. But all these would simply be preliminary phases of research to be undertaken in time. Of course, this happened frequently at the Center. True, if such a preliminary phase seemed overlong, one might gather that the staff member was temporizing in the face of the research-therapy conflict,[24] but if so, this delay would serve the image of himself as a worker who was using a unifying definition—not a disjoining definition. There would be no general expectations of his performing a role of a disjoining type, no expectations by any others that the psychiatrist would disjoin research and treatment in his work. There seems little likelihood that the covert disjoining definition would be used in a research hospital.

Role-Maintaining Techniques

Every social role performance is subject to both expected and unexpected threats that tend to upset the performance itself and the image that the person projects of himself in the performance. Thus each role performance will generally be accompanied by certain maintenance techniques that keep the role in operation,

---

24. Temporizing before the task of combining research and treatment in work with one's patients is not wholly a reaction to the potential conflict. Certainly one often pauses overlong before beginning any major piece of work. This may account for my impressionistic evidence of the frequency of this sort of action on the part of the research psychiatrist. There are other uses to which delay can be put, besides helping to resolve the research-therapy conflict. Role-maintaining techniques are not necessarily univocal in function. I will treat this matter in detail in the following chapter.

so to speak. For example, in my role as a potential customer at certain understaffed department stores, I have often been mistaken as a salesperson by a fellow customer who swoops down upon me with a glad cry. Under these circumstances, sustaining the proper role is occasionally a task of considerable dimension for me. I must tell the stranger firmly that he is completely in error and yet do this with the finesse and politeness that lets him know that I recognize his innocence. A small amount of cooperation from the stranger is necessary in order for both of us to get through the situation smoothly. All in all this role-maintaining technique of setting the other straight can be quite taxing. If possible, therefore, I try to forestall any such encounter by keeping a close watch; whenever I see a stranger approaching me intently, I am apt to suddenly pick up any random bit of goods to examine it ostentatiously as a customer might. That too is a role-maintaining technique. If I am successful, the stranger veers off. This forestalling technique is less expensive of time and effort, if more mendacious.[25]

The self can be heavily invested in any sort of role definition, but in contrast to such roles as that of customer, occupational roles are much more heavily invested with the self. In the performance of roles in the professions and other high-status occupations, there tends to be very little differentiation between the "real" self and the self as professional, while the professional role is actually being performed.[26] Any threat to such heavily invested

25. Probably the best recent discussion of these sorts of operations is contained in some of Erving Goffman's work. See *The Presentation of Self in Everyday Life*, *op. cit.*, and "Role Distance," pp. 83-152, in *Encounters*, *op. cit.*

26. Goffman's observations of surgical room behavior have led him to posit the condition of role distance, by which the person may perform his role but do so in such a way as to make it clear that he has not entirely invested himself in the performance. Surgical-room joking, for instance, is but a less exaggerated variety of the offhand behavior of certain aloof restaurant waiters or of job-seekers sitting on the benches of an employment office. All these people behave so as to indicate that a self resides apart from the situated role being enacted. However, as Goffman makes clear, much of the apparent role-distance behavior in the operating room, for instance, is actually functional for the role performance in the moments when there is the greatest need to perform the role properly. For example, mocking

roles can call out any or all of the full range of role-maintenance techniques.

The greater the investment of the self in the performance of a role, the more important it is to have a viable role definition that can be sustained. That is why the research psychiatrist at the Center could so easily be observed in operations that were designed to define and sustain the basic work role. The role was fundamental to the staff member's selfhood and required close attention on his part to maintain.

Of all the possible role-maintaining techniques that the research psychiatrist might use, I am here interested only in presenting examples of those that I observed to be utilized specifically for dealing with the research-therapy conflict and its threat to the psychiatrist's chosen role definition. The role-maintaining techniques that I describe were used, according to my observation, as a means for the resolution of the research-therapy conflict, while at the same time they operated to shore up the particular role definition within which they were utilized. However, such techniques are not univocal in function.[27] Therefore, while I am limiting my description to those techniques that are particularly adaptable to the resolution of role conflicts (and even more particularly to the conflict between research and treatment), it will be plain that many such techniques might be placed in the service of defending against some other type of threat to the role in which the actor's self has become invested.

27. Each empirical act can be analyzed, of course, on different levels, and according to which level one has chosen to view the act, it can be assigned different functions. The acts that can be viewed as functional for role-maintenance are concurrently functional or dysfunctional for, say, the actor's self-esteem on the level of personality analysis. Moreover, what is functional for role-maintenance in one relationship may be dysfunctional for role-maintenance in another relationship in the role-set. See Neal Gross, et al., op. cit.

the surgical operation or some part of it helps to ease tension that might interfere with a successful operation. The fact of role-distance behavior does not in itself negate the likelihood that the self is especially bound up in the performance of professional and other high-status occupational roles in our culture. See Goffman, "Role Distance," in Encounters, op. cit.

Moreover, such techniques have intended and unintended consequences for the scientific results of the worker. I shall begin in my tally of role-maintaining techniques with those of more diffuse and flexible function and proceed towards those that are increasingly more specialized for the resolution of research-therapy conflicts and have more obvious scientific consequences.

The first three sorts of techniques that may be used fall into an over-all class of their own: They are especially useful when the conflict is very short lived or momentary or when the acute conflict occurs only once or, at least, infrequently. The techniques are temporization, extenuation, and reconceptualization.

Temporization includes illness, vacations, and other absenteeism. It also includes the means of stalling for time that inhere in simple procrastination ("I'll think about it") and organizational procrastination ("The group will have to discuss it"). I have already described some instances of simple procrastination. As will be recalled, the principal investigators in the First LSD Project used temporization after the patients voiced their stand against the drug in anticipation of being formally asked to take it. The investigators dealt with the situation by putting off further action, in order to allow time for the heightened feelings to die down and the patients to become less opposed to the research. The delay in the research at this time allowed the two investigators to maintain their relations with the patients along the lines of the covert role definition that the psychiatrists had set up. The success of this role-maintaining technique as a quarantining process depended upon there being no recurrence of the initial threat; in many instances delay will solve a role conflict if the threat is not repeated. In the LSD research, however, the principal investigators expected to ask the patients to take the drug again. When the patients were again requested to take the drug, the conflict appeared again.

Simple procrastination can be successful if the situation can be expected to change—as it did in certain research conducted by Dr. Bates.[28] While I did not study his particular project, I

---

28. Dr. Bates, it will be remembered, was the ward administrator of the service on which the First LSD Project patients lived. He was involved as a research investigator in other projects not studied in my research.

heard a report that he made in a staff conference, April 7, second year, of a contretemps between him and a patient over a research procedure; this conflict was resolved while Dr. Bates temporized.

DR. BATES: . . . I wanted to do recording with a patient. I hadn't been doing it and then I proposed it to her. She hit the roof, and at the moment I was undecided, so I said, "We'll shut the thing [the recording machine] off and talk about it."

When I assessed this later after the hour, I became clear about the meaning to me of the recording and to her; and I went back the next hour, and used the machine and said, if she was afraid that I was not respecting the confidentiality of what she said in the hour (which was her overt objection), she had a right to quit. She walked out in a huff, but she came back shortly thereafter.

STAFF MEMBER: One thing you did not mention: You did turn it off the first time and became angry about it.

DR. BATES: I know. I was furious.

In this conference, Dr. Bates reported being angry at the possibility of not being able to make research use of the recordings. But he had delayed taking any action. The delay allowed him to become clear about his feelings and the issues involved. The situation then was changed when he reviewed with the patient the issues and reminded her that she had the prerogative of terminating their relationship if she felt he was not acting properly as a therapist. She tested that right, then decided forthwith that she did not need to exercise it. Of course, temporizing was not the only factor involved here in the successful resolution of a conflict between the therapy relationship and the research relationship, but its part in the resolution was significant.

Temporizing as a role-maintaining technique is ordinarily useful only on infrequent occasions. For longer-term and recurrent problems, temporizing must have a special legitimating role context that permits an extended moratorium[29] for the person from the problems that face him. The role of patient—especially

---

29. See the work of Erik H. Erikson, who has especially called attention to the moratorium period during the course of changing from one role to another in the growing-up process. Erik H. Erikson, "Ego Identity and the Psychosocial Moratorium," Chap. I, in Helen L. Witmer and Ruth Kotinsky, eds., *New Perspectives for Research on Juvenile Delinquency* (Children's Bureau Publication No. 356), Washington: U.S. Department of Health, Education, and Welfare, 1956.

of psychiatric patient—is a moratorium role. As a patient, the person can have a haven from conflicts engendered by his other roles. He can put off handling the conflicts until a later time when perhaps they can be more easily handled.

The patient role, therefore, is itself a means of temporizing. However, temporizing is also, interestingly enough, one of the chief tools in the psychotherapeutic or psychoanalytic treatment of mental patients. Certain responses of the therapist to the patient—silence in the face of requests by the patient, returning the patient's question with another question, and so on—temporize in the face of demands by the patient that threaten the therapist's performance of his role.[30] The psychotherapy process in general permits the therapist to wait out the effects of the patient's illness as well as actively to intervene in it. Thus, temporizing is a familiar technique and readily available to the psychiatrist for use in handling other sorts of problems, specifically the research-treatment role conflict. The special temporizing techniques of psychoanalysis and of psychotherapy in general were used by Dr. Thorpe in handling Mr. Pickett's concern about the LSD. Dr. Thorpe, as was pointed out, relied upon the noncommittal and reflective maneuvers of psychoanalytic treatment to prevent Mr. Pickett from recognizing the therapist's involvement with the LSD research. Temporizing by these maneuvers is clearly a quarantining measure. In contrast to most temporization these maneuvers can be used fairly frequently because they are embedded in the psychotherapist's role.

Quarantining the conflict is also possible in the technique of *extenuation*, especially if the acute appearance of the conflict is an infrequent or nonrecurring affair. Extenuation admits the person's failure in role performance but cites circumstances that permit others and himself to view his failure as due to more or less uncontrollable events. There is an implicit denial of the conflict by means of reference to some other agency of trouble.

---

30. John P. Spiegel has analyzed differing role responses available to a therapist, in a paper on the distinctions between pure psychoanalytic technique and other psychotherapeutic techniques. John P. Spiegel, "The Social Roles of Doctor and Patient in Psychoanalysis and Psychotherapy," *Psychiatry* (1954) 17: 369-76.

Extenuation diverts attention from possible conflict by focusing upon "acts of God" or upon some other fortuitous circumstances, such as "It was a communication breakdown," "I am only human," "The hospital just changed its policy," and so on. Such appeals can be accepted by all concerned once in a while, but not regularly. As with temporization, extenuation is successful in sustaining the image of the clinical researcher in his chosen role definition mainly if the threats posed by a conflict are very infrequent.

Extenuation is closely related to another of the role-maintaining operations that suffice for an occasional use, *reconceptualization*. Reconceptualization puts a different face on events by casting them into a completely different frame of reference. There are several varieties of this technique, which differs from extenuation primarily in terms of the more extended development of the new frame of reference. In extenuation, the conflict-inducing events are immediately redefined, for example, as acts of God. In reconceptualization, there is a somewhat more complicated elaboration required.

One variety of reconceptualization is the white lie, the fib, the half-truth, or even the outright lie. The person must engage in some kind of private rationalization, and sometimes collusion with others, if he chooses to use this technique of quarantining otherwise conflicting role expectations. It is not enough even for his own adjustment to make a statement that he recognizes as untrue. This technique is illustrated in the LSD research by Dr. Richards' statement to his patient, Miss Burton, that it was up to her whether she took more of the drug because it was Dr. Dirainey who was doing the research. In order for this sort of reconceptualization to be utilized, others, such as Dr. Bates, who presented the research to the patient, had to be involved in maintaining Dr. Richards' role definition that kept him, in the patient's eyes, uncontaminated by the research procedures. The reconceptualization broke down, of course, because the identical conflict recurred. In the end, Dr. Richards had to abandon the idea that the patient was free to make a choice and had to communicate this change to his patient.

Reconceptualization in general as a role-maintaining, conflict-resolving technique is very complicated, for it requires direct or indirect collaboration by others in constructing a different view of the conflict-inducing situation. Direct collaboration is illustrated in the LSD situation just alluded to. Indirect collaboration stems from general participation of staff in thoughtways that permit the research psychiatrist to maneuver freely in redefining or reconceptualizing a troublesome situation. For example, the absence of a clear consensus at the Center on the technical status of psychiatry as a research science—that is, on problems of interdisciplinary definitions—blurred the distinctions between research as a technical matter and treatment as a technical matter. Thus, especially in the earliest phases of the Center, whenever the opposition of research and treatment was suggested by some staff member, another might smooth things out by the anodyne that "all good clinical research is therapeutic in the long run," or more often, "all good therapy is good research." [31] By this means, the conflict was passed off in reconceptualization. In later phases of work at the Center such blurred distinctions could not survive, of course, as repeated conflicts and repeated examination of the technical meanings of research and treatment *in vivo* forced clarification.

Reconceptualization in frequent and continued use, like temporization, requires institutionalized supports. As Alfred H. Stanton has pointed out,[32] psychiatry offers to the practitioner certain built-in means of missing or masking the significant point of a troublesome affair. One of these, the very fact of dealing with mentally disordered patients, offers a ready-made reconceptualization of the conflict-inducing situation as the patient's problem. Thus one of the LSD investigators could say, upon being told that the drug made patients miserable, "But Miss Burton is always miserable." Or: "Mr. Pickett's guilt about refusing to take the drug will be bad therapeutically." The correctness

31. The Center was not unusual in this respect. For example, a study in another setting seeks to prove that patients on research projects are per se better off! See Harold A. Rashkis, "Cognitive Restructuring: Why Research Is Therapy," *Arch. Gen. Psychiat.* (1960) 2: 612-21.

32. Alfred H. Stanton, "Psychiatric Theory and Institutional Context," *op. cit.*

of such statements in and of themselves is not the issue in reconceptualization; they can be fully true and yet at the same time
can offer the opportunity of covering over the role-disturbing
conflict between the psychiatrist's research values and his therapy
values. However, it seems clear that such reconceptualizations
pose grave problems for scientific research in psychiatry, since
they so obviously restrict the clinical researcher's grasp of what
is happening. When the research therapist locates the trouble
in the patient's disorder, this serves to divert attention from
problems in the social context of the treatment and the research;
the result of this may in fact be visible in the form and content
of the psychiatric theories constructed by the research therapist,
as I shall illustrate later. Such theories will endure to the extent
that they meet social system problems. These theories can be
understood as a long-term form of reconceptualization.

I turn now to a group of role-maintaining tactics that are
more easily invoked over and over again and that routinely
provide for more enduring solutions to the research-therapy
conflict. These are decontamination, invocation, and technical
modification.

Decontamination singles out potentially disturbing features
of expected interaction and places them in a clearly differentiated
context where they can be more easily dealt with. Decontamination can be achieved through variations in the physical setting,
the timing, and the personnel of the interaction.[33] Different
physical contexts, for example, help the lawyer to vary his interaction with his opponent from enmity in the courtroom, to
courtesy in the courthouse corridors and anterooms, to con-
viviality at the local legal club—all in the course of exchanging
points about the same case with the same opponent. Similarly, the
clinical researcher can use spatial arrangements to make it easier
for him and the patient (or others) to keep clear as to what is the
specific business at hand, research or treatment.

Locating rooms for research at some distance from those used

---

33. There is a very close relationship between decontamination and the
use of "technical modification" as role-maintaining techniques. This will be
made evident in the discussion of technical modifications.

for clinical care was relatively easy at the Medical Research Center and made decontamination by spatial context a common feature of interaction between research physician and research patient. It should be remembered that one section of the building (one face on the stem of the Y) was devoted to clinical care and quite separate sections (the opposite face of the stem and the fork of the Y) were devoted to research laboratories, offices, and so on. Traffic among all the clinical units could go on without any contact whatsoever with the research areas, and vice versa. Some patients came into the research areas to their psychiatrists' offices for regular therapy appointments. These same offices might also have been used for research procedures with the patients; but even in the research areas, offices used for psychotherapy would rarely be used also for purely research contacts with the patients. Similarly, certain research procedures that appropriately might have been administered in the clinical area were relegated to the nonclinical section of the building. For example, although the first drug for Miss Burton on the LSD project was administered by the nurses in the clinical area under the auspices of the clinical ward administrator, later injections were given in the research area. Once the insulation of Dr. Richards from the drug research broke down and he was clearly defined as both therapist and researcher in the patient's eyes, the research procedures no longer took place in the clinical area. Insulation by means of spatial decontamination was substituted: Drugs, including the first placebo, were administered to Miss Burton in the research area—either in Dr. Richards' office or in his laboratory where certain test equipment was stationed.[34]

Decontamination can also be achieved through temporal

---

34. In this instance, I am inclined to feel that the decontamination technique was for the benefit of the clinical staff of nurses and so on, for Dr. Richards actually used fewer and fewer techniques to maintain the image of himself as a therapist as well as a researcher, ending with his final repudiation of therapeutic obligations when he transferred Miss Burton to another physician. Contrarily, it is interesting to recall that a later patient of Dr. Thorpe's who was given LSD as a therapy as well as for research purposes received the drug in every instance from the hands of a nurse and on the ward.

arrangements. For example, during the therapy hour the patient and physician can focus exclusively upon treatment as long as research procedures are scheduled for times quite distant from the therapy hour.[35] Finally, decontamination can be achieved through the employment of accessory personnel. The social situation can be modified by the introduction of additional persons. Just as a general practitioner may have his nurse present as he makes a physical examination of a female patient, so the therapist who is also doing research procedures on his patient may have a third person present when the research is being done, but may maintain complete privacy for therapy hours. The introduction of the third person may have no other value except as a denaturing of the emotional implications of research contact between persons who are in a therapeutic relationship.

The most extreme form of this interpersonal decontamination of the research situation for therapist and patient occurs when all research activity takes place between the patient and the accessory personnel. The part played by Dr. Dirainey for Drs. Thorpe and Richards was that of an accessory worker. Dr. Dirainey's observations could have been made by one of the principal investigators—in fact, that arrangement was contemplated for a time—but Dirainey was, in the end, employed to help the investigators maintain the role definition that they had constructed. Dr. Bates also served the purpose of decontaminating the therapy aspects of the role of clinical researcher by handling administrative matters with the patients. Dr. Dirainey and Dr. Bates were essential to the covert part of the role definition that Dr. Richards and Dr. Thorpe used. However, Drs. Dirainey and Bates could have performed the same role-maintaining service for Drs. Thorpe and Richards, even if the last two had chosen to construct an overt definition. In that case, the patients would have been clear that the drug research was being carried on by their therapists, but some of the problems of direct research interaction would still have been handled

35. It will be recalled that Freud (*op. cit.*) had suggested the extreme form of temporal decontamination, that is, postponing research until after the termination of the therapy relationship.

by the use of accessory personnel. For example, in the Therapy
Observation Project, the research psychiatrist stopped giving
research interviews to his patient, and another person took over
this task. The patient was clear that his psychiatrist was still
involved, but he was presumably less affected by his relationship
with the therapist when he answered the research questions
asked by someone else.

I shall deal only briefly with the next role-maintaining technique, *invocation*. Invocation is the act of calling up some higher
order of values that are not *prima facie* pertinent to the conflict
at hand. The consensus on these values is then applied for the
solution of the problem. For example, when all else fails, waving
the flag often re-establishes a common appreciation of what to
do, patriotism being the last refuge even of the conflicted traitor.
Religious consensus is another especially general possibility. The
social gospellers at the turn of the century urged that people
gauge labor disputes by the question, "How would Christ have
acted?" Invoking a higher order of values permits a wider consensus to be applied when the immediate and more narrow guides
for resolution of conflicting expectations seem inadequate.

The consensus that is invoked and applied will always be
on a fairly amorphous level. That is, invocation uses more generalized values because the more specialized values as sources of
normative action have failed and have given rise to the role
conflict. Religious and nationalistic value schemes are probably
the most flexible for invocation and application, but they are
also of such a high generality that they will be invoked only
when intermediate orders cannot be used. In ordinary circumstances, the clinical researcher would rarely need to reach to the
extremes of religious or nationalistic allegiances. He would instead be able to invoke generalized notions of etiquette and tact,
or notions of professional ethics, or even more specialized notions of technical considerations, such as what psychoanalytic
theory might presuppose. Any of these might be seized upon
as part of a general consensus shared by the participants in the
interaction and given a specialized application in the resolution
of conflicts in the clinical research relationships.

Two examples showing the invocation of different sets of values for the same kind of conflict can be drawn from the history of the First LSD Project. First, it will be recalled that in the initial conference called by Dr. Thorpe to discuss the patients' refusal to cooperate, discussion became focused on whether or not the request for cooperation was "friendly." Here the attempt was made to draw upon a generalized sense of values that was shared by all concerned, presumably including the patients. Much conference time was spent upon considering the patients' definition of the drug request as "unfriendly," and the physicians attempted to discover whether they too would apply the same distinction. Second, in a later, general meeting, values inherent in psychoanalytic ethics were drawn upon to resolve the difficulties in viewing the LSD Project. Dr. Lowe stated, "What we have come to is that . . . [in the first place] neither of the patients [on the LSD Project] was treated as if he were an equal, as we would theoretically expect from our psychoanalytic background." In other words, Dr. Lowe tried to invoke considerations of psychoanalytic values and techniques in the analysis of the conflict situation.

In these two examples, the invocation of general values— represented by ideas of friendliness or ideas of psychoanalytic equality—was an attempt to apply to a problematic situation items from a more generalized value consensus among the participants so as to establish norms for use in new situations of the same general kind. In the second example, it is interesting to note that Dr. Lowe reaffirmed his own solidarity with the group of workers and stated, "We have all been guilty of stepping aside from principles which we theoretically agree to." And he went ahead to give a recent illustration of his own misfeasance. However, as should be evident to the reader by now, the problem was not that the staff had stepped aside from well-known and accepted principles for action; the problem was to specify the application of those relevant principles to the problematic situations that arose. Invoking and applying a general value consensus is one of the most important role-maintaining techniques, for it tends to construct and disseminate a rationalized support for the chosen role definition. By invocation one seeks to find ways to fit a particular role definition (or role expectation) into the wider scheme of values and to draw from that integrating process a legitimation of one's activity and a guide for preferences among choices in future situations. In short, the role-maintaining technique of invocation helps to establish norms for the particular role definition being enacted.

The last technique I want to discuss, *technical modification*, crosscuts all the other role-maintaining techniques because it concerns the content as well as the procedure of role-maintenance. Technical modifications call mainly upon the actor's expertise in his field of specialized role knowledge, while the other kinds of role-maintaining techniques tend to tax only the skills of social adroitness. In technical modifications, the specific type of business between the interacting persons undergoes slight but significant changes in technical content. For example, a professional gambler will play for different stakes with other professional gamblers and will not use the same victimizing techniques that he would with amateurs ready for the fleecing. Also, in medicine, a doctor may choose between different possible therapies, according to nontechnical considerations, such as the amount of money the patient can afford to spend on drugs; if the doctor chooses with due regard to the patient's resources, his relationship is strengthened. The physician might select a slightly less efficacious therapy not only to save the patient money but perhaps to protect him from embarrassment, to save him extra effort or emotional expenditure, or to take account of any number of other considerations.

Technical modifications sustain the role definition of the clinical researcher in psychiatry through exercising his facility with his two expert crafts, treatment and research. The modifications occur in revisions of goals or procedures in either research or treatment. For example, the research goals of Dr. Thorpe and Dr. Richards were considerably modified when their patients refused the LSD. Although Dr. Thorpe had originally planned on a longitudinal study of each patient to gain acquaintance with the evolution of depersonalization as a psychological defense process, he settled for a three-month study on the third patient; Dr. Richards actually dropped the study of LSD and schizophrenia altogether. These goal changes, accompanied by changes in procedures, were at least in part a technique for maintaining the definition of the clinical researcher role that each psychiatrist had finally come to carry out. In Dr. Richards' case, the definition excluded the acceptance of obligations for therapy; he managed to find a place in the organization that did not require him to have medical responsibility for any patients, but this made it virtually impossible to pursue the same research goals that he had begun with. In Dr. Thorpe's case, the definition continued to combine research and treatment, but he imposed certain time limitations on himself and the patient whom he next admitted for study. By restricting the scope of his study to a cross-sectional rather than a longitudinal one, he could carry out his own conception of what was required in the way of both research and treatment in the hospital.

In the Trade-Off Project, research goals were finally defined in such a way as to be achieved by the normal outcome of the therapy process. Another project I studied was organized with the same technical arrangement: In the Schizophrenic Siblings Project, three therapists gathered together in weekly sessions to review their treatment of each of three brothers, with the intention of increasing their understanding of how the behavior of each of the siblings influenced the course of each of the others. Their research comprised an attempt to conceptualize the inter-sibling relationships as a factor in personality development and illness. Similarly, in the Trade-Off, the therapists came together for clinical conferences by which they hoped to find, in the productions of the therapy hour, clues to the family dynamics of schizophrenic patients. In each of these projects, the research goals were in little-known fields so that the exploratory nature of the therapy-hour data would be particularly suited for research purposes. This neat dovetailing of research and treatment resolved many problems that might have otherwise arisen if the goals in research had been more ambitious and precise.

The role-maintaining maneuver of technical modification is

clearly one of the most crucial areas for investigating the influences of social factors on the scientific (or clinical) process. Of course, not all technical modifications solve social problems met in the course of scientific research. Nevertheless, it would seem useful to study the course of any protracted scientific investigation in order to look for the social functions served by ongoing modifications in goals and in procedures. Such an inquiry cannot be made merely by collecting a quantity of examples of technical modifications and then subjecting them to analysis. While some generalized problems may be readily observed in any research laboratory—for example, problems of subordinate-superordinate relations in research direction problems [36]—the intricacies of the individual context of each project and modifications during its history requires a longitudinal case approach at this stage of our knowledge. I have intended this discussion of the technical modification as a role-maintaining device to be merely representative of the necessary considerations.

I should perhaps note here parenthetically that the interrelations of the various techniques can indicate their potential theoretical relevance to sociology, for they need not be considered merely as descriptive concepts. For example, invocation as a form of the integrating process bears a close relation to the hierarchization of roles and role obligations. Invocation is in fact an embryonic hierarchization, a kind of first step towards the institutionalization of specialized standards for choice in the role-conflict situation. While the ways of invoking values can be institutionalized, clearly the application of the invoked values to the conflict situation is not institutionalized. The choices are not previously programmed; they are problematical, hence the necessity for invocation. Similarly, decontamination is an incomplete and embryonic form of role segregation. Invocation and decontamination, as role-maintaining techniques, embody on a lower level of generality and organization, as compared to role hierarchization and role segregation, the fundamental processes

36. Herbert A. Shepard, "Superiors and Subordinates in Research," *J. Business* (1956) 29: 261-67. See also his "Patterns of Organization for Applied Research and Development," *J. Business* (1956) 29: 52-61.

of integrating and quarantining that prevent and correct social conflict. The accompanying schema presents these interrelations diagrammatically.

Conflict-resolution process	*Quarantining*	*Integrating*
Fully institutionalized	role segregation	role hierarchization
Role-defining technique	disjoining definition	unifying definition
Role-maintaining technique	decontamination	invocation

In general, I have presented only the merest introduction to the many considerations suggested by the major strategies of role definition and the minor tactics of role-maintaining maneuvers that the research psychiatrist uses to resolve the conflict between the research and the treatment aspects of his work role. I have tried to show that general social processes run through all these conflict-resolution techniques and that these can end by exacting changes in the content and procedures of research projects. The quarantining and the integrating processes of social action occur in the unifying and disjoining role definitions of both overt and covert types. The maneuvers that sustain any sort of role definition also exemplify the social tendencies that lead to the fitting together of discrepant social realities or their insulation from each other. Although the maneuver of technical modification of research or treatment goals or procedures has the most obvious effects upon the scientific process, certainly other sorts of role-maintaining operations also facilitate or impede the scientific awareness of the clinical researcher.

Seven

A PSYCHIATRIST'S IDEA
OF HIS OWN WORK
IS CHANGED BY HIS COLLEAGUES[1]

THE HONEYCOMB of rooms that piled atop and aside each other
to constitute the Medical Research Center swarmed with the
business of many specialists besides the psychiatric expert. Outside the psychiatric service itself were cardiologists, pathologists,
chemists, microbiologists, neurosurgeons, allergists, biophysicists,
and so on, and on, organized into smaller or larger cadres aiming
to subdue some one of man's ills by the scientific processes of
the contemporary world. The research psychiatrist operated
there within the context of a score of other programs, only
loosely related to some over-all organization. Any specialist
could, and most did, restrict their most frequent exchanges to
those who shared very much the same interests; who were
often, in fact, working on the same general problems. At the
Center, the members of the psychiatric service, like the members
of the other medical services, tended to form a group that was
usually only informally and infrequently penetrated by members
of the other services, who were left much to themselves.

Perhaps the compartmentalization of the various services im-

---

1. This chapter has been revised from "Observations on Social Processes
in Psychiatric Research: Definitions of Knowledge, Method, and Science
in Psychiatry," *Behav. Sci.* (1956) 1: 290-302

peded to some extent the potential spontaneous growth of knowledge from the crossing of intellectual boundaries that was physically possible in the social associations at the Center. Yet the geographic proximity of various different specialists did make it possible for the determined explorer to find what he wanted in informal intellectual exchanges right in the same building; perhaps he would find in the next corridor, the next floor up or down, at lunch in the common cafeteria, in the elevator, the person who could stimulate him with new views on an old problem. Even in the psychiatric service itself, not to speak of the other services, there were many of the specialties that I have mentioned—and more. It is perhaps no wonder that contact between the different medical services was not so frequent since a man could often find someone from another discipline within his own group to answer a question or puzzle over it helpfully, to suggest a book or paper, and so on.

The research in the psychiatric service was executed, then, in an almost overwhelming atmosphere of the multiplicity of modern scientific disciplines. It is on the effect of just one facet of this multidisciplined setting that I want to comment in the present chapter. I shall look at how the social and intellectual presence of one group of closely related scientists—the social scientists of sociology, social psychology, developmental psychology, and so on—exerted an influence upon the research psychiatrists' conception of knowledge (especially of science and its method) in his own work.[2] I am concerned with the sociointellectual meaning of these disciplines for the discipline of psychiatry under the social condition of collaboration or other close research association in the work setting. I shall argue that psychiatrists under these social conditions tend to devalue their own clinical operations, in terms of the desirable qualities of science and knowledge, and to overvalue the operations of the

---

2. For an examination of some reciprocal influences of psychiatric conceptions of the social scientists' work in psychiatric settings, see Robert N. Rapoport, "Notes on the Disparagement of 'Sociologizing' in Collaborative Research," *Hum. Org.* (1957) 16: 14-15. See also David M. Landy, "The Anthropologist and the Mental Hospital," *Hum. Org.* (1958) 17: 30-35.

quantitatively oriented social scientist.[3] In addition, this process of evaluation may take place with less concern for the intellectual or philosophical significance of the scientific operations involved than for the requirements of the social situation.

I am, of course, basing my argument primarily upon my observations at the Medical Research Center, but I shall also draw upon my experiences in other psychiatric settings, including clinical facilities in which little research was conducted and a psychiatric training institute. I shall also make use of anecdotal and other reports made to me by psychiatrists in other institutions whose experiences offer some rough check upon my own.[4]

The question of the generality of these observations and the formulations derived from them should be dealt with a bit further before I go on. First, some of the discussion is relevant primarily to the segment of the psychiatric profession that uses psychotherapeutic theory and techniques—especially the psychoanalytic orientation. But this will be clear in context, and the relationship of the intellectual orientation of that segment of the profession to the orientation of other groups within psychiatry will be indicated. It is appropriate to think of current American psychiatry as psychotherapeutic psychiatry, especially as it has been influenced by psychoanalytic theory, since it can be fairly safely assumed that such is the current dominant theme of American psychiatry. This would mean then that although I shall be talking about psychotherapeutic psychiatry, presumably what I have

---

3. The author's value judgment on this should be made clear: I feel that this tendency is unfortunate; that it is destructive of good psychiatric research effort of the nonquantitative varieties without bringing about a commensurate increase in the effectiveness of quantitative psychiatric research.

4. Of particular use has been a 250-page record of a conference on the research training of psychiatric residents. Papers of that conference and summaries of the record of discussion are included in "The Institute on Training for Research of Psychiatric Residents (Fort Lauderdale, Florida, April 10-11, 1959)," mimeographed for the National Institute of Mental Health, Bethesda, Maryland, 1960. An analysis of these meetings is presented in Stewart E. Perry and Helen Swick Perry, "A Report on the Major Areas of Interest and Emergent Findings of the Institute on Training for Research of Psychiatric Residents." Mimeographed with Institute proceedings, 1960.

to say will be applicable to most of the psychiatric profession rather generally.

Second, although I confine my attention in this chapter to psychiatry and its problems of defining method, knowledge, and science, the argument that I advance about psychiatry might be advanced equally about other branches of social science and clinical medicine.[5] Psychology and sociology especially have been dealing with the question of quantification for perhaps a century. Indeed, sociology from the time of its inception by Comte has dealt with the question of scientific stature in relation to quantification. Psychiatry, however, has more recently become involved in this sort of questioning.[6]

A general intellectual trend that may currently keep epistemo-

---

5. A parallel discussion for the field of entrepreneurial history is provided by Lewis Atherton, "The Research Center in Entrepreneurial History: A Personal Appraisal," *Explorations in Entrepreneurial History* (1954) 7: 105-10. In sociology, see Pitirim A. Sorokin, *Fads and Foibles in Modern Sociology and Related Sciences,* Chicago: Regnery, 1956. See also the following: *The Behavioral Sciences at Harvard* (Report by a Faculty Committee), Cambridge, Mass.: Harvard University, 1954, pp. 55f., 154f., 426f.); Robert Angell, "A Critical Review of the Development of the Personal Document Method in Sociology: 1920-1940," pp. 175-232 in Louis Gottschalk, *et al., The Use of Personal Documents in History, Anthropology, and Sociology* (Social Science Research Council Bulletin 53), Washington, D.C.: Social Science Research Council, 1945. An especially instructive paper is A. H. Maslow, "Problem-Centering Vs. Means-Centering in Science," *Philos. Sci.* (1946) 13: 326-31. See also Kurt W. Back, "The Game and the Myth as Two Languages of Social Science," *Behav. Sci.* (1963) 8: 66-71. For a discussion of the problems in medicine, see Hans Selye, *op. cit.,* and Donald Mainland, "The Clinical Trial—Some Difficulties and Suggestions," *J. Chronic Dis.* (1960) 11: 484-96.

6. One commentator believes that as late as 1949 medicine as a whole (presumably including psychiatry) was as yet unfamiliar with and antagonistic toward "modern ideas of [statistically controlled] design and analysis" of clinical techniques and therapies, but that by 1958 the diffusion of knowledge about this central conception of quantitative research technology had led to a "perversion of statistics" and a misapplication of the experimental design. See Donald Mainland, *op. cit.* See also S[tanley] C[obb], " 'Too Scientific,' " *Amer. J. Psychiat.* (1950-51) 109: 935-36. For one of the earliest assessments of the value of statistical techniques in psychiatry, see Franz Alexander, "Evaluation of Statistical and Analytical Methods in Psychiatry and Psychology," *Amer. J. Orthopsychiat.* (1934) 4: 433-48.

The general entrance of contemporary statistical thinking into the profession of psychiatry at large, however, perhaps may be dated from the invited lecture of Edwin B. Wilson, Professor of Vital Statistics of the

logical questions in the foreground of psychiatry and the other social sciences is the tendency toward interdisciplinary investigation and theory construction that focuses attention upon the techniques and methodologies of sister disciplines.[7] Perhaps just as important in the social science confusion over how to know things about human relations is the broader social context in which the social scientist operates: the American value system, which gives a high place to engineering and industrial technology and their associated techniques of mathematical investigation. It is interesting to contrast American social science in general with its European counterpart in this respect. In Europe, as the most cursory examination of the literature would suggest, library, qualitative, and deductive studies in all the social sciences command a greater respect than they do in the United States, where inductive, quantitative, and empirical studies are more developed. The remark of a leading American psychiatrist about another equally well-known psychiatrist points up the difference in evaluations: "I have heard from those who have no liking for him that he does his research in the library."

It might actually be said that the psychiatrist in his ordinary relations with his patient performs a general epistemological and ontological function. That is, his operations with the patient are aimed at reaching a consensus in defining what is real and what he and the patient need to know. He is concerned with

---

7. Much recent discussion has taken the form of examining the difficulties and uses of multidisciplined collaboration. A basic review and bibliography is provided by Margaret B. Luszki, *Interdisciplinary Team Research*, New York: New York University Press-Associated College Presses, 1958.

Harvard School of Public Health, to the eighty-third annual meeting of the American Psychiatric Association in 1927. This conjecture is suggested further by the relatively simple technical level of his address and of another paper read at the same meetings by two statistically trained physicians Henry B. Elkind and Carl R. Doering. See the 1927-28 volume of the *American Journal of Psychiatry*. These papers coincide with the first major philanthropic support of psychiatric research, as reported elsewhere in the same volume of the *Journal*, and with George M. Kline's presidential address, announcing the introduction of a mechanical, statistical reporting system for state mental hospitals in Massachusetts. Two years earlier, William A. White, as president of the Association, had recommended that the Association establish its first committee on research.

mapping out with the patient the latter's areas of difficulty in living and with clarifying with him what is and is not, in the patient's life—all this to the end that the patient will be able to solve his problems in living, if he has a clearer idea of his own participation in them. However, this aspect of the psychiatrist's role is not immediately socially relevant in terms of the definition of psychiatric knowledge generally, although in the performance of this function the psychiatrist may gain knowledge which he will then formulate for society at large in articles, books, and addresses. It is the goal of formulating information for a wider audience than the particular patient that makes the psychiatrist a knowledge-definer in the social order of science. Thus, to study the psychiatrist's social experiences and how they are related to his definition of psychiatric knowledge, one must look at his activity where it is more directly involved in producing, receiving, or transmitting knowledge in this wider sense. This means that one must be concerned not with his service function or purely therapy functions but with his research, learning or teaching activities.

In my presentation of the influence upon research of the conflict with treatment values, I was able to take the events occurring at the Center as if they had no particular prehistory. At this juncture, however, it is particularly important to investigate some of the experiences of the psychiatrist even before he arrives at a research setting. These experiences prepare him or make him especially vulnerable to the kinds of influences that his colleagues may exert on his conceptions of knowledge in psychiatric research. As a matter of fact, the psychiatrist need not participate in any such setting as the Center to face the sort of socio-epistemologial choices I shall describe.[8]

---

8. I have the impression that the situation is changing in psychiatric training. In the last two decades, only the rare psychiatrist might have been relatively immune from some of the problems of invidious comparisons of his epistemological and research conceptions with those of other disciplines, but today there are probably increasing numbers of psychiatric physicians who depart from the pattern I shall describe. Certainly psychiatry is not so shy now of the careful techniques of other experimental sciences as it once was. See, for example, Group for the Advancement of Psychiatry, *Some Observations on Controls in Psychiatric Research* (Report #42), New York: Group for the Advancement of Psychiatry, 1959.

As a matter of convenience for discussing the social processes involved in the psychiatric definition of knowledge, I shall proceed by describing more or less in developmental terms the way a psychiatrist moves into and accepts a knowledge-defining role as a scientist. This sort of career-line description has advantages in providing some contrast in the transition from a service orientation to a research orientation, when the psychiatrist accepts a job in which he is to do research. Conventional learning and teaching in psychiatry, as in other knowledge-related activities, will be described tangentially to this transition.

In tracing the microsocial development and definition of a scientific status by the psychiatrist, I shall describe three groups of social processes; each group corresponds roughly to a stage in the genesis of the psychiatrist's definition of psychiatric knowledge insofar as this definition is conditioned or accompanied by relevant social processes. The first group of processes is that inherent in the psychiatrist's training and experience before he assumes a research role. The second group has to do with the expectations engendered by the actual research situation. The third group includes those reactions or responses to research that the psychiatrist may see in his associates and that he may emulate and use in his own definitions of knowledge, method, and research.

Psychiatric Training and Experience

At least three features of the psychiatrist's background and training in psychiatry seem to have importance in his later definition of psychiatric knowledge as a researcher: (1) He tends to have little or no academic exposure to research methodology or the philosophy of science. (2) The opinion of other segments of the medical profession about the status of psychiatry as a scientific discipline is not high. (3) There is the common practice in medicine of doing research with patients by using the ordinary clinical procedures that would be used for treatment purposes anyway, a practice leading to a certain lack of intellectual distinction between clinical procedures and research. Each of these three features of the psychiatrist's background may be seen simply as an experience that tends to set up accompanying scientific ideologies and professional values.

Training. It will have to be granted that the psychiatrist who goes through the ordinary course in America rarely, if ever, receives any training specifically in research philosophy or methods. Even if he goes on to take a good deal of advanced training, such as the course of a psychoanalytic institute, he is not required to pay much attention to the research and scientific status of his tools, techniques, and philosophy.[9] In short, the physician learns under intensive training how to practice psychiatry and psychoanalysis, but he is not led to understand self-consciously the methodological and scientific underpinnings of his profession as medicine in general and as psychiatry in particular. Although typically he will not have been familiarized with research operations in his psychiatric training, the psychiatrist may, if he plans to be a researcher, seek special training

---

9. In 1960, the psychoanalytic community published a survey of its training practices: Bertram D. Lewin and Helen Ross, *Psychoanalytic Education in the United States,* New York: Norton, 1960. This book notes that since 1950 "scientific method" has been a required part of the curriculum for approved institutes. Yet, as my own review of the training bulletins of the individual institutes indicated in 1955 and 1963, this requirement was rarely met. (See "Observations," *op. cit.,* esp. 293n.) Even as late as 1963, scientific method, or its cognates, is not listed or explicitly provided for in many of the classical psychoanalytic institutes, nor is there any indication of a change in a recent review of the psychoanalytic training programs. See "Psychoanalytic Education," *J. Amer. Psa. Assoc.* (1962) 10: 118-65. It should be noted also that the deviationist institutes rarely offer courses that examine the scientific methodological and philosophical underpinnings of psychoanalytic theory, classical or deviationist. "Research" courses in some training settings tend to be a noncredit "opportunity to collaborate" with senior staff or merely a presentation of case materials organized around some topical or diagnostic category. Some training institutes, notably the Menninger School, offer considerable sophisticated research training for the psychiatrist. But the 1950 standards of the American Psychoanalytic Association do not show the same level of attention; the Association's standard syllabus of the required course work in "scientific method" is as follows:

"Psychoanalysis is presented as a method and as a synthesis of empirical observations.

"Special consideration is given to primary postulates, to basic require-

before taking a research job. But the fact that the psychiatrist's apprenticeship as a student in medical school, as a resident in hospitals and clinics, and as a trainee in a psychoanalytic institute is so prolonged militates against his further prolonging his education by special training for research.[10] His research training is apt to be an on-the-job affair, after he has accepted a research post.

The psychiatrist, then, who takes on the role of researcher—by accepting a specific job as a researcher—is apt to come to it relatively naive as to how he will perform his research functions. He will understand to be sure, that his training background is the reason he has been hired, and so he expects or presumes that the techniques and approaches he is accustomed to use in previous work will be the ones he will use in a research job. His expectation may be either supported or challenged by his work group when he assumes his new position—a point that will be discussed in a moment.

Inter-profession standing. Another characteristically profes-

---

10. See Lawrence S. Kubie, "Some Unsolved Problems of the Scientific Career," *American Scientist* (1953) 41: 596-613; (1954) 42: 104-12. Research training as a specialized program is offered, for example, at the Menninger School of Psychiatry in a two-year stretch to take place after the third year of residency!

---

ments for utilizing the method of free associations and to logical means for interpretation. Applications of criteria to clinical material provide continuity with the course on dreams." Syllabus quoted entire from "Standards for the Training of Physicians in Psychoanalysis," *Bull. Amer. Psa. Assoc.* (1950) 6: 1-5.

Criticisms of the training situation have been forcefully made by leading representatives of the profession. For example, Edward Glover has felt that psychoanalytic teaching militates against a research attitude and "preserves many of the disadvantages of mid-Victorian pedagogy and few of its advantages." Edward Glover, "Research Methods in Psycho-Analysis," *Int. J. Psa.* (1952) 33: 403-409. A recent report of the American Psychiatric Association says that psychiatry "does not have a strong research orientation. It lacks research models, research training opportunities for young people, and tools to implement their research inclinations." American Psychiatric Association, *Training the Psychiatrist to Meet Changing Needs* (Report of the Conference on Graduate Psychiatric Education, 1962), Washington, D. C.: American Psychiatric Association, 1964.

sional value-idea-experience complex that the psychiatrist brings to his research job is his peculiar role as a specialist within the medical profession. This experience is, for most psychiatrists, remarkably similar: that is, they feel that their specialty is regarded by other medical students or practitioners as a most unreliable and diffuse discipline. In the view of other medical men, psychiatry may be something that is rather strange and even anxiety-provoking, but most of all it is simply a step-relative, not a real relative, of the medical sciences and professions. The psychiatrist is thus almost an outsider so far as the other medical men are concerned.[11] To be sure, he is held in higher esteem than the osteopath—after all, a psychiatrist does have an M.D. degree [12]—but the respectability of his subject matter is looked at a bit askance.

This question of respectability is not so imperative if the psychiatrist defines his field of interest as being the neurological and physiological aspects of psychiatry. Defined thus, psychiatry is closer to traditional medicine in practice and theory. If, on the other hand, the psychiatrist is primarily concerned with the psychological and interpersonal aspects of human living, his subject matter is far removed from the medical, and it demands a great deal of understanding for his medical confreres to accept his specialty as a real part of medicine. For one thing, behavior as defined psychologically and interpersonally is less amenable to many of the common techniques of medical research. That is, the psychiatrist doing behavioral research cannot operate very easily in a laboratory; he tends instead to operate in a clinical, person to person relationship with the patients whom he is studying. The psychiatrist must usually be content with this one

---

11. See Harvey L. Smith, "Psychiatry: A Social Institution in Process," *Social Forces* (1954-1955) 33: 310-16; and "The Relationship of Psychiatry to the Other Medical Professions," paper presented at the American Sociological Society Meetings, 1955. Revised version published as "Psychiatry in Medicine: Intra- or Inter-Professional Relationships?" *Amer. J. Sociol.* (1957) 63: 285-89.

12. The emphasis that medical psychotherapists place upon the medical degree in their relations with nonmedical psychotherapists may be related to a need to maintain a certain status under this adverse pressure from other medical colleagues.

approach to his data. He must be a clinician par excellence. In fact, his professional standing within his specialty will depend upon his powers of sensitive perception in his relationship with his patients. The difficulties of conducting psychiatric research (of the mentalistic or psychological type) [13] according to laboratory techniques analogous to other medical research techniques, therefore, tend to prevent the psychiatrist from using standardized and quantitative means to demonstrate the validity of his frame of reference as scientific in comparison with other medical fields.

Research as a Minor Activity in the Service Setting. The research-psychiatrist-to-be brings also to his research role a certain confusion between service and research. The traditional clinical method in medicine—that is, everything that is involved in diagnosis and treatment—is service to the patient, his family, and the community. Most doctors are in service positions, there being more demand for service than for research. It is not unusual then for the medical man interested in research to carry on his research on a bootleg basis, sandwiched in between his service functions. Research carried on this way must be done ever so economically, and there is the added impetus to do the research with the identical procedures that will be used anyway in the treatment. Research thus may not be differentiated from the purely service or clinical function of the doctor—except in terms of the additional value (for research) placed on the treatment procedures by the doctor for himself.[14] Psychiatrists have shared with other medical men this sort of global experience of treatment-cum-research. An indication of the close relationship of

---

13. See George Devereux, "Practical Problems of Conceptual Psychiatric Research," *Psychiatry* (1952) 15: 189-92. Devereux maintains that the psychiatrist's medical training is not research-minded anyway or, at least, what he is taught is unsuitable for psychiatric research and separated from an understanding of the general problems of logic and scientific method. One of Devereux's complaints about the practical difficulties in conducting psychiatric research—the lack of funds—is certainly outdated, as is his suggestion that a psychiatrist who collaborates with social scientists loses status in the eyes of the usual dispensers of medical research funds.

14. See Flanders Dunbar, "Research in Private Practice," *Amer J. Psychiat.* (1950-51) 107: 739-42.

ordinary clinical, treatment routines and research in medicine (especially newer branches of medicine) is provided in the literature by the many instances of reports on a single case or studies of very small numbers of cases.

Psychiatric Research in an Organizational Setting

With this sort of background the psychiatrist approaches the situation in which he consciously sets out to do research in an organizational and group setting. The central expectation which, like any other researcher, the psychiatrist experiences is, of course, that he produce research results. "Results" means basically some sort of scholarly or professional publication or some systematic communication of one's work to one's peers.

This demand for results means that the worker is expected at some point not too long postponed to stand up and say, "This is the final report on what I have been doing; this is the result, the reward to science (and/or to me and to my organization), from the time I have spent and the work I have done." The researcher in any field is required to put himself out on a limb thusly, and so, too, the psychiatrist. This demand is so much a part of research that it is to be presumed that a researcher at least tolerates it easily or even accepts it with alacrity, so long as he feels he is capable of fulfilling the expectation. It is only when the researcher feels an impotence, real or fantasied, in the face of the expectation or demand, that he will resist it. At the point of growing resistance to the demand for results there is an increase in the worker's counter-demands for the resources and facilities that may be useful for meeting the demand for results. For example, there may be increasing requests for supporting personnel and equipment or for additional salary. If these requests are granted, there is a corresponding increase in the original demand that sparked the request for more support. There is a cyclical process: The more equipment, personnel, space, or whatnot the researcher has placed at his command, the more responsibility he is likely to feel in terms of using these facilities to get results. There is thus an inescapable complex of interlocking expectations—and physical buttresses to those expectations—that reinforces the whole research system, so that the researcher must develop ways of maintaining his own confidence in his ability to meet these expectations.[15]

The maintenance of one's self-picture as a researcher is important for the purposes of this chapter in that in at least psychiatric research one of the maintenance processes involves the definition of scientific knowledge in the research field. Before discussing this point, however, I think it is important to probe the psychiatric research setting for some of the elements that will tend to threaten the maintenance of an acceptable self-picture and thus call up a social adjustment that has intellectual consequences. For this purpose let us consider, as the typical setting, the multi-disciplined setting like the Center in which most psychiatric research currently takes place. Much psychiatric research necessarily is done in collaboration with other disciplines, and if not, then the research is done in close physical or intellectual proximity to research going on in other disciplines or with other disciplines. This fact is due to the growth of team research and also to the need for institutional resources. Psychiatrists tend to do

15. Tremendous pressures are built up in the individual researcher, which can take a physical and psychological toll. When one is given everything in equipment, assisting personnel, and salary, in return for which mere miracles are expected, results must come out in terms of miracles or in terms of symptoms, as Nellis Foster has observed in banking and business situations. This "Nellis Foster syndrome" was reported by Alan Gregg, M.D., in "When to Change Jobs—And Why," *Harper's Magazine* (August, 1955) 211: 71-76.

At the new Center the atmosphere of psychological expectation of great things to come from the researchers was tellingly and amusingly illustrated in one of the elements of the orientation lectures given by housekeeping supervisors to any new janitorial and cleaning staff. They were told, in effect, "If you see one of the researchers sitting with his feet up on the desk and just looking out the window, don't get upset that he isn't working and you are. The fact is he is undoubtedly thinking very hard." Such breathless regard from the cleaning supervisors may not have been known to most of the researchers, but it formed part of a general pattern that the researchers did know and feel.

research in institutional settings or in collaboration with others who are in institutional settings, and therefore are very likely to be in some kind of contact with workers in other disciplines. For example, general hospitals, universities, research organizations, and mental hospitals are loci for specialists in other social or medical disciplines. The private practitioner as a lone-wolf researcher is almost unknown in these days,[16] and even if a psychiatrist operates by himself physically, he would find it difficult to avoid the intellectual influence of interdisciplinary work done by his psychiatric colleagues. The interpenetration of the social sciences is thus an almost inescapable intellectual influence.

In the multidisciplined psychiatric setting the (psychologically oriented) psychiatrist comes in close contact with social scientists [17] who apparently are studying the same sorts of human behavior that the psychiatrist studies. However, for studying the same thing the social scientists are able to choose from among a greater assortment of tools than the psychiatrist ordinarily has at his disposal. First, there are those techniques and tools of which the psychiatrist may not have any intimate knowledge and which the social scientist may flaunt before him. The techniques of experimental science, adapted or maladapted by social sciences from the arsenal of the physical sciences, are the special case in point. These techniques, generally quantitative and thus sometimes requiring advanced mathematical knowledge for appropriate use, are reminiscent of the laboratory medical sciences, and they may therefore confront the psychiatrist with the same stern, hawk-nosed visages that he experiences within the pecking order of medical specialties. Second, a social scientist may also have some of the most advanced training a psychiatrist can claim. For example, there is the important experience of personal analysis,

---

16. Joseph Ben-David has studied the deviant roles of those, like Freud, making the important advances in the medical fields. His data suggest that the more or less unaccepted, marginal man is more likely to do the important creative work. See Joseph Ben-David, "Roles and Innovations in Medicine," *Amer. J. Sociol.* (1959-60) 65: 557-68.

17. Although psychiatry can be considered one of the social sciences, I use the term *social scientist* here to refer to psychologists, anthropologists, sociologists, and the like.

which the social scientist is quite likely to have undergone if he is interested in research that brings him into much contact with a psychiatric setting. The social scientist may even have undergone systematic psychoanalytic training as a therapist, although, of course, such training would generally have taken place outside of the classical psychoanalytic institutes. In other words, the psychiatrist may experience difficulty maintaining his self-picture as a researcher because (1) he does not have certain research tools of high social (and intellectual) value that are currently available to his associates and/or (2) he has virtually no tools restricted to his own profession.[18] This contrasts sharply with the ordinary work situation of the psychiatrist in a clinic or hospital, and particularly in private practice, where his own functions are considered by himself and by nonmedical associates as by far the most important, where he receives greater financial return and authoritative standing, and where his operations are closer to being socially unique.

At this juncture I should like to give a few illustrations of the fact that psychiatrists often find it necessary to make some socio-intellectual arrangement or integration of the clinical operations in research and the operations that are closer to laboratory, experimental, and mathematical models. One almost across-the-board experience is the evaluation, in research and other medical institutions, of the neurological, brain-metabolical, and so on, studies as being somehow more "basic" than studies that cannot use the physiochemical, laboratory methods. Thus

---

18. The purely medical training that distinguishes the psychiatrist from nonmedical practitioners in his field is, as he will sometimes assert, relatively useless to him in most instances in the practice of psychotherapy or in the study of the interpersonal processes of behavior with which psychotherapy is concerned. On the other hand, for ceremonial and other purposes emphasis may be placed upon the relationship between the psychotherapeutic and other medicine—an emphasis that serves to strengthen the respectability of psychotherapy and conversely weakens the position of nonmedically trained psychotherapists. A presidential address to the American Psychoanalytic Association begins: "Psychoanalysis is biologically based and body bound. Historically, its most intimate relationship has been as a medical discipline. . . ." M. Ralph Kaufman, "Psychoanalysis in Medicine," *Bull. Amer. Psychoanal. Assoc.* (1951) 7: 1-12.

in the Center, two divisions of research were distinguished, each organizationally on a par with the other. One was named Clinical Studies; the other, Basic Research. The Basic Research Division was, of course, the branch which was most concerned with laboratory techniques and with neurophysiology and neuro-chemistry and the like. The Clinical Studies Division dealt mostly with actual patients and was the group that used less the labora-tory or experimental method than the naturalistic method. It is interesting to note a further implication in the differences be-tween the two names. *Studies* is a much less rigorous term in science than is *research*. Further, within the Clinical Studies program one unit was less concerned with mentalistic or inter-personal investigation than it was with physiologic functioning. This unit, interestingly enough, was termed the Laboratory of Psychiatric Sciences, whereas the unit that was most concerned with psychotherapy with adults was termed the Laboratory of Psychiatric Studies; subsequently that name was changed to Psychiatric Studies Group, making the difference in the names even more striking.

These organizational titles, of course, not only reflect the underlying intellectual philosophy of research and science, they may also support it. Although the public evidence of this intel-lectual orientation may not be as striking in, for instance, uni-versity departmental settings, still those who have been connected with them can testify to similar relative scientific standings of subject matter and methods of systematic inquiry.[19]

At this point, let me take some more informal illustrations from observations at the Medical Research Center:

A group of researchers (including sociologists, psychologists, and psychiatrists) discussing their work over coffee was asked by one of its members for advice on placing an article already completed. A certain psychiatric journal was suggested by a sociologist, but the reply was, "I mean a scientific journal—you know, one that publishes papers with statistics."

---

19. See, for example, David Riesman, *Constraint and Variety in Amer-ican Education*, Lincoln, Nebr.: University of Nebraska Press, 1956.

Although the journal in question does in fact regularly publish "papers with statistics," it undoubtedly publishes less of that sort of material than some others; for that reason it was not considered "a scientific journal."

The informal situation is perhaps especially likely to reflect the nonintellectual influences upon the work being conducted. This may be true not only when colleagues discuss the homely details of publication outlets but also when they consider seriously their own work, as another coffee discussion illustrates:

A research psychiatrist studying psychotherapeutic processes expressed concern over criticisms of his nonquantitative research procedures. He remarked, "Those guys [psychologists] may have something when they talk about reliability, but all I know is that I have to do my kind of work." But was his kind of work *science*, he wondered.

However, even in more formal settings, the general atmosphere of doubt can make itself felt.

In a formal staff meeting, Dr. Lowe talked of his work, addressing a heterogeneous group of fellow researchers in the field. "Of course," he said, "we can't prove scientifically that psychotherapy works, but I intend to spend the rest of my professional life in a commitment to study it, in the faith that there is something to it."

In spite of his unchallenged status and reputation in psychiatry at the Center and in the larger community, this psychiatrist apparently felt it necessary to be apologetic about the scientific standing of his field, a matter of "faith" rather than science.

A final example comes from my own collaborative relationship with two psychiatrists who had sought my assistance in analyzing interview materials they had collected. Our work together was fruitful but troubled by their expectation that I would somehow make something quantitative and scientific out of their own significant and original work. I had repeatedly to point out the greater importance of their own formulations in comparison with some of my work on the same data, in which I subjected the data to some minor statistical manipulations. My particular experience in this project is only illustrative of a general tendency in collaborative research in the mental health field.[20]

The psychiatrist, then, is more or less forced to make adjustments to the technological arsenal of the social scientists (or laboratory scientists) in the multidisciplined research setting because he (or others) cannot escape making comparisons of the gross scientific standing of his own work and that of his associates. The comparison that the psychiatrist makes may be invidious in terms of (1) techniques; (2) results; and (3) criteria to evaluate techniques and results. That is, the psychiatrist may begin to assume that his techniques are not as sophisticated as the instruments of the psychologist, for example. Both his techniques and results, he knows, are less precise and less communicable, operationally speaking. Moreover, the very criteria with which he is accustomed to evaluate his own hunches and work are suspect, for the psychiatrist is apt to judge his clinical hypotheses and results by the following yardsticks: (1) Did the patient respond in the direction of improvement? In other words, did the psychiatrist's operations succeed empirically? (2) Do the various facts brought out in the course of treatment from all sources—from the patient and from those with whom the patient has had contact—fit together into a relatively coherent pattern? In other words, is there a tendency towards mutual confirmation of all data?

The first criterion is, as the psychiatrist himself will admit, susceptible to self-fulfilling prophecy; moreover, "cure" or "improvement" is a term that defies ready definition. Thus, by standards of reliability it does not stand very high as a criterion of the scientific status of a piece of work. The second criterion, mutual confirmation or coherence of data, is a relatively respectable yardstick in the history of science. However, its use in psychiatry requires that one assume a large body of untested and vulnerable theoretical formulations. That is, various items of data can be considered coherent and compatible only within a context of a theory that can manage them. Most current psy-

---

20. See Margaret B. Luzski, *op. cit.*

chiatric theory is only uneasily accepted for want of anything else, and thus data may fit into such a theory and still not receive full credence. The psychiatrist, viewing his own standards, may come to the conclusion that in comparison with chi-squares, correlation coefficients, and probability scores in quantified social science research, his own work looks rather weak.[21]

What also makes inescapable the comparison between his specialty and social science is the fact that in the sphere of the psychological-interpersonal the psychiatrist's subject matter is very similar to the interests of the psychologist or social anthropologist, for example. He is threatened by eclipsing forces in his own heaven. The threat often appears to him to come through the superior power of the social science techniques. Such a threat is presumably important, because there is competition within a research field, just as much as in the real estate business or commercial baseball. That is, the fruit of successful competition is professional standing or advancement, which apart from its economic advantages is a basic source of one's self-picture in an achievement-oriented society.[22] The competition within a research program does not simply take the form of seeing who will do his work better than whom; it can take many other forms. One of these is especially marked by irrationality: staking out claims in the lands beyond the horizon of current knowledge and maintaining such property against potential claim-jumpers— as if somehow the wealth of unsolved scientific problems could be exhausted. In this manner, certain areas of investigation may be jealously guarded, or access to researchable patients refused. There are more obvious forms of competition in terms of amassing facilities that investigators use in their work: equipment of any sort, but especially expensive equipment, and supporting personnel, either junior assistants or senior consultants.

In the psychiatric research situation the competitive game

21. It is ironic that the psychiatrist can become as dazzled as he sometimes does with the paraphernalia of precision. With rare exceptions, one cannot say that the paraphernalia has been used to brilliant advantage in the social sciences.

22. See Warren O. Hagstrom, *The Scientific Community*, New York: Basic Books, 1965.

tends to suggest to the psychiatrist that he must adopt an aggran-
dizing attitude toward research problems, facilities, and techniques. Instead of sharing his interests he may indicate they
are closed to nonpsychiatrists. Instead of being challenged intellectually and thus presumably satisfied, as a scientist, with
examining his own clinical operations, he may desert the study
of patients and look for other fields to conquer. Instead of the
usual clinical facilities, he may seek out intricate equipment to
observe the patient: The first prerequisite to psychiatric research,
but only the first, may be a high fidelity tape recorder and a
one-way observation screen. And he may look for collaborators
or technicians who can provide him with the key to Science.
In a sense then, the psychiatrist may come to see certain forms
of science as being the substance of science. If he does so, he
begins to equate the social scientists' tools of quantification with
a competent piece of investigation. In short, scientific research
becomes inextricably confused with someone else's technology.

The Range of Responses

I have discussed some of the kinds of experience that set up
pressures toward the low valuation of the common psychiatric
clinical operations as scientifically respectable. Now I should like
to describe some of the socio-intellectual adjustments that the
research psychiatrist makes to his perception of the relative
position of his own operations versus the more quantitatively-
expressed operations of other researchers. There are a number
of ways by which the psychiatrist can make an adjustment to
this perception, which poses a potential challenge to his self-
picture. As he enters a research institute, for example, he can
choose a response process from among those that he sees in
his fellow workers with an established *modus vivendi*. Some of
these response processes maintain the necessary self-picture by
adjustments having relevance to the definition of psychiatric
knowledge, the fruits of the research operation. I would like
to describe briefly two such processes: The first of these may

be called *conversion*; the second, *orthodoxy*. These terms are chosen to emphasize the social and ideological nature of the knowledge-defining response, as opposed to its intellectual content.

In the throes of conversion the psychiatrist sees the light: quantification is the end-all and be-all. He recognizes his past transgressions: the crude fumbling of psychiatry's clinical investigations. As a convert, he vows to follow the pure call of Science ever after. To this end, he may painfully acquire the quantitative and other skills or information he has not picked up in medical training.[23] Or he may attach himself to possessors of such skills and become thereby an appendage who hopes to produce the ideas that will be studied in sterilized laboratory detail by his purer associates. Or he may limit his research to problems that are amenable to the statistical description and the laboratory instrumentation that he can execute by himself. In any case, he considers the clinical method too crude to use, and he may treat a few patients "only in order to keep my hand in," for purposes he considers unrelated to his research interests. The conversion process results in the definition of psychiatric research in terms not very distinguishable from other behavioral research; it ends in the rejection of the traditional psychiatric clinical procedures with individual patients in favor of any method that uses statistical procedures; thus it rejects the validity of information that churns around in the psychiatric brain rather than in the mechanical calculating machine.

The other main process that may be present in the psychiatrist's definition of his research role, and derivatively present in his definition of psychiatric knowledge, is the process I have called orthodoxy. It is antithetic to conversion. Its fundamental intellectual premise is that psychiatry is a discipline *sui generis*, a discipline that should not be contaminated by the introduction

---

23. A doctor is generally required to take academic courses in mathematics, either in premedical training or in medical school. The application, however, of this academic knowledge is ignored in his training, and it may be as useless to him for research purposes as having studied the bony structure of the foot is to the practicing psychoanalytic psychiatrist.

of heretical concepts or technologies derived from the social sciences. Psychiatry in terms of this process comprises phenomena far removed from the ordinary subject matter of social science; it is purely the study of mental aberrants, of people who need to be helped. The study can be undertaken only by someone with the sixth, or clinical, sense; by the same token, the clinical understanding of what is necessary for the well-being of the patient is a *sine qua non*. Orthodoxy thus commits the psychiatrist to the study of mentalistic phenomena for the most part; it also commits him to therapeutic goals in the course of his study.[24] In short, he is primarily interested in what goes on between him and the patient in the course of treatment, and he may thus be awfully concerned with the so-called intuitional processes.

Orthodoxy is regarded as magical thinking, by the psychiatrist who has been converted to quantification. In turn, orthodoxy suggests to the apostate convert that there are more things in heaven and earth than are dreamed of in his statistical orientation. The antithesis between conversion and orthodoxy may be expressed by a member of a research program in the following train of thought: "Quantification does not respect the individuality and uniqueness of the whole person; therapy requires such respect; on therapeutic grounds, therefore, all the sorts of procedures necessary for quantified research results are out of order." Orthodoxy then can provide a rationale for the psychiatrist to refuse to allow his patients to be used for validating a psychological test, or for any other quantitative procedure.

The two processes may thus be found in conflict with each other, and within a psychiatric research program, individual staff members may come to symbolize for each other these typical processes. The two processes are found, to be sure, in any individual staff member who assumes the occupational role of psychiatric researcher. They may, therefore, result in a synthesis that might be called *reform*. This synthesis is signalled when the psychiatrist tries to reconcile both methodological schools, but

---

24. On the other hand, the psychiatrist's prior commitment to therapeutic and mentalistic interests may influence him in his choice of the *orthodox* point of view on the science of psychiatry.

does so only on the rather simple rationale that "both approaches have something to offer." The reform process is expressed when the psychiatrist delivers the opinion that clinical investigations comprise a phase in the broad development of science, or comprise a necessary, though rough section of the road that leads to investigations by more exacting techniques and with more precise results. The reformist response is, in short, merely broad-minded and tolerant. In this tolerance the psychiatrist is free to use the techniques and concepts of his past training, but he must also show himself as being deeply interested in interdisciplinary work. The reformed psychiatrist does not usually have time for interdisciplinary work himself, but he will couch his reports to colleagues in terms that show a sensitivity to multi-disciplined feelings. He may be somewhat humble and suggest that he does not aspire to be a precise researcher, but he feels you will agree he has a darn good therapy project.

These, then, are some of the possible patterns in the psychiatrist's response to the new demands that a research career places upon him. As patterns of response, they are marked by a singular absence of any examination by the psychiatrist of the meaning and structure of the methodologies he uses or those he envies. These responses are, in fact, socially conditioned definitions of knowledge, method, and research in psychiatry, but they are lacking in intellectual content, so to speak. That is, the internal logic of such definitions is not developed.

As social definitions, these points of view or responses to the research situation can develop into divergent schools of so-called thought within the same research program. Such schools of thought are marked more by social isolation from each other than by intellectual boundaries. As time goes on, however, the social isolation may be accompanied by the development of truly idiosyncratic techniques that are not tempered by the interest and contact of other points of view.[25]

There is, of course, always the possibility of a more intel-

_____
25. See Florian Znaniecki, *The Social Role of the Man of Knowledge*, New York: Columbia University Press, 1940, esp. Chap III, "Schools and Scholars as Bearers of Absolute Truth."

lectually effective response to the research situation. A psychiatrist may figuratively sit himself down to puzzle out exactly where his particular clinical operations come into the picture of scientific methodology. In so doing he develops a viable intellectual rationale for his work, but unless this rationale can receive acceptance within the social situation of the research work group,[26] he may find it an inadequate adjustment to the need to establish a viable social image of himself as the researcher he is in intellectual fact. His methodological position, like others within his setting, will probably proceed toward its own logical extreme in inverse ratio to the capacity of adherents of the other positions to understand its fundamental intellectual structure. In the process of this development toward extremes, the social acceptance of the definitions may take the form of the development of methodological schools of thought, as previously noted, and the schools themselves may become the significant feature of the research group atmosphere rather than the content of the methodologies. For the content—the internal intellectual structure—of the scientific position or frame of reference must in such cases be free from possible examination, lest the whole social adjustive structure collapse. That is, the definition of acceptable method and of scientific knowledge in psychiatric research will depend upon what the social structure of the research setting requires, rather than upon what the logical nature of subjects for research might dictate.

In this chapter I have tried to describe some characteristics of the social structure of psychiatric research, as they influence the psychiatrist's definitions of psychiatric knowledge and of how that knowledge is obtained. The socially conditioned defini-

---

26. To a great extent the likelihood that this response pattern is used will depend upon such potential acceptance. Particularly it will be encouraged by favorable attitudes toward the naturalistic research of clinical observation held by those members of the staff who are prestige figures. For example, the continued encouragement of the top research director can, to a certain extent, offset unfavorable attitudes held by what might be called the researcher's peer group. Cf. Kenneth Mark Colby, *An Introduction to Psychoanalytic Research*, New York: Basic Books, 1960.

tions described herein overvalue the methods of quantification—positively or negatively—and undervalue the methods of clinical investigation. Because the need for a rationalized methodological position in a research setting is highly social, the psychiatrist's attention is often focused on what will meet the social need, to the point of ignoring what will meet the scientific or methodological need. The responses that he makes to the social situation tend to become institutionalized; and only marginal workers are likely to pay attention to questions of scientific method per se. One is apt to conclude that the clinician requires a developed and communicated scientific rationale for the problems he chooses to study and for the methods those problems require. The institutionalization of such a rationale by deliberate orientations in the early stages of psychiatric training and by the full development of clinical research programs will provide the psychiatrist with an internalizable frame of reference that is not only intellectually sound but socially defensible.

Eight

A PSYCHIATRIST'S THEORY
EMERGES FROM
HOSPITAL PRESSURES[1]

✎§

I N THIS AND the next chapter I shall carry my argument another step to show that, like the day-to-day process of research and like the general idea of proper scientific research, the actual products of the research (the theoretical formulations) are intertwined with the trellis of social order that gives them the chance, the support, to grow. I shall discuss a theory that evolved about how professional psychiatric staff should deal with a certain kind of schizophrenic patient. It was constructed, like most clinical theories, out of the cross fire of conflicting forces in the care of a patient. Also, like most clinical theories, it was first presented in its nascent form to the members of the hospital staff in which the patient was being treated—to the psychiatric staff of the University Medical Research Center. For me the story began with two clinical research conferences in which the two doctors concerned presented what they had learned about the patient and his management on the ward.

It will be, I hope, easier for the reader to follow the story if I supply some preliminary guides, for example, names for the doctors, the patient, and the nurses involved (see Table 3). As

1. This and the next chapter draw upon Stewart E. Perry and Gertrude N. Shea, "Social Controls and Psychiatric Theory in a Ward Setting," *Psychiatry* (1957) 20: 221-47.

*Table 3: Chief Participants in the Evolution of the
Transference Diffusion Theory*

Mr. Pickett The schizophrenic patient whose upsetting behavior started people thinking.

Dr. Thorpe The patient's therapist; later also administrator of his ward; developer, with Dr. Adams, of the transference diffusion theory.

Dr. Adams The patient's personal administrative psychiatrist; collaborator with Dr. Thorpe in developing and presenting the theory.

Miss Holton The chief nurse on the patient's ward.

Dr. Bates The psychiatric administrator of the ward, succeeded by Dr. Thorpe.

Dr. Lowe The research director who urged work on the problems posed by the patient.

a matter of fact, two participants in this story are already familiar to the reader: Dr. Thorpe and his patient Mr. Pickett. The events took place a little less than two years after the end of the First LSD Research. Mr. Pickett had in the interim been discharged and then readmitted. Dr. Thorpe had then resumed his treatment of Mr. Pickett, at the Center, hoping to learn in more depth about the treatment and the personality processes of a patient who showed extreme classical symptoms of depersonalization. I had known that Mr. Pickett was back in the hospital, but at that time I was involved with work on the children's ward, so that I was ignorant of anything that was going on in the ward on which Mr. Pickett was treated. Incidentally, for no reason I can understand, I never happened to meet Mr. Pickett, and as a matter of fact I never did see him that I know of, during either of his hospital stays.

Mr. Pickett's Ward. Mr. Pickett was readmitted to the same nursing unit he had occupied in his previous stay at the Center. The patients on that unit, both male and female, could be diagnosed as schizophrenic, and they were all in intensive psychotherapy, the only treatment in general use. There were many recreational facilities and a high ratio of nursing staff to patients —an average of about one nurse or nursing assistant to three patients for all shifts. The nursing staff lived in close psychological and physical proximity to the patients throughout each eight-hour shift. They ate with patients and participated with them in the round of recreational and other activities. Since they were relieved of many housekeeping and routine administrative duties, they were thrown more completely into participation with the patient population.

Great emphasis was placed upon the therapeutic potential of the nurse-patient relationship and, correspondingly, there were strong implicit and explicit demands that the nurses and nursing assistants actively involve themselves and the patients in the business of living on the ward. For example, the nursing staff had considerable freedom to define their individual relationships to the patients, with the expectation that the nurses would in turn permit the patients a great deal of freedom in determining their life on the ward. Also, senior nursing personnel made themselves very accessible for help and consultation to the ward nurses, expecting that the ward nurses, in turn, would make themselves accessible to the patients for the same purposes.

These twin precepts of *permissiveness* and *sympathetic availability* were regarded by nurses and doctors alike as a necessary basis for therapeutic nursing organization and function. It will be clear to the reader that permissiveness in this context as in other institutional contexts connotes a situation in which higher status persons indulge lower status persons with opportunities for self-determination. Indulgence at the Center was generalized in an across-the-board attitude held by the nursing staff that patients, having been deprived of opportunities for self-determination and many other values in the past, ought to be indulged in these values by the staff and the hospital environment as a milieu-therapeutic technique to redress lacks in the patients' experience. It is evident, then, that the supervisory nursing philosophy was consciously guided by social-psychological principles that indicated, first, how working groups could operate with maximum satisfaction to each member and, second, how such satisfaction could be translated into positive, beneficial relationships with other people in the work situation.

The ward had been in operation for a little over two years

at the time of this study, and the development of the ward philosophy and staff organization was a dynamic influence in ward events. In other words, staff members were continually engaged in the process of refining and revising their ways of working. This, it must be assumed, is not an altogether comfortable process. Nor is it one that can be avoided in a psychiatric community. The staff recognized that the precepts of permissiveness and sympathetic availability were not sufficient and indeed might have disadvantages. For example, a therapist reported what his patient told him of her perception of the nursing staff:

She gave me a little lecture the other day about what goes on in her ward as far as the nurses [are concerned]. . . . And I think it's quite accurate as far as it goes. . . . They [the nurses] had a need to prove that they were needed. . . . She felt that they had a need to make out the patients were sicker than they really were. She thought [the nurses] addressed themselves to the sick part of the patients all the time, sort of solicitously were concerned about helpless people, which was a way of justifying their having the job on this ward as a nurse.

Such considerations had led to continuing review and re-evaluation of nursing policy in the nurses' own conferences.

The physicians' psychiatric philosophy also viewed the clinical operations of the ward in social-psychological terms. The psychiatrists were sensitive to the idea of considering what goes on with patients in terms of the whole ward structure, and not merely in terms of the individual dynamics of the patients. For example, considerable research and administrative attention had been paid to "the milieu" and its structure and function in relation to mental illness, and especially its relation to what happens in the psychotherapy hour. The felt importance of "ward structure" was also reflected in the fact that frequent conferences —"problem seminars"—were scheduled between the doctors and the nursing staff, to discuss difficulties with particular patients.

Mr. Pickett was seen in psychotherapy off the ward four times a week but, of course, most of his time was spent in the wide variety of recreational and other activities provided on the ward and in the hospital. He was quite able to make use of such activities, and in fact impressed the staff by his capacity to maintain relatively conventional behavior in those activities. But he also evidenced a great deal of hostility, combativeness, and sarcasm toward the nursing staff—so much that it would be hard to overestimate the patient's impact on them. Most of the staff felt that he was the most difficult patient they had ever dealt with in any setting.

Research Conferences at the Center. In a clinical setting of any kind, staff have routine conferences. On the psychiatric service of the Medical Research Center, there was a special weekly research conference, the most important of the myriad meetings that took place. These alternated between presentations of some current or recently completed research by a staff member (or sometimes an outsider) and the presentation of one or more cases of patients who posed clinical problems with theoretical implications. The latter were clearly clinical research conferences; they were not on the order of the clinical conferences traditionally held in psychiatric hospitals for the purpose of reaching or communicating clinical decisions or diagnoses.

The two conferences on Mr. Pickett were fairly typical of the clinical research conferences at the Center. Dr. Lowe, the program director, had suggested Mr. Pickett as an appropriate subject because the patient had posed so many operational problems for the entire ward staff. These problems had often been brought to Dr. Lowe for discussion, and Dr. Lowe had finally suggested that the case be presented to the whole staff, jointly by Dr. Thorpe, Mr. Pickett's therapist, and by Dr. Adams, Mr. Pickett's administrative psychiatrist.[2] They were both relatively well prepared to do so. Dr. Thorpe had already organized some materials from his experiences with this patient and other similar patients. He and Dr. Adams had been holding frequent dis-

---

2. The reader should recall that it was common practice on the entire psychiatric service for the psychotherapist to see the patient mainly in the therapy hour, delegating to another doctor authority and responsibility for the ward routine and care of the patient. The administrative physician thus was concerned with the patient's ward privileges, medications, and so forth.

cussions with each other and with other staff members about this particular patient. Dr. Adams was also in the process of preparing a relevant paper; both he and Dr. Thorpe later presented their materials at an international meeting.

The conferences on Mr. Pickett were, as I have said, not ordinary clinical meetings but, for the Center, fairly standard clinical research discussions, except in two respects. It was these two features that set me to studying again, long after the First LSD Research, what was happening with Mr. Pickett. First, the general atmosphere of staff interest at these two meetings was more intense than usual. Many in the audience seemed impressed by the presentations. In fact, interest and curiosity seemed to be so general that Dr. Lowe suggested that the two physicians return for an additional session in two weeks' time, to which they agreed with pleasure. This was an unusual amount of attention for one patient and the ideas that he stimulated. All this indicated that Drs. Adams and Thorpe had touched upon matters of crucial concern to many staff members. Second, and perhaps most important, I was struck by the fact that in both conferences, discussion of highly significant information about the patient was omitted or elided within the conference room, but came to light outside the conferences. The information that seemed to me inexplicably omitted was the following: As of the first conference the patient was on "escape" from the hospital; and as of the second conference the patient had returned from escape and then been discharged against the advice of his physicians. Neither of these facts was mentioned in the conferences.

This phenomena of group selective inattention to crucial facts about the patient in the staff discussions so puzzled me that I began interviewing staff members, searching through clinical records, and so on, to find some explanation.

The Two Conferences

I told Drs. Adams and Thorpe that I wanted to do a natural history of their presentation. I showed them a retrospective summary of each meeting, as I had reconstructed it. According to their own recollections, they corrected these summaries (incidentally, in very minor ways that seemed proper to me too), and I present them now.

The first conference. At the first meeting Dr. Thorpe (the therapist) and Dr. Adams (the administrator) presented a talk entitled "Problems in the Management of the Diffusion of Transference in the Treatment of Schizophrenia." In this presentation they discussed Mr. Pickett (the patient), who was impressively hostile in much of his behavior and quite difficult to handle on the ward. The case was used to illustrate the concept that patients may develop relationships with nurses or nursing assistants that interfere with the course of therapy in the doctor-patient relationship. The problem involved was described in the following terms: The patient tended to diffuse transference feelings throughout his environment instead of concentrating them in his relationship with his therapist, Dr. Thorpe. A theoretical description of schizophrenia was presented by Dr. Thorpe, who noted that it is an illness pattern in which this transference-diffusion phenomenon often occurs.

Dr. Adams then discussed a frame of reference to describe types or phases of behavior in a schizophrenic who makes progress toward recovery. If the patient is to get better, he indicated, one certain type of behavior must be manifest; that is, the patient must begin responding to his environment in a more accepting way: He must accept the restrictions of life on the ward and deal with them realistically, and not always manipulate the staff to avoid these normal, therapeutically necessary restrictions. Dr. Adams said that Mr. Pickett was adept at manipulation and that his own role as administrator had been set up to minimize such manipulations, to set limits for the patient. He felt this task was made difficult by the fact that the patient was not remanded by a court and therefore could at any time act out against the restrictions by leaving the hospital; as a matter of fact, the patient had done just this *at another hospital.* [Italics added later.] Dr. Adams doubted that such a patient could be handled unless he was legally committed. The pathology of the patient was such that if he could avoid making adjustments to the restrictions, he would remain ill. Excerpts from Dr. Adams' recorded interviews with Mr. Pickett were played to show the patient's reactions to Dr. Adams' attempts to place limits on his disruptiveness and to let him know that, instead of acting out his problems on the ward and trying to remake the ward to suit himself, he would have to take up his problems with his therapist. In other words, Dr. Adams' efforts were designed to put limits on the patient's diffusion of transference.

The audience response to this presentation was especially favorable and the discussion, lively, continuing up to the limits of the time set aside for the meeting. The clinical director, chairing the meeting, suggested that a second meeting be called to continue the discussion, and this second conference on the same patient was held two weeks later.

The second conference. Dr. Thorpe began the second conference by reading a somewhat satirical description of the ideal mental hospital atmosphere, in which everything would be arranged to surround the patient with gentleness, kindness, and helpfulness. He then commented that, of course, the description was not realistic. In practice, the hospital itself and the staff also have needs, and things happen to fulfill those needs. He then went on to detail the kinds of things patients do that make the staff anxious, that is, that set up needs or frustrate them. He noted various characteristics of the average schizophrenic patient that provoke staff anxieties: the incorporative nature of schizophrenic love and similarly the schizophrenic's fear of incorporation; his free expression of much hostility, and especially his expression through violence; his expression of feelings in terms of sexuality; his unpredictability, and his quality of being hard to understand; his large doses of anxiety, which are contagious; his not getting well, but rather remaining ill so long; and his seizing on a staff member's weak points. This last-mentioned characteristic, Dr. Thorpe said, is an important source of staff anxiety. However, he felt that the schizophrenic patient is not inordinately sensitive to staff weak points; rather, the schizophrenic strikes out against his environment so much that, like buckshot, some of his attacks are bound to hit vulnerable areas.

Dr. Thorpe went on to say that the staff could deal with these anxieties in a number of different ways: by denial, withdrawal, hostility, discussion, and supervision, and by restructuring the ward. He felt from his own experience that discussion with the nursing staff is not an adequate means of handling the problem. And then he turned the meeting over to Dr. Adams to discuss some aspects of ward structure.

Dr. Adams discussed ways of thinking about relations on the ward, illustrating possible types of ward structure by three simple diagrams: (1) a horizontal line; (2) a vertical line; (3) a kind of latticework. The first represented a concept of structure in terms of everyone being equal on the ward; the second, in terms of a hierarchy; and the third indicated that the relationships of the patient with some staff members proceeded by going through other staff members, and not directly. He made the point that in type (2) the hierarchy is not rigid—that is, sometimes the patient might think he is on top, and other times, on the bottom. In reply to questions, he suggested that what is necessary is a direct relationship with the therapist, rather than a relationship through the medium of some intercessor—a nurse, or ward activity and what not. He felt that the extent to which the doctor-patient relationship is direct and can be expressed in verbal interchange is a measure of how well the setting is structured to induce therapeutic change.[3]

Now, presumably Dr. Thorpe and Dr. Adams presented all the information about the patient's hospitalization that they considered necessary and relevant. However, they did not present any illustrations or examples of nursing participation in the transference diffusion. In addition, those two specific facts that remained undiscussed seem to me not only relevant but important data for the theory presented. The first undiscussed fact was that the day before the first staff conference, the patient had run away. He was out walking with a nursing assistant and simply walked off, with an apology to the nursing assistant for perhaps getting him in trouble. The patient could not be located, but three days later he returned to the hospital of his own volition. That he had run away was disclosed to me by a staff member (unconnected with the patient's treatment) in a casual conversation a few minutes after the first conference.

The second undiscussed fact was that about six days after the patient had returned from escape—a day or so before the second conference—he left the hospital, presumably for good. Upon his return from escape he had been confined to a seclusion room, from which he emerged only for a few minutes each day. Apparently he had previously arranged with his family that if he did not telephone them after he had returned, they were to seek his discharge. This they did, and the patient was discharged on the request of a family member and against medical advice. The fact of his departure and the inferences involved were communicated to me by Dr. Adams in a casual conversation the day after the event, the day before the second staff conference.

_____

3. The conference records presented here were submitted to Drs. Adams and Thorpe for corrections three days after the second conference. They therefore represent a consensus on the significant highlights of the meetings. However, certain data on discussion from the floor have been omitted as irrelevant for the purposes of this chapter.

To spell out why I consider the two undiscussed facts to be important and pertinent, it should be recalled that Dr. Adams and Dr. Thorpe paid some attention in the conferences to the notion that such a patient as Mr. Pickett could not be successfully treated unless he was legally committed. Dr. Adams had mentioned in the first staff conference that Mr. Pickett had left another hospital when he was placed on a stricter regime; Dr. Adams noted this event as indicating the need for commitment, but he did not note that the patient had escaped the previous day from the Center. Also, in the second conference, it might be presumed that the psychiatrists would have brought up the fact that the patient had again been discharged against medical advice, and thus document the contention that commitment was necessary. It was Dr. Adams who, as administrator of the patient, was most concerned with the problem of commitment and who particularly discussed it in the two staff conferences. Dr. Thorpe shared his opinion, and although he did not participate in efforts to persuade the patient to allow himself to be committed, he did tell Mr. Pickett that if he left the hospital, treatment would not be continued on an outpatient basis.

At least eight or ten out of the forty or so staff members present at the conferences knew about all or some of these undiscussed events. These people included doctors, nurses, and social scientists, some of whom were connected with work on Mr. Pickett's ward. It should be pointed out that, in the second conference, I myself might have brought up these facts about the patient and his hospitalization, but did not do so.

A Brief History of Mr. Pickett's Experience at the Center

As in my report on the First LSD Research, I now want to present a short, preliminary history of the events that I shall later describe in much more detail. Briefly, what follows is the story of Mr. Pickett's hospitalization at the Center.

The reader is already familiar with the fact that Mr. Pickett had been a patient on the LSD research project. At that time, Dr. Bates was the ward administrator, and the head nurse on the ward was going through a period of basic disagreement with him, culminating in her resignation. This head nurse is important in the story primarily because she was particularly interested in Mr. Pickett and wanted to do things for him that Dr. Bates felt were too indulgent.

Shortly after the nurse's resignation, Mr. Pickett was transferred to another hospital where Dr. Thorpe continued to see him in therapy for seven months before readmitting him to the Center. In the meantime, a new head nurse, Miss Holton, had joined the ward staff. She and Dr. Bates and Dr. Thorpe worked together on Mr. Pickett's case for several months until Dr. Bates left the Center to enter private practice. At that time, Dr. Thorpe became ward administrator for all patients, including Mr. Pickett, but continued also to treat Mr. Pickett on the ward.

As I have mentioned before, it was the practice in the hospital that a patient would have two physicians concerned with his care: his psychotherapist, and the administrator of his ward, who was concerned with all other therapeutic and management questions outside of the psychotherapeutic hours. Thus, it was probably only natural that in time Miss Holton and Dr. Thorpe should come to the conclusion that another physician should be chosen to act as administrative psychiatrist for Mr. Pickett so that the two therapeutic functions would not be lodged in the same person. At any rate, this solution was tried at the end of the ensuing period of three months or so in which the nursing staff in general grew increasingly dissatisfied with what was happening between them and Mr. Pickett and finally asked Dr. Thorpe to discharge him. Dr. Thorpe took up the matter with the senior psychiatrists at the Center, and Dr. Adams was selected to deal with the ward problem, and became the administrative psychiatrist for Mr. Pickett. Dr. Thorpe remained as the ward administrator, the administrative psychiatrist for all other patients on the ward.

It was shortly after this that the first of the clinical research conferences by Drs. Thorpe and Adams was scheduled, as it turned out, for the day after Mr. Pickett's escape. The second conference was scheduled at the close of the first conference, for two weeks later. About two days after the first conference Mr. Pickett returned to the Center and a week later he was discharged against medical advice. Soon thereafter, the second of the two clinical research conferences was held, as scheduled.

As this capsule history indicates, Mr. Pickett's experience at the Center was a hectic one, marked especially by disturbed relationships and very sharp disagreements about him among the staff and between him and the staff. I want now to go into some detail about these disturbances, for they throw into high relief aspects of the ward structure and requirements of the staff and patients living together that show up in the psychiatric theory propounded by Dr. Adams and Dr. Thorpe. I shall present the details from the point of view of the nursing staff, as this became evident from interviews and from a review of the routine records that the nurses were required to keep on Mr. Pickett's ward life. The nursing staff materials will balance the presentation of the physicians' point of view as they reported it in the conferences. Also, there is a richness of detail to be mined, since of course nurses are apt to have a more intimate acquaintance with the patients than the physician can usually acquire by his rather limited contacts.

Nursing Problems with Mr. Pickett

In interviews with members of nursing staff ample evidence appeared, first of all, that Mr. Pickett posed a serious strain on the nurses' self-picture. That is, he often refused to be treated as a patient and thus did not allow the nursing staff to act as nurses with him. Implicit in the nurses' discussions of the patient was their concept of the nurse's role. This role involved actions that permitted and accepted deviant behavior on the part of a patient; but it also required actions that assumed a protective responsibility for a patient when he was not able to assume that responsibility himself. Mr. Pickett did not present himself consistently as a subject for such role action. Within the rules of the social order of the ward, therefore, there was no way to treat him. Second, Mr. Pickett posed a serious strain on the solidarity of the nursing staff group through—as they saw it—his manipulation of one staff member against another. Third, he aroused fear and hostility by his physical aggressiveness. Fourth, he confused the staff by appearing quite "normal" at times, throwing doubt on their perception of him as a patient at all.

The first interview I held was with Miss Holton, the head nurse at the time of my study, a competent and verbal spokesman for her staff who freely discussed her perspective on the situation. In the beginning of the interview she expressed her inability to understand why the role of nursing staff with the patient was considered by Dr. Adams and Dr. Thorpe a problem now. It was true, she said, that when the former head ward nurse was there it had been a problem, but an attempt had since been made to correct the situation.[4] She told me:

The first time Mr. Pickett came to live on the ward, the then head nurse took over the therapist role, so his admission was messed up. [After a few months he was transferred to another local hospital and for a time seen by Dr. Thorpe there.] Then he was admitted again. This time I was the head nurse; Dr. Bates was still ward administrator. I insisted that since he was a difficult patient, we needed to have some structure—some meetings about the patient. We had these meetings, but they did not seem to be enough; though we discussed and discussed, still we went on in our own way and still we were anxious and felt inadequate and inferior in response to the devices the patient used. . . . The nursing staff did know that it was not us, our problem, that was making us anxious but Mr. Pickett and his problem; nevertheless, we had great hostility for him. . . . The staff never came to grips with the situation. . . . Finally I told Dr.

---

4. Later, Dr. Thorpe said that although the former head nurse was "the classic example" of a focus of transference diffusion, a number of other nurses later played the same role, but to a lesser extent. He also felt that the same sort of transference diffusion occurred with Dr. Bates—the former ward administrator—and Dr. Adams. "In Dr. Bates's case," Dr. Thorpe reported, "the patient's day-to-day difficulties in living were taken up by Dr. Bates and dropped out of the therapy hour."

Thorpe that there was a growing dissatisfaction in the staff about the doctors not giving enough orientation about the patients. . . . In a meeting . . . the nursing staff said that Mr. Pickett ought to be discharged, and they kept on saying this . . . for the next two weeks with increasing intensity. . . . Anyway the viewpoint of the nursing staff was finally taken up in a medical staff meeting [at which the nursing staff was not present], and the medical staff came back with the message [for the nursing staff] that this [situation with the patient] should be considered a challenge—[that the nursing staff should try] to work with the patient and work it out.

The staff . . . stopped talking to Mr. Pickett—they were giving him the cold treatment. It was a real sitdown strike. There was another medical staff meeting [which the nursing staff did not attend], and I assume that at this time Dr. Adams volunteered or was drafted to be the administrator for the patient.

This patient was always difficult. He is a man whose main job is manipulating. We were taken in by his arguments and were uncomfortable about any decision we made regarding him. [This manipulation represented] an intolerable situation for a staff of 18 to handle. [The large number of staff provided a large number of opportunities for inter-staff manipulation.] Also, the unit started off with the philosophy that you give the patient anything that he asks for that is reasonable, and as soon as possible. That is my theory still. But I don't think this patient was schizophrenic. He acted very normal and it was hard for the staff to see him as a patient. All of his demands seemed reasonable, yet there was always something behind them. He took your identity from you. If you talked with him, you became all tangled up. Finally we had a sort of rule that no one would talk with him alone for more than an hour; that was all you could stand. I always timed myself for 15 minutes; that was all I would spend with him at a time. Besides that, my time is not for patients but for the staff. People really liked him though; at the same time they hated him. He could make you look like a real fool. You don't mind that if you are alone with a person, but he always chose a time, say at mealtime, in front of everyone. You just have to get together, stick together, and not let him manipulate one against the other.

When Mr. Pickett was first admitted, he was practically the assistant head nurse—he was running everything. That was the kind of arrangement he had with the head nurse who was very involved with him. She resigned. But Dr. Bates [as ward administrator] did not change his way of doing things, even when she left. We would say [to each other and in meetings with Dr. Bates], "What is this patient doing with all these privileges? Isn't he a patient? Can't we be more restrictive and deal with him with ordinary nursing care procedures?" Of course, he needed no physical care; he was very independent and took care of things himself. But sometimes he needed a [relaxing period in a therapeutic] tub or pack [in a hot or cold wet sheet] and it was hard to get him to take it, even though you knew he was tense and needed it. You could not insist with him because he took complete responsibility for himself.

He would discuss one staff member or patient with another. He had his "black list" that he had written up with all the names on it. You had a check after your name if you were okay, or an X mark if you weren't, or a question mark if he wasn't sure about you. Finally we [the nursing staff] did get together and agree that we had to stick together and provide a united front; we finally came to the decision that it was not us, but him [who caused the anxiety]. . . .

He wanted the complete love of everyone. . . . He could be very reasonable, but he wanted everybody's time. He would interfere with you when you were spending time with other patients. He would get what he wanted. . . . How could you refuse? For example, he wanted maybe to cook sausage at two o'clock in the morning. With the schizophrenic it would be okay; you would be overjoyed that he wanted to do it. Of course I'm exaggerating, but the point is if the ordinary schizophrenic shows that much interest in the environment, you want to respond to him. But with Mr. Pickett, he was pushing a point always. That was why it was hard to have him with a ward of schizophrenics. I would call him a psychopath, but he was also a schizophrenic, I suppose.

I disagreed with Dr. Adams' program only [when it changed] after Mr. Pickett escaped. The patient had [earlier] been told that if he escaped he could not stay; he could not come back to the ward. But by the time it happened we changed our minds; we had become very hopeful with the new rules. So we figured it out that if we went and got him and made him come back, that was okay, because it was our decision. Actually he came back on his own, although he knew we would have gotten him back if we could have found him. He went immediately into seclusion [with a new set of rules for his management].

Dr. Adams' [new] plan was, pretty much, isolation. Mr. Pickett could have someone with him when he ate his meals, but no other time. And he could have a cigarette afterwards. He was not allowed to make phone calls or see anyone. I felt that he should be allowed out on the ward for a little while each day. But Dr. Adams said I was soft. I didn't think I was soft. I thought it was necessary for him to have some contact. Dr. Adams said no one [of the female nurses] was to go in unless four men accompanied them. Well, this was pretty impractical, because we only had two of the men on duty at one shift, and Dr. Adams said no one was to work any overtime. We did get some change made: The patient was allowed to have someone with him for a cup of coffee, and then again someone would go in with the nourishment [evening snack]. . . .

Dr. Adams said that he had to be committed and that he could not stay under the old plan. Mr. Pickett had been in seclusion six days and then suddenly a member of his family appeared at the door of the ward to take him away. Mr. Pickett must have had some pre-arranged plan with his family that if they didn't hear from him or something then they were to do something. Dr. Adams' idea was that this handling would get Mr. Pickett angry and that it might be good if he actually broke [that is, had a definite psychotic episode]. I did not agree with this—however, I have not talked with Dr. Adams about this.

I do not know why they [Dr. Adams and Dr. Thorpe] were using his case as an example for their presentation. Mr. Pickett always acted toward everyone the same; at least we all experienced his liking, then his hostility.

A few days later, when I saw Miss Holton again for the purpose of checking my record of our interview, she volunteered further information which is excerpted here, in her own words.

As I think about it, the problem we had to deal with had to do with a process we go through with all patients, and which with Mr. Pickett was intensified: giving; expectations; disappointment; hatred.

When Mr. Pickett was in seclusion, I had the discussion with Dr. Adams when he said I was being soft. Mr. Pickett was in there with nothing to do. I wanted him to have a magazine; I thought he would go crazy with nothing to do.

[After the first set of rules were in effect] no one on the nursing staff wanted to talk about Mr. Pickett when I brought it up in a conference. They said that they did not feel guilty about it. I would have expected that they would have some feelings about it. We had never treated a patient like this before. But the whole staff seemed to agree with Dr. Adams. . . .

Once Mr. Pickett was in seclusion, there was no discussion among the staff about him. I guess it was because we knew what to do. [The rules were] cut and dried. It just didn't come up in our con-ferences. . . .

Since we've never done this kind of nursing, I wondered why people didn't say anything about it. I think if we had made the deci-sion ourselves, we couldn't have stayed with it. But because it was Dr. Adams and he was definite, that was different. . . .

I think that the staff must have been pretty much in agreement with Dr. Adams on [the seclusion room rules]. I was not here when he communicated these rules to the staff when Mr. Pickett came back. But I would have received some call on it, if there had been some trouble. One time [at the inception of the first set of rules] I did get a call. Dr. Adams had given the rules to Mr. Pickett and then right after that he went to a case conference with the staff and reversed himself there. The staff were concerned about it. The next morning I got in touch with Dr. Adams and Dr. Thorpe and talked with them. Dr. Adams admitted that he had yielded to Mr. Pickett's pleading and was reversing himself, and he went back to his first position. But they did not call me [at home] that week end [when Mr. Pickett returned from his escape]. So I think they must have been in agreement.

Using as an introduction Miss Holton's summary of the course of Mr. Pickett's hospitalization, I shall now present other data in the historical order of the events themselves—beginning with the period shortly after Dr. Thorpe assumed the duties of ward administrator. Although Mr. Pickett had already been a source of difficulty for the staff, at about this time he became a frequent topic of discussion between Dr. Thorpe and the nurses in the nursing problem seminar.

Miss Holton in her first interview with me described a series of such discussions in the following words:

There was the feeling that nothing was being accomplished. Dr. Thorpe expressed some discouragement, too. The nursing staff felt that they were not accomplishing anything and that their efforts were not acknowledged. They were tentatively mentioning that the "patients cannot be our satisfaction in working here." Dr. Thorpe said that work with acutely ill patients [rather than chronically ill ones, like Mr. Pickett] is more satisfying and rewarding. "But," he said, "since we do have chronically ill patients here, what are the satisfactions you can get out of working with Mr. Pickett?" He complimented the nursing staff [on the fact] that they had been able to handle Mr. Pickett so far.

Despite these conferences, the nursing staff apparently felt themselves more and more pressured in their work with the patient. They communicated their feeling to Dr. Thorpe that the patient was untreatable, that they could no longer work on the ward with him, and that he should be discharged. Dr. Thorpe discussed their feelings on this matter with the senior staff clinicians, who took the responsibility for deciding to keep the patient in the hospital. They noted that the nurses were stepping out of bounds to suggest that the patient be sent off and suggested that the nursing staff should consider Mr. Pickett a challenge to their nursing capacity. This was greeted by the nursing staff with both resentment and amusement, although there were no more threats of resignation, nor did the nurses continue to ask for Mr. Pickett's discharge.[5] However, their problem with him continued. At about this time Mr. Pickett, using a table, battered open the ward door one evening, ran off for a few hours, and got drunk, but returned to the ward on his own. This dramatically illustrated the lack of control that the nursing staff experienced in the situation.

The nurses' silent treatment of Mr. Pickett began the following week, as indicated by their notes in the patient's chart.

[A nurse reports: Today Mr. Pickett] came to the supper table and talked to [other patients] but not to the staff—not that we gave him the opportunity. I sat directly opposite him and did not even so much as glance in his direction. Being fed up with all the patients and their shenanigans, I did not trust myself to speak to anyone. . . . Conversation petered out . . . but staff felt *très* comfortable.

[Another nurse reports: Mr. Pickett has] seemed quite worried this P.M. with no staff members to talk to. . . . Many whispered powwows with other patients.

[The next day still another nurse reports: Mr. Pickett] has seemed quite concerned over the silent treatment he received from staff last night. Questioned me about it. All I was able to say was that I didn't know any more about it than he. . . . At lunch time, Mr. Pickett stated that the patients were all frightened by the silent treatment last night, but that he was more curious than anything else.

[The next day Mr. Pickett overstays for a few hours on off-ward pass, and returns to be greeted with reproaches for his misbehavior.

---

5. The capacity of the medical staff to maintain the conventional doctor-nurse structure was greater than the nurses' capacity to maintain the conventional nurse-patient structure. This passing along of the experienced difficulty between patient and nurse into difficulty between nurse and doctor seems analogous to the passing along of a patient-therapist difficulty to the therapist-supervisor relationship, as described by Harold F. Searles, "The Informational Value of the Supervisor's Emotional Experience," *Psychiatry* (1955) 18: 135-46.

The following day, a nurse reports: Mr. Pickett] blamed the present situation on the silent treatment. . . .

It should be re-emphasized that the staff had tried all sorts of techniques by this time to deal with the situation. Among them was the use of sedation when the patient was acutely anxious, this having once been suggested by the patient himself. However, as with all the other efforts, sedation had accomplished nothing. Lesser amounts of the drugs in use then had not been effective, and the patient had not been able to tolerate physically a dose that did have a psychologically calming effect. Despite these repeated failures, the staff still attempted to discover what was wrong and what could be done. The next day after the last cited nurses' note appeared in the chart, a tape-recorded conference was held among the nursing staff and with Dr. Thorpe, in which the group again attempted to arrive at some formulation of the difficulty, with efforts toward frank self-examination. The following is transcribed from the recording at the point that Miss Holton has asked Dr. Thorpe to present his ideas about what was wrong.

DR. THORPE: I gather more by the grapevine than directly that there has been considerable dissatisfaction with [my] administration . . . that there is a general feeling that I'm too soft . . . that the patient has thrown—oh, I don't know—sand in my eyes or something like this. Now this may or may not be so, but, at any rate, I think that the group and I ought to deal directly with it . . . dealing with a patient, both as therapist and administrator, is not an easy task— and particularly with such a patient as this. It's easy to make mistakes. . . . But I would like to hear some sentiment as to how the administration of this patient can be better carried out. . . . [For example, the other day] the [nursing] group felt pretty strongly that I confront Mr. Pickett with some of the more malevolent transactions he has indulged in—which I did. I don't think this was a particularly useful maneuver—perhaps because I didn't feel it was going to be useful. [With this sort of confrontation] maybe he should behave a little better. But I don't think we can expect . . . too much from this. . . .
[There is a discussion about Mr. Pickett's overstaying his off-ward passes, in which a nurse notes that this occurs when the staff member most responsible for his returning on time is one of those most close to him.]

DR. THORPE: I think this is what makes dealing with him so hard. I don't think it's mainly that he's extremely aggressive and nasty, but I think basically what he does disappoints us. . . . I have discussed with [another psychiatrist] . . . how to manage him—[such things as] "Do we keep him [here as a patient]?" [and] "Have we not made a bad error in giving in to him all the time?" Of course here . . . I don't have the feeling of having given in to him all the time, but others may differ. . . . [One of the doctors] feels that the error is not in refusing to say "no" but in giving him all this permissiveness and then being disappointed—having too many expectations of him. . . . I think that the treatment may never convert him into a pleasant personality; it may only relieve his [situation]. . . .

STAFF NURSE: I see your position is a difficult one, of course. . . . If you say "Yes"—that this patient can go out—[and if] we as nurses step in and say "No," [then that] puts you in a position of a pretty weak sister. . . . It would seem to me that another administrator for Mr. Pickett . . . could certainly work more directly with the nurses and . . . you would [not] be blamed.

Two weeks later Dr. Thorpe arranged for Dr. Adams to take over the administration of the patient's ward life. Dr. Adams held his first conference with Mr. Pickett, and he also met with the nursing staff to discuss his ideas about Mr. Pickett's management. In conversations with the nurses he maintained that such patients as Mr. Pickett were not treatable in a hospital setting and should be discharged. However, considering the established policy to keep Mr. Pickett in the hospital, Dr. Adams did not press his own position on the matter but set about to suggest changes that would make the clinical management problem less difficult. He stated that Mr. Pickett needed limits set for him but that those limits need not be punitive, and he provided the staff and the patient with a list of rules, quoted here without change:

(1) Dr. Adams is administrator for Mr. Pickett.

(2) Dr. Thorpe is Mr. Pickett's doctor.

(3) It would be preferable if Mr. Pickett spoke of personal feelings and attitudes and problems with Dr. Thorpe.

(4) It would be preferable that Mr. Pickett remain in his room or return to it when he feels particularly upset. If he desires it and feels comfortable, someone may sit with him to talk; if he wishes to be alone, he may have this privilege.

(5) He may receive a tub or pack on his request or at the discretion of the staff. The scheduling of these will be at the staff's discretion.

(6) Mr. Pickett will handle all communications referring to privileges and orders, activities, etc., with the team leader of each shift only. Assistants and nurses other than the team leader will be instructed to refer him to the team leader, who will then consult with Dr. Adams about these and a group decision will be made.

(7) Phone calls permitted—two per night, only after 5 o'clock in the afternoon. He may have visitors for two hours at a time, twice a week only, beginning today until further decision is made.

(8) One hour accompanied walk on grounds *twice* per week until further decision is made.

The above rules are necessarily incomplete and will be subject to additions and changes with notice from Dr. Adams directly or usually through the Head Nurse [Miss Holton]. These privileges may be suspended or cancelled temporarily, depending upon what seems to be going on with the patient in the discretion of the staff and Dr. Adams.

We are with you.

In order to assure consensus on the meaning and application of the rules instituted by Dr. Adams, Miss Holton held a number of discussions with him and then wrote an extensive rationale and explanation of the program which was distributed in typed form to members of the nursing staff. This rationale, entitled "Why This Plan for Mr. Pickett," spelled out in detail the purpose of the plan, the fact that it was not intended to be punitive, and the necessity for a united front on the part of the nursing staff. It specified what Mr. Pickett had been told in regard to the rules, and what the nurses were to do and say in given situations. For instance, under "Dealing Directly with Mr. Pickett," the rationale stated:

This is probably the most difficult area of Mr. Pickett's care for us. Our usual philosophy here has been to deal pretty directly and fully with patients, and what they say to us. Mr. Pickett is a clever talker (how many times now have we bought the Brooklyn Bridge?) [He is] a master manipulator. About the only safe topics left for free participation with him are impersonal, neutral ones, such as sports, music, news, etc. What to say then, when Mr. Pickett starts griping to you?

First of all, there are some things that staff does *not* discuss with Mr. Pickett:

(1) Your personal feelings. The only thing he has to know and should know about your feelings on *any* matter related to him is, "Mr. Pickett, I'm interested in you and in carrying out the plan for your care here."

(2) The actions of another staff member or what they are like. "I don't care what so-and-so did. I'm interested in sticking to these rules, and this is the rule. You discuss your feelings about the staff (or the doctors) with Dr. Adams or Dr. Thorpe, not with me."

(3) The reasonableness or unreasonableness of any decisions or rules. Again this is referred back to Dr. Adams. "This is what has been decided for you by the group, Mr. Pickett, and any changes must come to you through Drs. Adams and Thorpe." Remind him that this kind of material belongs in his therapy.

(4) His pathology, how sick he is, the forms that his illness takes, etc. We can *listen*, but not profess to understand, and again remind him that that is stuff for his doctors. To Mr. Pickett, professing to understand him leads him to believe that you are "on *his* side" [and] see things *his* way; and that you might be a tool by which he can hope to gain special considerations that other staff members would not [give him]—a dangerous wedge for him to play with.

If Mr. Pickett makes any sort of request that you question, don't feel that you have to give him an immediate answer. Say that you don't know, but will find out or talk with him later about it. When he says that we are being unreasonable in not doing something for him, etc., then we can remind him that "Our interest is to take care of you according to the plan that has been set up." Any further discussion of the plan is between him and Dr. Adams.

This may eventually sound terribly repetitious, but it's *meant* to, in the hope that he will really begin to hear what we are trying to say to him.

The rationale concluded with a number of "other considerations in his care," including the following:

A *walk* means a *walk*—no stops at his car, barber shop, snack shop, and no sitting in the lobby. . . . His family or another patient may shop for him. Emergency requests are handled through the team leader. If it is the decision of the group or team that something is a *must*, then it will be done by the group. He will not know what individual took care of it for him, and his dealing will be with the team leader. . . . The nursing staff is in *no way* responsible for his car or its care. DO NOT GO NEAR IT. . . . The main channels of communication are between Mr. Pickett and the team leader [and also between] Mr. Pickett and Dr. Adams. Dr. Adams makes the decisions, the team leader carries the plan out, and refers all Mr. Pickett's requests back to Dr. Adams. . . . Deal with his family in the same way that you do with Mr. Pickett. We are interested in caring for Mr. Pickett according to the plan. Any questions further about Mr. Pickett will have to go to Dr. Adams. . . .

The day after Dr. Adams assumed the role of administrator for Mr. Pickett, the nurses' notes in his chart began to indicate a change in mood—for themselves and for the patient:

[A nurse reports: Mr. Pickett] talked freely with [a male nursing aide] whom he hasn't spoken to for months. Still did not speak directly to me but included me in general conversation about . . . a cook-out. . . .

[The aide notes:] Mr. Pickett talked to me a bit about his new administrator. Feels things will work out fine, feels that there is good and bad in his planning, but realizes a large degree of sincerity.

[Another nurse reports:] Mr. Pickett has been talking to me quite freely this evening. Yesterday he gave me an opening to speak—which I accepted. Since then things seem to have reverted to what they were before the period of silence. . . . Talked about [his] privileges to [a patient]. Told her that he certainly wasn't going to get in the rut he was in before—"going into [town] every day, then having to come back practically on hands and knees. I think it will be better to work up to full privileges gradually" [he said].

[The following day another nurse reports:] Mr. Pickett repeatedly said that the sort of program set up [by Dr. Adams] is just what he needs and has needed for a long time. Said there was nothing to make a decision about: he willingly would go along with us. Much talk about fear of "accumulation effect of incidents."

[The same day still another nurse reports:] I came on duty and poked my head in Mr. Pickett's door to wish him a "Happy birthday" —first time I've spoken to him in three weeks. He . . . said a rather surprised "Thank you." However, met him in the hall later and he spontaneously started to speak, saying he was sorry that none of the cake was left. We joked about it, and that was that.

[The following day a nurse reports:] Mr. Pickett talked quite a bit about the new rules handed him [a day or so before]. Mr. Pickett said, "I don't think I can hold out." He said, "This is too much for me to take all at once. But I will give it a trial."

Thus Mr. Pickett was doubtful but hopeful about the workability of the new set-up. The nurses, too, felt hopeful. In fact, the nurses, the therapist, and the administrator were all pleased with the initial success of the new arrangement, but some of the other physicians on the unit criticized Dr. Adams and Dr. Thorpe for it. In medical staff conferences—which excluded the nurses —criticism was at times frankly derisive. One doctor character-ized the new regimen for Mr. Pickett as "the cowboy school of psychiatry," referring to Dr. Adams' statement to his colleagues that "this patient was much like a wild mustang and would have to be broken." As Dr. Adams said later, "My mustang phrase was dramatic [or metaphorical]. My implication was that such a self-centered personality would require limits in order to func-tion properly in any setting."

According to the nurses' notes, in the following two weeks the patient is quoted as saying, usually ambivalently, that he will have to leave the ward, that he cannot take the new regimen, and that he will have to discuss his discharge with the staff doctors and nurses. At the beginning of this period of ambivalence, his therapist, Dr. Thorpe reported on an interview with the patient, putting notes on it in the patient's chart, for the benefit of the nursing staff.

He [Mr. Pickett] wondered whether I was trying to drive him away [out of the hospital]. I assured him I was not. I raised the question, How was it [that this idea] came up? He said, "Then you must be trying to break me, just like Mom did." [The patient had earlier reported that when he had temper tantrums as a child, his mother reacted by beating him senseless to conquer him.]

At the end of two weeks, the following entry by a nursing aide appears in the chart:

Mr. Pickett requests to go on a walk. . . . We walk. . . . Mr. Pickett seemed pleasant and talkative. Mr. Pickett said to me, "This is it, Jerry. I am going to take off. It has to be this way. This is the easy way out. Goodbye, Jerry, take care of yourself." [Thereupon the patient ran away.]

The next day the first general staff conference was held on "Problems in the Management of the Diffusion of Transference in Schizophrenia." The following day, early in the morning, Mr.

Pickett returned to the ward. The night nurse reported the following in the patient's chart:

Mr. Pickett arrived on unit at 6:05 A.M. Taken to seclusion; started making requests. Dr. Adams was called about sedative. He said it was out for now; might do Mr. Pickett good to break. Mr. Pickett was told that there were other patients to be taken care of and if he needed anything we would be around to fulfill his requests insofar as this was possible. All articles removed from seclusion room, door locked, and Mr. Pickett fell asleep at 7:30 A.M.

[A nurse who came on duty later writes:] Mr. Pickett was out in dining room drinking coffee and conversing with the other patients this A.M. It was decided that if Mr. Pickett wanted coffee, he would drink it in the seclusion room . . . regardless of what he wanted to do, it would be done in seclusion. [The nurse goes on to report that in the process of taking Mr. Pickett back to the seclusion room a fight ensued, although, once in the room] Mr. Pickett simmered down. However, later in the morning he took his bed and broke open the door. . . . He was removed from the first seclusion and placed in a second. Visited by Dr. Adams. . . . [Later] he also took one of the buttons off his pj's and attemped to scratch his arm.

A new set of rules was organized by Dr. Adams for Mr. Pickett's management. These, too, were communicated to the nursing staff in writing.

(1) Is to remain in the seclusion room ALONE.
(2) NO TUBS.
(3) NO PACKS.
(4) Both doors locked.
(5) Visited by 3 men at regular intervals to take him to the [bathroom] and to give him water and/or milk.
(6) Taken his food on paper plates and paper cups by 3 men. If he throws the food, then he must wait until the next meal to have more.
(7) May have hot coffee.
(8) Only one person will talk to him at a time, and the fewer words the better. The only thing necessary to tell him is what we are going to do and why. DO NOT become involved in any sort of a conversation or long explanations. Don't fall for wheedling, etc.— "you don't know."
(9) No magazines.
(10) Can have only the sponge rubber mattress on the floor; hospital pj's, no robe. Blanket at night, if necessary.

(11) If he defecates on the floor, then it must wait until the next regular staff visit to be cleaned up.

(12) Knock before entering. Treat him civilly and with as few words as possible.

(13) The seclusion room will be his room and Mr. Charles [another patient] will be moved into his old room.

(14) Try not to increase the staffing. If you need 4 men, get one from the other unit. He expects that we will all work overtime for him again.

(15) We are not attempting to just get him to conform. We want him to get angry.

(16) Shave and bath, and cigarette after 10 A.M. each day.

(17) Do not explain or discuss Mr. Pickett's treatment with any patient. This is not their concern; strictly between Mr. Pickett and staff.

(18) May have spoon to eat with. Be sure you collect spoon when Mr. Pickett is finished with meal.

Rounds made regularly—do not go in to talk to Mr. Pickett at this time. This is just a check to see if he is all right.

Coffee at 2:30 P.M.—may have one staff visit for 15 minutes. General topic [sic] of conversation.

These additions were made to the rules in the next two days:

Out on unit for 15 minutes after bath in A.M.

Out on unit for 15 minutes after bath in A.M. and 15 minutes in P.M.

These rules were in effect during the succeeding five days. In this period the nurses' notes indicated that Mr. Pickett was quiet and pleasant to the staff. Several times, one or another staff member quoted Mr. Pickett as remarking that another patient, in an adjoining room, was quieter and better. Then, at the end of this time—exactly one month after the appointment of the new administrator for the patient—Mr. Pickett was discharged against medical advice. When Mr. Pickett was being discharged, Dr. Adams made the recommendation to him that he try to get along without entering a psychiatric hospital, because such a treatment setting was not to the patient's advantage.

In actuality, Mr. Pickett did make a fairly good adjustment outside of the hospital. In the year following his discharge he made what appeared to be an appropriate marriage and was holding down a regular job. It was Dr. Adams' opinion that his concept of such patients was borne out in the patient's termination of treatment and subsequent adjustment.

I interviewed the assistant head nurse about three months after the patient's discharge. Her perspective on the patient-staff relationships, especially during the period that Mr. Pickett was in seclusion, provides an excellent summary of the nurses' feelings and their concept of the difficulties that the ward experienced. She told me:

Before Mr. Pickett came back [from his escape], it was decided that if he did, he would go into seclusion right away. He came back [around 6:00 A.M., and I came on duty about 8:00 A.M.]. When I heard from the night staff that he was back, I said he had to go into seclusion. He got mad, and there was a fight. He was a very dirty fighter, and [the male staff] were furious. I was, too. However, it was a good thing that happened, because the rules which were decided later were extremely severe, but the staff was ready to put them into effect and not go back to being lenient with him, remembering about the fight. I was the one who decided that he should go into the seclusion room, until Dr. Adams could be consulted.

Dr. Adams came at about 9:00 or 9:30, and he decided that it was time to show Mr. Pickett who was running the show. So he and I sat down and worked out the rules. They were the type of rules the staff were looking for. There wasn't a murmur of protest from the staff, although these rules were not anything like what we were used to doing with other patients. . . .

If I were to make the same sort of decision with Bob or Jean [two other patients]—to send them to seclusion without anyone to stay with them—the staff just wouldn't go along. They'd say, "You're crazy," and go on in and stay with the patient. That is just not the way we would treat the other patients. With Mr. Pickett the staff was relieved that we were finally in control of the situation. . . .

Even though this treatment [for Mr. Pickett] was the best thing—because you [as a nurse] are feeling hostile, you feel guilty for fear you are acting on the hostile feeling—getting too much satisfaction out of doing this [enforcing the rules with Mr. Pickett]. . . .

He is terribly sick, extremely immature. I do not know enough about psychopaths to say that he is one, but he seems to fall into that pattern. I feel he *learned* schizophrenia. I think that it is possible in some areas of behavior to pretend to be schizophrenic, and be somewhat convincing.

[What leads me to believe that he was not a schizophrenic:] . . .

he had some pretty personal material in [a file box] . . . diary stuff about how he felt and what he did—[it was] not schizophrenic [material]. The stuff became more sophisticated as time went by. Also, there was his way of manipulating people, relating to them. Also, his way of thinking—autistic, but not necessarily schizophrenic. It's funny that I can say so little about what I feel sure about. . . .

We liked the first set of rules [pre-escape rules], but with them you still had to listen to him. When he was in seclusion, it was easier, because you didn't have to talk to him, listen to him. For some reason, his outrageous blasts were very anxiety-provoking. . . .

By their very nature, of being in this kind of work, the nursing staff tend to be rather giving. Yet of him it was said that he was a bastard, and when he got well he would be a well bastard. . . .

Everybody has remarked on how different the place is now that he has gone. I feel more free. You feel hostile to patients from time to time, but in this case, it was a real personal hostility that we felt. . . .

The depth of negative feeling towards this patient is in itself a clue that something more than his own personality was involved here. The nurses felt that when he got better, he would simply be a healthy "bastard," and even his therapist conceded that psychotherapy might never make him over into "a pleasant personality." These conceptualizations or personifications of Mr. Pickett seem to be rooted in the wider seedbed of the ward, as I shall make clear.

Nine

THE SOCIAL ORDER
SHAPES
THE THEORY
&

To UNDERSTAND the socio-intellectual forces that eventuated in
the theory of transference diffusion and in the staff conferences
on that theory, three foci of these forces need to be kept in
mind: first, the values, ideas, and understandings—the philosophy
of psychiatric care—shared by staff as to what is appropriate
behavior with patients who do not respond in the ordinary,
acceptable modes of social interaction; second, the actual organization of this philosophy in the social structure of the ward—
that is, the roles and statuses of the participants; and third, the
socially constructed and shared portrait of Mr. Pickett himself—
that is, his personality, as it appeared in the ward interactions. I
mention Mr. Pickett last to emphasize that as important as he
was and as essential in the development of the theory, his personality is only one of the features of the presenting situation.
There were also other features than the three I am emphasizing
here—for example, the kinds of socially engendered conflict that
had already involved Mr. Pickett during the LSD study, and so
on—but I believe it is possible to take these other features for
granted as of less importance. For example, I am sure that the
personalities of others besides Mr. Pickett were also factors in
the history of this theory, but my analysis will not require that
I deal with them. I intend to demonstrate the influence of the

social forces in the situation (as they coalesce in these three foci), but I do not hold that these forces totally and exclusively explain the form and content of the transference diffusion theory.

The philosophy of psychiatric care—the scientific and ideological perspectives of the staff—varied in some respects, no doubt, across status lines in the staff and among members of any one status, even in this one ward.[1] The nursing philosophy had developed relatively independently of the medical staff, for example, so that the nursing staff philosophy provided a continuing social orientation for its members despite changes in medical staff or any absence of guiding perspectives from the psychiatrists. However, the perspectives of all staff coincide at least in the two central precepts that were important in the definition of the problems posed by Mr. Pickett for all staff.[2]

The first central precept is *permissiveness*. That is, in one's relations with the schizophrenic patients on the ward, one is accepting and indulgent of inappropriate behavior that one would not accept in other social situations and in other people. Second is the precept of *responsibility*. That is, the mental patient is ill and unable to take care of enough of his own needs to live outside the hospital, and therefore the staff member must take a certain amount of responsibility and initiative in seeing that these needs are met. In other words, the patient is cast in a help-receiving role while the staff member takes on a help-giving role. These two precepts are established values or ideals in most psychiatric settings.

The essential test of these values as social guides is, of course,

---

1. One of the earliest systematic studies of the variations in these perspectives within a single clinical setting is the dissertation by Doris C. Gilbert, "Ideologies Concerning Mental Illness," Unpublished doctoral dissertation, Harvard University, 1954. Hers and other relevant work is briefly reported in Greenblatt, *et al.*, eds., *op. cit.* See also Anselm Strauss, *et al.*, *Psychiatric Ideologies and Institutions*, New York: The Free Press, 1965.

2. It is only to be expected that psychiatric nurses, physicians, and others working with mental patients will have some understandings in common if they come out of a basically similar training tradition—for example, emphasizing either somatic or psychological aspects of mental illness. In this instance, the key physicians and nurses were indeed mainly trained and experienced in psychoanalytically oriented settings.

what social relations are maintained in the contexts in which they are applicable. As Dr. Thorpe pointed out in his presentation at the staff conference, action that puts these ideals into practice is not all that goes on in the mental hospital. However, on Mr. Pickett's ward, there was a great deal of evidence that these ideals were reflected in patient-staff relationships.

Without entering into an enumeration of the "permissive" and "responsible" activities of the psychiatrists and nursing staff, I will simply call attention to two items of staff-patient inter-action. First, to take the hyperbolic example that Miss Holton mentioned, if a patient wants to cook sausage at two in the morning, this is acceptable behavior. Second, if a patient must be locked in seclusion, a staff member will stay with him to give him attention, to take care of his needs while he is there—especially his needs for reassurance about his social isolation. Now, cooking sausage at 2.00 A.M., when everyone else is asleep, is a privilege or indulgence not ordinarily acted on or accepted in most social situations, even in a well-staffed mental hospital. Similarly, in most hospitals, if a patient must be secluded, he is often left to his own devices until he is more tractable. By contrast, in nonpsychiatric situations—for instance, in prisons—the maximum responsibility taken for a secluded person is in minimal physical care. In both examples of the permissiveness and responsibility characterizing the ward staff, the very fact that the personnel both reported spontaneously that such action was not taken for Mr. Pickett and noted that its omission would be unusual with regard to the other patients, further attests to the existence of permissive and responsible social relations.

Mr. Pickett's behavior, as described by those who were concerned with his psychotherapy and ward therapy, showed the following characteristics: (1) incessant demands for special privileges and manipulation of staff in order to obtain those privileges; (2) frequent infraction of the explicit rules for all patients as well as those made specifically for him; (3) disparaging acts and words; (4) threats or actions of physical combativeness; (5) occasional attempts at suicide; (6) temporary, yet intensive positive or negative feeling for one staff member or another; (7) autistic activity, for example, hallucinations; (8) periods of normal-seeming—and appealing—behavior; (9) refusal to accept nursing suggestions, for example, packs, tubs, and so on, on the grounds that he knew best what to do for himself.

It is highly probable that the same characteristics would be detailed by staff members in this hospital or other hospitals as applying to many specific (paranoid) schizophrenic patients. The difference, one must assume, between Mr. Pickett and other patients is that those characteristics that are most difficult to handle are exaggerated in him. For example, in respect to combativeness, the patient was found to be hiding a section of lead pipe under the bed. Yet, in this respect, one must consider views of the patient by staff of other hospitals he had entered. My review of his records from four other hospitals, over a period of several years, showed that his diagnoses varied: catatonic schizophrenia; psychopathy; chronic undifferentiated schizophrenia; alcoholism; undifferentiated psychosis; psychoneurosis. At the hospital where Mr. Pickett stayed in the interim period between his two admissions at the research hospital, nursing staff reported that Mr. Pickett was "friendly, cooperative, helpful," and emphasized his excellent ward adjustment. The physicians there reported the same picture. It is true that records of earlier hospitalizations—with that one exception—emphasized sarcastic, irritable, and manipulative behavior, and one hospital noted: "He . . . is the kind of person who incites a desire for retaliation, even among professionally trained people." Yet, several years before Mr. Pickett came to the research hospital, one physician reported in a clinical note: "He is perhaps one of the best adjusted patients on the ward, is very friendly and pleasant toward patients and personnel and is well liked by all." One of the research hospital staff members who had known Mr. Pickett at another hospital commented that "he was just one of the mob." In other words, Mr. Pickett looked different in different settings, to different people, at different times.[3]

---

3. It seems, incidentally, that the more favorable reactions to Mr. Pickett were accompanied by diagnoses in the spectrum of psychosis; the less favorable reactions tended to occur in hospitals where he received other

Strains in Role Performance and the Treatment Philosophy

The situation in which the two staff conferences finally took place was a complex of social, intellectual, and historical forces or pressures surrounding the treatment of one patient, whose personality was only one of the important elements, since it, in fact, seemed to vary depending upon which hospital he was in. The combination of these various forces resulted in a continuing strain upon the performance of the roles of everyone involved and cast doubt upon the basic philosophy of treatment upon which the social structure of the nursing unit rested.

To begin with the nurses: Their role activity was to give the patient a great deal of permissiveness and indulgence, and they were supposed to find their own place in the social system by taking care of him as they did the other patients. Yet they felt themselves overrun and abused by the fact that he demanded and, for the most part, obtained extraordinary privileges and freedom. Further, he pictured himself to them as not needing their care, as knowing himself better than they knew him, and as therefore being the person who should decide how he was to be taken care of. In short, there was an utter frustration of the nursing role. If the nurses could not take care of the patient, then why were they here and why was he here? If he was a sick person, a patient, then why should they not take care of him? But if taking care of him meant giving him the freedom to abuse them, how could they handle that?

The psychotherapist, Dr. Thorpe, was in a similar situation,

---

sorts of diagnoses. The relation between settings, diagnoses, and patient-staff relations seems to be a fertile field for social-psychological research.

The central difficulty for a patient in establishing a favorable image or identity for himself that will be ratified by others is illustrated with vivid case material in Donald Burnham, "Identity Definition and Role Demand in the Hospital Careers of Schizophrenic Patients," *Psychiatry* (1961) 24, suppl. to no. 2: 96-122.

especially during the period in which he was also the patient's administrator. His own philosophy of psychotherapy enjoined him to accept the patient's frustrating behavior. Since he was not in the position of having to accept it for much more than the daily hour of psychotherapy, and since, even as an administrator, he had less contact with him than the nurses, the patient's behavior was not so personally frustrating. But the patient posed for Dr. Thorpe another problem: Dr. Thorpe could not support what he regarded as the patient's privilege to be unconditionally accepted without alienating the nursing staff in their relations both with him and with the patient. Therefore he had to mediate somehow between the nursing staff and the patient—a problem that was particularly insistent while he was also administrator of the ward. Somehow he had to recognize the vulnerabilities of the nursing staff as well as the needs of the patient.

The patient himself, one can presume, was no happier with the situation than anyone else. Since he could not determine exactly what was required of him, yet was aware that the staff was extremely dissatisfied with him, he alternately either sought by badly expressive behavior to define his own privileges and methods of care, or tried to comport himself in a dutiful manner that he hoped would cause the staff to regard him more favorably.

As to the staff as a whole, the most immediate preoccupation deriving from this situation can only have been the continued threat to such self-esteem as was bound up in the adequate performance of their professional roles, for it became the feeling of all staff members that the operation of the clinical program for Mr. Pickett was not going well.[4]

On the level of the staff ideological or value schemes, doubt was cast upon the accepted treatment philosophy and values as guides in social relations with this patient and, presumably, with other patients, by extension. It may be said generally that if the professional roles—the occupational roles by which people are accustomed to live at least somewhat successfully in the hospital

---

4. For purposes of simplicity, I shall not discuss the results of the clinical program—whether it actually produced any changes in Mr. Pickett's mental health that could be assessed favorably.

situation—begin to be questioned by those who take the roles, there is a threat to the entire professional ideological system, which in turn threatens the established and mutually recognized patterns of expected behavior in the psychiatric setting. Thus at the Center this threat to the professional role and its values, together with the other felt effects in the presenting situation, led through time to various courses of action designed to redress the threats to the ideology, to the social structure, and to the professional identity and self-respect of all concerned.

Rudimentary Hypotheses and Corrective Actions

Under circumstances of such acute and continuing strain, the maintenance of the role positions of all concerned naturally included a good many rudimentary analyses of the trouble and attempts to derive courses of action from them. In a sense these analyses embodied hypotheses, usually not very precisely or thoroughly developed, that could be tested in the crucible of the treatment situation and found either wanting or appropriate. The hypotheses varied considerably according to the position of the person in the ward structure and the opportunities open to that person (or group) for deriving corrective action.

I shall first deal with the patient's hypotheses and how he acted on them: Mr. Pickett volubly expressed to chosen audiences his feeling that certain members of the nursing staff were all right, but others were mentally unbalanced; that although his therapist and friendly staff members were perhaps sincere, perhaps they were actually insincere or at least mixed up, and if so, the patient could not work with them any more. So Mr. Pickett quite consistently disparaged or black-listed those members of the staff he felt were against him and quite ambivalently attempted to continue relationships with his therapist and members of the nursing staff with whom he felt more secure.

The nurses were also the main subject of other hypotheses,

some held by themselves and others by the doctors. The nurses looked at the difficulty as residing in themselves in that they had not achieved a united front in dealing with Mr. Pickett. They had "to get together," they felt, and not let the patient manipulate them. Consequently, their attention was focused on the need for detailed discussions about handling Mr. Pickett, which they conducted in their problem seminars. The rationale written by Miss Holton for her staff on how to deal with Mr. Pickett was another means taken to achieve staff consensus.

From the doctors' point of view, the explanation of the difficulty as residing in the nursing personnel was formulated as (1) the inexperience of the staff in dealing with such patients without getting overinvolved with them; and (2) their fears and anxieties that Mr. Pickett mobilized by his aggressive and disparaging behavior. The appointment of Dr. Adams as Mr. Pickett's special administrator in order to provide guidance to the nursing staff was a move toward redressing the situation according to this hypothesis.

There was also a rudimentary explanation of the situation centering on the fact that it was difficult for Mr. Pickett's therapist to act also as his administrator. The selection of Dr. Adams as the patient's administrator finally solved this problem, but it clearly was not the definitive solution to the whole situation. A further hypothesis, held by the nurses, localized the difficulty in the doctors generally, in that they did not give the nurses adequate supervision and advice for dealing with difficult problems. The solution proposed was additional conferences with the ward physicians, as both Dr. Thorpe and Miss Holton noted.

Still another group of rudimentary hypotheses localized the difficulty in the patient. One of these, held by members of the nursing staff, was stated frankly as their feeling that "Mr. Pickett is a bastard, and when he gets well, he will be a well bastard." Action taken by the nurses on the hypothesis that Mr. Pickett was not a patient but a bastard was the "silent treatment," as well as the nurses' request that the patient be discharged from the ward. Another hypothesis advanced by the nurses was that Mr. Pickett did not fit into the ward because he was not like the other patients, and he should therefore be discharged. Still another, held by Dr. Adams, Dr. Thorpe, the nurses, and Mr. Pickett, was that the patient himself needed more guidance. On the basis of this explanation, the first set of rules as outlined by Dr. Adams was instituted.

Probably none of these rudimentary hypotheses ruled out the others as partial explanations. Almost all could be entertained at the same time by any of the participants, with the possible exception of the patient. And, in fact, it seems evident that most of them were floating around during the same general period. Several had one characteristic in common—that is, each explanation located the trouble in participants other than those holding to the explanation. Considering the highly emotional coloring of the situation, one can hardly doubt that all participants imperatively needed to avoid the anxiety of seeing themselves as the locus of the difficulty. Yet it seems true that at one time or another almost every participant did give some public, as well as private, consideration to the possibility that his own input into the situation was a source of difficulty: the therapist's feeling about the difficulties presented by his being the ward administrator; the nurses' feeling about their lack of coordinated action; and the patient's recognition of the fear and anxiety provoked by his aggressive and independent behavior.

Two hypotheses received more developed attention than those that have been listed: the nurses' tentative conviction that the patient was not a schizophrenic but a psychopath, and the theory of transference diffusion presented by Dr. Adams and Dr. Thorpe in the staff conference.

The Hypothesis of a Diagnostic Error

The nurses I interviewed were extremely tentative in putting forth the hypothesis that Mr. Pickett would be more appropriately diagnosed as a psychopath, stating that they, of course, were not expertly qualified to make a competent diagnosis. Yet they had obviously given some extended consideration to the likelihood that they were operating on the wrong premise as to what Mr. Pickett's pathology was and what it implied for nursing care.

To analyze the nurses' theory according to their social situation, they were committed to an ideology and role that did not seem to fit their day-by-day relationships with the patient. To act toward him in a different pattern, however, required a redefinition of the situation, in which the patient could be literally expelled from the social system in which he did not seem to fit: Mr. Pickett is a psychopath; he cannot therefore respond to our usual way of treatment; accordingly we do not have to deal with him in the same way we deal with the schizophrenic patients; we can therefore be more strict, less permissive, less indulgent. Under this formulation, a rationale was provided for following the rules which Dr. Adams instituted. It was especially appropriate to Mr. Pickett's seclusion: To leave a schizophrenic in seclusion all day long is wrong, but for a psychopath, perhaps it is the correct procedure. In the absence of some other ideological support for the revised nursing procedures, it seems likely that the hypothesis of an incorrect diagnosis played an auxiliary function in permitting the nurses to redefine what was expected of them in the treatment of this patient.

The Theory of Transference Diffusion

Three central propositions are inherent in the theory of transference diffusion presented by Dr. Thorpe and Dr. Adams: (1) the patient was acting out the transference processes in his everyday life rather than concentrating them sufficiently in his relationship with the therapist; (2) the nursing staff, without intending to, were encouraging the transference diffusion; (3) one of the prerequisites for the necessary control of the patient's behavior was a legal insanity commitment. This theory, which can be considered the "final" stage of an explanation of the situation from the doctors' point of view, was the most elaborated of the descriptions and explanations—a scheme that sought to put the events into some meaningful relationship. And it can be considered, for the purposes of this chapter, an intellectual product that synthesized the functional requirements of the ward social system, the psychiatric ideology, and the historical facts of the patient's hospitalization.

Now, how do the social and ideological influences that participated in the development of this psychiatric theory appear in its form and content? In its over-all structure, the theory might be called individualistic, as indicated in the first proposition. That is, it localized the presenting problem primarily in the pathology and personality of the patient. It was *his* diffusion of transference. It was, again, "his problem, not ours"—his characteristic behavior which set off the "problems in the management."

While there is a long tradition in psychiatry and psychology that structures conceptual schemes in terms of the individual— his instincts, his feelings, his behavior—this tradition cannot fully account for the fact that the transference diffusion theory was couched in individualistic terms.[5] The strong theoretical counter-development in psychiatry, and again, in psychology, that uses the situational, interpersonal, or field approach was present in the specific training and experience histories of the participant psychiatrists and was a significant part of the intellectual culture of the hospital under inquiry. Thus, it cannot be said that the conceptual tools were lacking for a formulation of the subject matter in interpersonal or situational terms. Nevertheless, the individualistic approach is by far the most widespread and strongly developed conceptual framework in psychiatry at this time, and the scales were probably tipped in its direction.

If the conceptual tools available do not fully explain the

5. It must, of course, be recognized that the concept of transference diffusion did not emerge out of an intellectual vacuum. See, for example, Benjamin Wolstein, *Transference: Its Meaning and Function in Psychoanalytic Therapy,* New York: Grune & Stratton, 1954. Cf. John P. Spiegel, "Some Cultural Aspects of Transference and Countertransference," in Jules Masserman, ed., *Individual and Family Dynamics,* New York: Grune & Stratton, 1959.

individualistic cast that the theory took, another possibility may be singled out: The individualistic approach is much more compatible with dissociating the social system and all of its members from any responsibility for the difficulties posed by mental illness in the patient. That is, if a theory can conceive a "pathology" as residing in the patient, it sets up certain intellectual barriers to seeing the "pathology" as something like an interaction or transaction involving others. In fact, one might speculate that the society of "mentally healthy" people—as mental health is socially defined—has contributed historically a good reason for conceptualizing psychiatric and psychological theories in individualistic terms. It is easier for everyone to see the other person as being a queer one; to think otherwise is to revise drastically a good many of one's most cherished social institutions and ideas.

To turn now to the second proposition in the actual content of the diffusion theory, although the theory is individualistic in structure, it insisted that the patient's transference diffusion is encouraged by activities of the nursing staff. Here is an embryonic conceptual recognition of the participation of other, nonpatient factors in the pathological situation, but this is not the same thing as conceptualizing the events according to a situational or interpersonal framework. For the patient remains the center of pathological emanations with which others—the nurses—simply go along. Nevertheless, the pathological situation is seen to have other aspects than the patient himself. One can hypothesize here that the psychiatrists' lesser involvement in the ward ideology and its operating, day-to-day social structure made it possible for them to see nonpatient sources of encouragement of transference diffusion.[6]

---

6. On an abstract, generalized level, Dr. Thorpe emphasized that doctors and others besides the nursing staff have needs that determine some of the things that go on in a mental hospital. By implication, he said that such people may also participate in the patient's pathology. Furthermore, in response to a nurse's comments during the conference, he stated that nurses' difficulties with patients may be related to the jealousy of doctors who do not want nurses interfering with their patients. But he did not say in the conferences what he privately said later, that Drs. Bates and Adams also participated in the transference diffusion.

The third proposition in the theory is that, in order for the staff to establish control over the transference diffusion, a patient should be legally committed to a mental hospital. This implies that the psychiatrists treating such patients will need to be free of certain legal restrictions. If the patient is legally able to leave the hospital at any time, he can thus avoid the mobilization of anxiety that would be caused by the concentration of transference—that is, by the enforcement of rules for ward behavior so that the patient's dissatisfactions with his hospital life will be taken up with the therapist instead of being acted out through obtaining changes in his environment.

On the level of its social functions, this proposition can be seen as supporting the ward social structure by more definitely placing the patient in the role of patient—by getting a court order to define him as a dependent person who needed to be taken care of. Mr. Pickett denied the nurses their proper role of taking care of him. His commitment would undoubtedly define the situation so that he required care and the staff had the responsibility for decisions about his care. A committed patient is in a poor position to say that he knows best how long to give himself a tub or pack.

The probability that commitment would consensually establish the role expectations of the actors is indicated by the patient's own refusal to accept it. The doctors had, prior to the staff conferences, discussed the need for this legal commitment with him, and at one time he seemed to accept their point of view. He changed his mind, probably because he could not accept the very definite recognition of his patient status that would be entailed. He would not agree to refrain from contesting a legal commitment procedure, and so the physicians did not try to institute the procedure—which would have been difficult to press favorably.

Group Process in the Staff
Conferences and Afterwards

To complete my inquiry, the social or group processes in the staff conferences and shortly thereafter must be briefly analyzed. The presentations were made by and to professional people whose roles as doctors, nurses, psychologists, and so on, involved at least a working commitment to the ideology that has been described. The presentations were in part a defense of that ideology. But in addition they were an attempt to remake it or elaborate it in small measure to meet the pathological situation under discussion. They were undertaken by psychiatrists who occupy a high status position in the system vis-à-vis other clinical professionals, and who are therefore in some ways the leading spokesmen for the system. In their presentation, as was noted earlier, certain information was not discussed, although that information was pertinent and supportive of the theoretical position that was presented.

Consensus on the Selective Inattention of Certain Data. The two general areas of data that were not discussed as such in the meetings were documentative data—if any existed—to support the proposition that nurses had operated in ways that interfered with the patient-therapist relationship; and two events in the current hospital status of the patient—his escape and his discharge.

Since one of the main propositions of the transference diffusion theory is that nurses had actively participated in the diffusion of transference, it would have been appropriate (and possible) to document this proposition with some observation or other data, such as records from the ward experience. Also, since another proposition of the theory is that patients like Mr. Pickett should be committed, his escape and his discharge could appropriately have been cited as indicative of the way in which he avoided a concentration of the so-called transference feelings. It can be assumed without doubt that the two psychiatrists who held the conference were competent and were aware of the pertinence of the information that was not brought up.[7] Moreover, the explanation cannot lie solely in the personalities and professional needs of the two psychiatrists, since a number of other people in the conference were aware of the same material, but made no reference to it at the time. Thus the omission of this information can probably best be explained in terms of the social and ideological functions that it served for the total group. This is particularly true in view of the fact that the group passed over the opportunity to look at the data not just at one meeting but at both of them.

How did the group consensus on selective inattention to these vital facts serve to reinforce the structure of the social system in which the group members were participants? How did the selective inattention of pertinent and apparently supportive data fit into the requirements of the therapeutic theories of the nurses and of the physicians? On the basis of the materials presented on the story of Mr. Pickett's hospitalization, a number of interlocking, if tentative, conclusions can be reached on these questions.

First, the omission of any possible information about nursing intervention in the psychotherapy relationship seems to have been related to the mutual expectations of professional courtesy and respect for staff problems in dealing with difficult patients. That is, everyone is at some time curiously and unproductively involved in his relationships with patients; and private attention in a two-person group to such problems, rather than public discussion in a large group, is the general rule.

Furthermore, the avoidance of specifics in the case of any particular nurse permits avoidance of specifics in the case of other staff members; the code of public reticence works in terms of mutuality. So long as the conferences recognized only in abstract terms that some of the nursing staff had problems with the patient, there was no necessity to see whether the same problems occurred systematically—that is, throughout the rela-

---

7. My conversations with Dr. Adams, described later, indicate this.

tionships of all staff members, all doctors, and so on, who had significant contact with Mr. Pickett. The problem was localized; it was the problem of only certain unnamed nurses; it was the problem of only a few members of the social and ideological system. Thus, the system itself was protected from criticism. But if it were publicly recognized that the same problems were experienced by all members of the group, then there might be a greater pressure to subject the structure and ideology of the group itself to critical scrutiny. The problem would have to be viewed as possibly systematic, rather than as localized in a few persons. When events force a group to conclude that certain of its basic social values and guides for behavior are askew, the stability of the understandings among them as to what to expect from each other is severely threatened. That is, the roles performed by the members of the social unit are no longer adequate and can be expected to undergo some sort of change. In consequence, the personal security invested in the performance of the roles is also threatened. Under these circumstances there would be the possibility of a major social reorganization, a reinterpretation of the guiding values and the activities of everyone within the system—which, in relatively stable social systems, occurs only in times of crisis.

Members of a social system do not participate in a reconstruction of their system unless they see this as absolutely necessary. In the instance of Mr. Pickett's ward, no necessity existed, for similar problems of such degree were not experienced with other patients whose illness did not take the form that Mr. Pickett's did and, moreover, the problem was rather conclusively disposed of by Mr. Pickett's discharge. It is not so surprising then that the group did not have to inquire deeply into the data that bore on nursing staff or other staff participation in the "diffusion of the transference" and that the group thereby did not have to re-evaluate the significance of its psychiatric philosophy.

Now, in regard to the inattention to the patient's escape and discharge, the conference consensus helped to avoid two potential implications. The first of these is the implication that operations of the high-status figures—that is, the psychiatrists—as well as of all other clinical personnel involved were poor and inappropriate. This is, of course, not a necessary inference; indeed, it may be entirely erroneous.[8] But the point is that it would have had to be examined as a possibility if the facts of the patient's final, complete evasion of treatment were brought up. This examination would have implied criticism of the responsible high status members of the group, which is ordinarily avoided when there are no challengers for the positions that the leaders of a group occupy. And certainly there was no one in the conference who might displace the psychiatrists who were presenting the case.

The second potential implication is that something was awry in the set of social rules by which a hospital deals with patients like Mr. Pickett. This was in part an inference that could be drawn from the entire presentation by Dr. Thorpe and Dr. Adams. Their presentation was a sort of elaboration and revision of the standing principles of patient management, one that did not disturb the central propositions of the psychiatric ideology—permissiveness and staff responsibility—that suggest that the patient is in the dependent role. Yet it was those two propositions that the history of Mr. Pickett's hospitalization most contravened, and that the facts of his escape and discharge dramatically challenged. To overlook these facts is to maintain the rightness and stability of the guiding philosophy and its two central propositions. .

The theory of transference diffusion defined the means of handling such a patient as Mr. Pickett in a manner that left the two propositions theoretically untouched, while, at the same time, it suggested the technique of commitment as an answer to the problem of controlling the intolerable aspects of Mr. Pickett's behavior. It defended the existing ideology, yet provided a technique for handling a problem that the ideology did not sufficiently provide for.

---

8. For example, some physicians at the Center and elsewhere see it as a sign of progress or potential progress when a schizophrenic patient runs away from a hospital—especially a previously withdrawn patient—and can maintain himself without being rehospitalized by someone else.

The problem posed in the clinical management of Mr. Pickett is not a problem peculiar to him, or peculiar to schizophrenics, or indeed peculiar to inpatient treatment settings. Every psychotherapist and every psychotherapeutic setting does evidence certain means of social control—certain means that adequately or inadequately deal with the problem of a patient's transgressions of accepted social behavior. That is why the conference presentations were of intimate interest to all staff personnel who dealt with patients on one level or another. The presentations proposed a means for handling the problem in the hospital; they suggested an explanation for the problem; and at the same time they maintained without basic change the familiar rules and expectations by which psychiatric workers define their relations with patients. The conference consensus on not upsetting the apple-cart by looking at possibly contradictory evidence followed the pressures of the social situation in which all were participants, but it also served to reinforce the intellectual understandings, in the ward philosophy or ideology, with which the clinical staff operated.

Relaxation of Restricted Attention After the Meetings. The staff conferences were intensified moments, so to speak, of an on-going situation. Although the structure of the situation around Mr. Pickett did not materially change in the immediacy of the conference meetings, the conferences had their own social imperatives. When each of these group meetings was over, the social demands and expectations inhering in them became somewhat attenuated. So, with the ending of each conference, the group consensus on inattending the unmentioned data and their implications began to dissolve. Thus it was that immediately after the first conference, I was told, by a psychologist over a cup of coffee, that the patient had escaped the previous day. This fact was communicated not casually, but as a significant event, and with an expression of puzzlement as to why it had not been mentioned in the conference. Further, I was in a car pool with Dr. Adams and we of course had the opportunity to chat informally in the period between the two conferences, before I actually began to study the episode. I once asked him whether he thought the patient's escape was especially pertinent to the presentation that he and Dr. Thorpe had made. Dr. Adams agreed that it was and went on to say that he himself had decided not to bring it up because it was a decision within Dr. Thorpe's province; however, he had not talked about this matter with Dr. Thorpe. A few days later, Dr. Adams spontaneously reported the fact that Mr. Pickett had just been discharged, and he noted the relevance of this fact to the proposition that patients like Mr. Pickett should be committed. Yet, neither he nor anyone else brought up this point in the following staff conference.

Thus, outside the meetings the group consensus of inattention to certain specific information was weakened. The consensus was also weakened to permit critical examination of the transference diffusion theory itself, of the exponents of that theory, and of the basic psychiatric philosophy and social structure of the ward.

It would seem to be a general group phenomenon that after a meeting is over, twos and threes get together to discuss things that somehow they were unable to discuss in the meeting itself and that they nevertheless feel are important. Even though group discussions may avoid certain topics or facts, by that very avoidance they may also stimulate the discussion of those topics afterwards. Thus, the fact that Dr. Adams and Dr. Thorpe did make formally public some events and considerations around Mr. Pickett's case is likely to have stimulated the consideration of other topics that were not brought up in the conferences. In other words, the conferences contributed not only to a consensus of inattention, but also to a focusing of attention on the inattended topics and facts, after the conferences.

To return to illustrations of how the consensus of inattention dissolved in the period after the conferences, one of the two psychiatrists himself undertook a reexamination of the theory: Dr. Adams revised a paper he had written, which dealt with some of the same ideas. Similarly, the nurses undertook in their interviews with me to cast doubt upon the proposition that any nurses had acted in a way that appreciably interfered with Mr. Pickett's therapy relationship with Dr. Thorpe. They recognized that the head nurse who had preceded Miss Holton had acted in the manner described by the physicians as diffusing the transference. Yet even this nurse was defended for that behavior. One of the staff insisted that only this nurse had ever been able to achieve a really good relationship with Mr. Pickett.

Other staff members criticized the transference diffusion theory in casual discussions about the case. In a more private situation, they found it easier to criticize those who held a high status in the group. A final example is my own beginning examination of what was involved in the total history of the conferences and in the psychiatric ideology that played such an important part in that history and in the entire group structure.

It will be instructive to note that despite many discussions of the patient's history, the staff conferences, and so on, in the course of the present study, one significant fact did not turn up until over a year later, when a manuscript report of my study was being circulated by Dr. Thorpe. One of the senior clinicians, who was especially responsible for relations with the community around the hospital, recalled after reading the manuscript that in the first conference Dr. Thorpe had made a (humorous and elliptical) reference to Mr. Pickett's escape from the hospital: Just as Dr. Adams had been about to play excerpts from a tape-recorded interview with the patient, Dr. Thorpe had said something to the effect that the patient "is on the loose, and I wouldn't want him to hear this tape, considering his paranoid personality!" And he had peered out the conference room door as if to ascertain whether Mr. Pickett were eavesdropping at the keyhole.

Upon being reminded of this incident, Dr. Thorpe immediately recalled it, as did I. The fact of Mr. Pickett's escape was therefore actually referred to in the conference, albeit ambiguously and humorously ("on the loose") and in a way that was not meaningful to those, like myself, who at the time did not know Mr. Pickett had escaped. The reference was so slight, indeed, that even Dr. Thorpe did not recall it unaided, although in the intervening time he had discussed my formulations with me on several occasions. This is specifically the hallmark of selective inattention, as formulated by Sullivan and distinguished from the process of denial or repression; that is, an event may in some way be actually experienced and even explicitly referred to at a later time but its implications will not be examined, and in that manner the event may as well have never occurred so far as any learning from it is concerned.[9] Not only did the conference members overlook the fact of Mr. Pickett's escape, they overlooked, if they recognized it, Dr. Thorpe's tangential reference to the escape.

The history of Mr. Pickett's hospital stay and of the group processes provoked by the problems posed in his care is also the history of the emergence of various ideas used by the staff to grapple with those problems. The various conceptualizations seem to have emerged in forms that "fitted" the social requirements of life at the Center. The ideas, including the theory of transference diffusion, were constructed in shapes congenial to their social and intellectual context. They fulfilled requirements for the persistence of the pattern of relationships and mutual understandings that characterized the ward.

The explanation that the shape and content of scientific ideas are subject to social pressures inherent in the environing structure of relationships and understanding is deducible from the sociological conception of the persistence of integrated social systems. That is, within any relatively stable and integrated social order, behavior explicitly valued by members of that order operates, for the most part, to maintain it in its recognizable and stable form.[10] (Whether or not the members of the order are fully aware of this significance of their behavior does not affect its significance, although, of course, awareness may affect the frequency and strength of the particular behavior.) It follows then that if, within such an order, intellectual products are definitely at a

9. See Harry Stack Sullivan, *Clinical Studies in Psychiatry* (Helen Swick Perry, Mary Ladd Gavell, and Martha Gibbon, eds.), New York: W. W. Norton, 1956, especially Chap. 3.

10. For an extensive discussion of this perspective, see Robert K. Merton, "Manifest and Latent Functions," Chap. I, in *Social Theory and Social Structure, op. cit.* For a definitive presentation in the context of a general theory, see Talcott Parsons, *The Social System*, New York: The Free Press, 1951.

premium, the products and the producing process will also tend to be stabilizing for the social order, that is, to be functional for it.

It is not possible to conceive theories as patterned mainly to fit the social order in which they occur unless that order is rather highly integrated. That is, the social order must be governed by a set of fairly harmonious values, towards the realization of which the various elements of the order are primarily geared; and the members of the order must, as in the small primitive society, typically studied by anthropologists, be fairly well isolated from contact with others and living the total round of life within their own social order. These conditions are relatively well realized in the social order of a psychiatric ward or hospital, in that the long-term, intimate, day-to-day contact of staff and patients (particularly on the locked wards) tends to describe a coherent pattern for a total round of life activities— eating, sleeping, recreation, work, even sexual activity, and so on.[11] Indeed, the psychiatric inpatient setting is perhaps one of the very few possible settings in a complicated society such as ours in which the social order is so integrated. Under these circumstances, it may be supposed that theories arising within this setting are especially sensitive to the necessities of local social life.

Yet even in the most uncomplicated of social orders in the back wards of forgotten hospitals, there are impinging social values and pressures indicative of competing elements within a hospital and outside it. On Mr. Pickett's ward, the competition of varying perspectives appeared clearly in the fact that the nurses had different answers to the questions posed by the patient's care, as compared to the physicians' explanations. Moreover, there is in the environment of any theory that is presented as scientific, the whole body of values and rules of life inherent in the social system of science itself. These demands, as described in earlier chapters, interfere with whatever else might be going on in the social order. The precise interdigitation of the social system of science and that of the particular institutions (such as

---

11. See, for example, Erving Goffman, *Asylums*, New York: Doubleday Anchor, 1961; and William Caudill, *The Psychiatric Hospital as a Small Society*, Cambridge, Mass.: Harvard University Press, 1958.

hospitals, universities, industrial laboratories, so-called nonprofit research corporations, and so on) in which research is conducted is an important area for research in the sociology of the knowledge-producing process.

The systematic review of problems requiring study in the special area of psychiatry as a knowledge-producing activity, as a science, can be organized much as follows. I offer this outline (and a few representative works) only as a means of orientation to possible topics. It should be emphasized that all sociological studies of psychiatry as a science must rest upon a general conception of psychiatry as a social and cultural phenomenon. For example, psychiatry as it is practiced must be considered as a social control activity—that is, an activity directed toward the neutralization or correction of certain types of socially devalued behavior. An understanding of this basic social nature of psychiatry as a social phenomenon is essential to studies of the development of science in psychiatry.

Areas for Research into Psychiatry as a Science

A. Psychiatric research as an organized social activity—as social subsystem and social structure.
  1. Institutional setting: private practice as a research setting; the research hospital; the research ward in a service hospital; and so on.[12]
  2. Roles: research directors; investigators; assistants; subjects; and so on.[13]
  3. Processes: social change; integration; rates of production; and so on, viewed across roles and institutions.[14]

---

12. Dunbar, op. cit.

13. Irving Ladimer, "Ethical and Legal Aspects of Medical Research on Human Beings," *J. Pub. Law* (1954) 3: 467-511, esp. 483-85; William J. McEwen, "Position Conflict and Professional Orientation in a Research Organization," *Adminis. Sci. Quart.* (1956) 1: 208-24.

14. Leslie Schaffer and Leila C. Deasy, "Deference, Social Mobility, and Conflict in Psychiatric Settings," paper presented at the meetings of the American Sociological Society, Washington, D.C., 1957; Leslie Schaffer and Leila C. Deasy, "Social Mobility and the Value Context of Psychiatry," paper presented at the meetings of the American Psychiatric Association, San Francisco, 1958; Stewart E. Perry and Lyman C. Wynne, "Role Conflict, Role Redefinition, and Social Change in a Clinical Research Organization," *Social Forces* (1959) 38: 62-65.

B. Psychiatry as a body of ideas and methods in relation to other ideas and methods—as cultural subsystem.

   1. Mutual influence between psychiatry and general ideas of logic, consistency, coherence, pertinence, and so on: the development of internal consistency and logico-meaningful relations within psychiatry; deviations from coherence, as a function of inconsistent premises or lack of fit between data and theory; and so on.[15]

   2. Mutual influence between psychiatry and other more or less organized bodies of ideas and methods, for viewing objects of cognition: philosophical orientations (such as existentialism); religions (such as Zen Buddhism); scientific theories from other fields (cybernetics); and so on.[16]

   3. Mutual influence between psychiatry and the generalized evaluative and orientational scheme of the participants in the culture within which psychiatry exists: interdependence with local notions of morality and of personal responsibility for deviant behavior; and so on.[17]

   4. Mutual influence between psychiatry and particular subcultures in which it has been or is especially imbedded: psychoanalysis and the Jewish subculture; Pavlovian psychiatry and Russian communism; American psychiatric understandings about the behavior of patients from subcultures of the United States other than white, middle-class groups, and so on.[18]

---

15. John R. Reid and Jacob E. Finesinger, "Inference Testing in Psychotherapy," *Amer. J. Psychiat.* (1950-51) 109: 894-900; Group for Advancement of Psychiatry, *op. cit.*

16. Rollo May, *et al.*, eds., *Existence: A New Dimension in Psychiatry and Psychology*, New York: Basic Books, 1958; Ernest Becker, *Zen: A Rational Critique*, New York: W. W. Norton & Company, 1961; Jurgen Ruesch and Gregory Bateson, *Communication: The Social Matrix of Psychiatry*, New York: W. W. Norton & Company, 1951; Harry Stack Sullivan, *The Fusion of Psychiatry and Social Science* (with introduction and commentaries by Helen Swick Perry) New York: W. W. Norton & Company, 1964.

17. Jacques Barzun, *The House of Intellect*, New York: Harper & Row, 1959; George Devereux, "Cultural Thought Models in Primitive and Modern Psychiatric Theories," *Psychiatry* (1958) 21: 359-74; Iago Galdston, ed., *Man's Image in Medicine and Anthropology*, New York: International Universities Press, 1963, esp. Pt. IV.

18. David Bakan, *Sigmund Freud and the Jewish Mystical Tradition*, Princeton, N.Y.: D. Van Nostrand & Co., 1958; Kingsley Davis, "Mental Hygiene and Class Structure," *Psychiatry* (1938) 1: 55-65; Frank Riessman, *et al.*, eds., *Mental Health of the Poor: New Treatment Approaches for Low-Income People*, New York: The Free Press, 1964. John R. Seely, "Social Values, the Mental Hygiene Movement and Mental Health," *Annals Amer. Acad. Pol. Social Sci.* (March, 1953) 286: 15-25.

C. Psychiatry as a body of ideas and methods in relation to social structures and social systems.
   1. Mutual relations with the over-all internal institutional structure of psychiatry: relations between psychiatric training in medical schools, hospitals, and clinics and the "medical model" for understanding social deviants and subculture members as "mental patients." [19]
   2. Mutual relations with the structures of the primary groups in which psychiatry is created, used, and maintained: the social two-group structure of doctor and patient and the dyadic cast of psychiatric theory; interdisciplinary research institute organization and methodological inventions in psychiatry; and so on. [20]
   3. Mutual relations with concurrent institutional structures of the family, government, business, education, and so on: family structure and the pattern of psychoanalytic thought as it originated in Freud's Vienna; American pluralism and American eclectic psychiatry; and so on. [21]

19. Thomas S. Szasz, *The Myth of Mental Illness: Foundations of a Theory of Personal Conduct*, New York: Harper & Row, 1961; Erving Goffman, *Asylums*, Garden City, N.Y.: Doubleday & Company, 1961.

20. Doris C. Gilbert, "Ideologies Concerning Mental Illness," Unpublished doctoral dissertation, Harvard University, 1954; Stanton, 1954, *op. cit.*; Stanton and Schwartz, 1949, *op. cit.*; Erika Chance and Jack Arnold, "The Effect of Professional Training, Experience, and Preference for a Theoretical System upon Clinical Case Description," *Hum. Relat.* (1960) 13: 195-213; Erika Chance, *et al.*, "Professional Background and Themes in Clinical Case Description," *Hum. Relat.* (1962) 15: 53-61; Milton Greenblatt, *et al.*, eds., *The Patient and the Mental Hospital*, New York: The Free Press, 1957; Luszki, *op. cit.*; Frederick Wyatt, "Climate of Opinion and Methods of Readjustment," *Amer. Psychol.* (1956) 11: 537-42.

21. Jurgen Ruesch, "The Trouble with Psychiatric Research," *Arch. Neurol. Psychiat.* (1957) 77: 93-107; Iago Galdston, ed., *Freud and Contemporary Culture*, New York: International Universities Press, 1957; Max Lerner, *America as a Civilization*, New York: Simon and Schuster, 1957.

Ten

THE PSYCHIATRISTS REVEAL
SCIENTIFIC TRUTH
AS SOCIAL BEHAVIOR

THE EXPERIENCES of my colleagues at the University Medical Research Center—the dilemma of Dr. Richards and Dr. Thorpe when Miss Burton refused to take the LSD, the uneasiness of Dr. Lowe about the scientific status of his psychotherapeutic skills with patients, the plight of Mr. Pickett—all these and more, as they have passed through my own processes of review and analysis, seem to me to raise many more questions than their concreteness as facts can ever clarify. Yet the psychiatrists and their associates and patients, systematically focused as they were upon their own participation in the total process of treatment, of research, and of life in the hospital, delineated deliberately as well as accidentally the fundamental nature of science. Moreover, once their own self-awareness was mobilized, they could formulate for themselves many of the implications that I want now to draw from this study—for science. for social science, and for that conception of true knowledge that underlies the whole scientific process. Particularly, I think, continued experience in conducting clinical research in psychiatry at the Center would and did lead many of them to the sort of practical recommendations that I will now outline—and that hold within them a conception of scientific knowledge and how it is produced.

The Practice of
Psychiatric Research

I conclude from the projects I studied a number of suggestions for the concurrent conduct of research and treatment. First, the physician should ordinarily develop explicitly and directly the understanding with his research patients of how he is studying them as well as treating them; that is, he should adopt an overt unifying role definition. Second, his understanding with patients must be periodically reviewed and changed or renewed. Third, the physician must be prepared for recurrent crises of conflict between research and treatment, and he must be prepared to find that he has often automatically used a variety of stabilizing operations—what I have called role-maintaining techniques—to meet these crises. Fourth, the psychiatrist can and should use the appearance of these operations in his own behavior as a signal that something important is going on in either treatment or research, or both—that is, as a clue that will lead to something scientifically and/or therapeutically enlightening.

Let me review some of the considerations that lead to these recommendations. In support of the recommendation that the research psychiatrist choose a role definition that openly combines research and treatment with each patient, I should point out that the histories of the projects at the Center indicate that other types of role definitions are unstable. For example, concealing the existence of research in the First LSD Research was ineffective, and the role definition based upon it broke down. Also, disjoining research and treatment in the Trade-Off Project, even though the arrangement was explicit, was only temporarily useful. Further, the splitting of duties between two staff members seemed to pose a substitute problem: To what extent must the treatment physician, for therapeutic considerations or whatever, participate in and even change decisions about research

taking place on his patient? [1] In the end, the physician seems to
be forced into research, and thereby moves towards a combination of research and treatment considerations in his relations
with the patient.

It seems, therefore, that so long as the job of the psychiatrist
is to conduct therapy as well as to conduct research, he will end
by adopting a job adjustment, a work style, that openly combines
the two activities in his relations with his patients.[2] A work style
that tries to combine the two in a concealed way is unstable
because the consensus upon which it rests is incomplete and
therefore vulnerable. Separating the two activities in different
relationships with different people attempts to compartmentalize
the basic interests of the physician; but these interests seem to
inevitably coalesce in relationships with the research patient. In
short, the recommendation that the research psychiatrist adopt
an overt unifying role definition is based upon the observation
that it is the only viable and stable work adjustment.[3]

It should not be concluded that the research-therapy problems
are solved in such a work adjustment. As a matter of fact, they
are not, for they require periodic review of the way in which
the psychiatrist and his patient have agreed to work with each
other. At least two inevitable consequences of human interaction
require this periodic review. One of these is the natural growth

---

1. Juliana Day reports on the problems of maintaining a psychotherapeutic relationship with a patient when someone else is conducting
research on the patient: "The Role and Reaction of the Psychiatrist in
LSD Therapy," *J. Nerv. Ment. Dis.* (1957) 125: 437-38.

2. Of course, the psychiatrist's job does not always call for him to
continue to do both treatment and research; he can avoid the conflict by
doing only one sort of work, if he is satisfied with giving up the other.

3. As I noted in Chapter Six, the concealed separation of research and
treatment—what I have called the covert disjoining role definition—did not
appear at all in the projects or program I studied. It is now clear why that
was so. If the covert element of a role definition is unstable and the disjoining element is also unstable, the combination of the two elements in a
work role definition will obviously lead to a very unstable type of adjustment. Such a definition would probably make only a fleeting appearance,
if it appears at all.

of sentiments arising out of continued interaction.[4] This increase in the affective significance of the relationship (recognized, in part, in psychotherapy as transference-countertransference) will cause over time a kind of misfiring in the doctor-patient relationship, which in turn leads to a questioning of the bases of the relationship. In other words, what has seemed satisfactory begins to have unsatisfactory features. For example, what seemed like a reasonable amount of time, for Miss Burton, to spend upon psychotherapy became onerous for Dr. Richards under the working conditions of the Center. Again, a research patient may decide that what he had once agreed to he later finds too difficult, as Mr. Pickett decided when he told everyone he would not take LSD.

A second natural consequence of continued interaction is the inevitable appearance of the unexpected in the course of a relationship. This too can threaten even the most workable role definition. It may even force a complete change. For example, the physician may receive a promotion or an offer from another institution that is too good to turn down; or the patient who has agreed to the use of stressful drugs may unexpectedly develop a severe heart disorder, and so on. In either instance, the relationship between doctor and patient would probably terminate. Life always offers something that cannot be programmed for ahead of time. The specific mutual understandings between doctor and patient in a research setting will never provide for all contingencies. The partners cannot devise a perfect contract.[5] The contract that they settle on will depend upon a penumbra of trust in each other and of confidence in the possibility of working out ongoing difficulties. Of course, this trust and confidence are in one sense a product of the personal relationship that

---

4. Cf. George C. Homans, *The Human Group*, New York: Harcourt, Brace, 1950. Robert R. Blake, "The Interaction-Feeling Hypothesis Applied to Psychotherapy Groups," *Sociometry* (1953) 16: 253-65.

5. Durkheim demonstrated this early in the history of social science. Emile Durkheim, *Division of Labor in Society* (George Simpson, translator), New York: Macmillan, 1933. (First, French publication, 1893.)

builds up. But fundamentally important also is the parallel adherence of each partner to a generalized set of value commitments within the society, for in a sense, the applicable guides for meeting the novelties of the relationship are deduced from these commitments.[6] The explicit deduction, when it becomes necessary, of a common way for meeting a puzzling crisis in the relationship is complicated of course by the somewhat different interpretations of the fundamental values and ideas that the partners presume they share. This no doubt was a significant part of the difficulty in working out a clinical program for Mr. Pickett. Everyone knew that a psychiatric professional should act responsibly and yet indulgently with a patient—including even a difficult patient like Mr. Pickett—but that did not enable them to decide effectively on his care.

In summary, simple answers about what are appropriate interactions and agreements between doctor and patient in the research setting cannot be laid down. The answers in a sense have to be built up *ad hoc* even though there may be guidance from general principles.[7] All research goes on in an environment of ignorance; it is inconceivable then that all research decisions on a project especially in psychiatric research, can be foreseen in

---

6. Since the severely ill mental patient ordinarily is disturbed also in the realm of such commitments, the psychiatrist and the patient may experience considerable difficulty in finding common ground. The psychiatrist has to guard against the imposition of his own choices among values. The problems of such a delicate task are complicated enormously because the whole process determines what the psychiatrist will oblige the patient to do for him and what the patient will expect of the psychiatrist.

7. I am not sure I would conclude, for example, that all social science research with human subjects should necessarily be conducted according to the outlines suggested here for psychiatric research with patients. But I would certainly assume that the lessons of psychiatric research would have to be carefully examined for likely applications. For instance, social science research with children may be a very close analog. See Alfred Baldwin, "The Study of Child Behavior and Development," Chap. 1, in Paul H. Mussen, ed., *Handbook of Research Methods in Child Development*, New York: Wiley, 1960. A. B. Hill offers important guidelines for clinical research, but he finds it impossible to "reduce the broad principles to precise rules of action that are applicable in all circumstances." His discussion of exceptions is especially instructive. Austin B. Hill, "Medical Ethics and Controlled Trials," *Brit. Med. J.* (1963) 1: 1043-49.

detail. The research psychiatrist and his patient will have to review their relationship often just at the point of such decisions.

Thus, if the research psychiatrist recognizes that there will be recurrent crises in the doctor-patient relationship, he will then be prepared for the fact that he will be using continually a variety of stabilizing activities in order to keep his work going, in order to salvage both research and treatment goals from the recurrent threat of disorder. Moreover, since in general the research psychiatrist will be confined to a single choice among the possible role definitions—that is, to the role definition that openly joins research and treatment—his maneuverability in the situation will depend upon responses within that definition; that is, the role-maintaining techniques. In short, the use of role-maintaining techniques will be frequent and fundamental to the continuity of the relationship between doctor and patient and to the work accomplished.

The ubiquitousness of role-maintaining activities in the clinical research situation must not be allowed to obscure their crucial significance. The psychiatrist can utilize them as signals of the occurrence of events shaping his research and his treatment. To this end, I want now to examine the *fundamental* importance of the role-maintaining techniques in the procedures and products of psychiatric science, for these maneuvers can be recognized as either facilitating or retarding the progress of science. In this respect, the basic effect of these social techniques can be found in that process in which the attention of doctor and patient is diverted from recurrent obstructions in their relationship. Let me try to make this clear. In any instance of research or treatment in which progress toward these goals depends upon the doctor-patient relationship—for example, if any of the research data are obtained in a psychotherapeutic interview—the structure of that relationship determines the structure of the results of research and of treatment. Thus, if the role-maintaining maneuver stabilizes inattention to certain influences upon the relationship, it has assisted in shaping the information available in the relationship. Some of that inattended information may be simply tangential, distracting, and irrelevant;

but some of it may be crucial. In the simplest sense, ignoring it may therefore be either facilitative or obstructive to the research; but on the most basic level, in either instance, the information that is obtained is different.

The simplest example is the unconscious withholding of information on the part of the subject who selectively withdraws in direct response to the particular way that the psychiatrist chooses to handle a minor research-therapy conflict. A single instance of such restricted interchange between the research patient and his physician is ordinarily unimportant; what is important is the patterning of such interchanges as a stabilized means of handling the conflict. In the development of their mutual adjustment through role-maintaining techniques, the research and treatment are significantly shaped. That is, the doctor and the patient come to collaborate in the standardization of the data drawn from their interaction.

It is not accurate to say that the data are therefore wrong; they are simply different from what they might have been, because of unrecognized parameters. The scientific recognition of the difference then depends upon the work of others who come afterwards. However, the follow-up and potential description of the social parameters in the data (and in formulations derived from them) may become virtually impossible because of the traditionalization within the entire working group of researchers of particular role-maintaining techniques. In other words, the development and support of a role definition for the research psychiatrist may come to be institutionalized in his field with a consequent social standardization of data, theory, and methods.[8]

Any role-maintaining maneuver used in the service of stabilizing the research-treatment relationship of doctor and patient can have a part in the process of shaping the research or the treatment. Perhaps there are some special effects particular to

---

8. My study took place in the early organization of a research program, before it had jelled. A return to the program some years later might permit an examination of this phenomenon. For an informal discussion of the idea of traditionalized scientific truth, see Vilhjalmur Stefansson, *The Standardization of Error;* London: Kegan Paul, Trench, Trubner, 1928.

different sorts of maneuvers; that remains to be studied. Quite evidently, however, the maneuvers employing technical modifications of research or of treatment embody the most direct effects upon the data and ideas of the research psychiatrist. In the use of technical modifications, the creativity of the researcher is challenged to circumvent or resolve the research-treatment conflict threatening the relationship between scientist and subject. For example, the fact that certain technically simple experiments upon human beings are ruled out by adherence to therapeutic or humanitarian social values restricts possible scientific information; but it also requires the scientist to find alternative means to the knowledge he wants. Since knowledge is so completely bound to the methods used to obtain it, the very content and scope of the building-blocks of the science are thereby influenced. Even technical modifications in research or treatment design and procedures may be carried out by the worker without direct awareness of their implications. If the research psychiatrist and the social scientist in general are to act truly in the scientific mode, they must apply their skills in observation of human behavior to the activities that they use to circumvent and neutralize the inevitable conflicts between research and non-research considerations.

The Validity of
Psychiatric Research

The observational materials I have put forth offer evidence that in a variety of ways the social forces occurring in the environment of day-to-day research in psychiatry find expression in the procedures, ideas, and theories that come out of that research. The problem for the scientist in this is how to evaluate these procedures, ideas, and thories as approximations to valid knowledge. One answer is to regard all knowledge, of whatever degree of validity, as a property of the social system in which it occurs. In this manner, then, social forces are to be considered not as impinging upon scientific operations and their products but as, in part, constituents of them. Scientific truth is a social property in another sense, as well. It is something that is shared, and without being shared it does not exist. I shall deal with this viewpoint in general terms a bit later, but the argument for it within psychiatry can be rather simply stated in terms of what I have already described in the activities of the researchers at the Medical Research Center, with particular reference to the role-maintaining techniques and the role definitions used there.

The epistemological significance of the various role-maintaining techniques or role definitions that might be used in solving social problems during scientific research derives from their meaning as operations necessary to the research. Since knowledge, in science or elsewhere, is the product of operations undertaken to accumulate the knowledge, the social operations necessary to the development of scientific knowledge in psychiatry, for example, are inextricably a part of that knowledge.

The sharing of particular social maneuvers—their use in common by researchers—offers the same avenue towards common knowledge as the sharing of the specific technical operations of the scientific disciplines involved. Moreover, deliberate variation or a recognition of the natural variation in the use of such maneuvers permits the calibration of their individual significance in the structure of the common knowledge obtained.[9]

The penetration of the social conflict of research-versus-treatment in the case of psychiatric research is but a particularly observable example of the general penetration of the social context in scientific research of any kind, visible primarily because of the methods and subjects of the projects I studied. The qualitative and natural historical methods used by the researchers in the LSD project, for example, were a technical element in the research that made the entrance of social influences especially visible. Those same methods in the development of the theory of transference diffusion were similarly important. However,

---

9. This is a particular statement on the microsociological level of the general principle of "relational knowledge" advanced by Mannheim, *op. cit.*; see e.g., Chap. 5, sec. 4.

tangential social forces, not immediately relevant to the ideas and technical systems of the science, are also present, if more obscured, in studies that use more specific and precise research techniques, for example, the statistical evaluation of drug effects.

In more precise studies, special procedures such as the double-blind technique in experimental design (by which neither the patient nor the researcher knows until the end of the project who got what drug) can be used to winnow out some tangential matters like the social or personal atmosphere of optimism about a drug. In general, a large number of technical operations can be used to shunt off certain aspects of the unnecessary participation of nonscientific elements in the research. The fact that other kinds of studies, or other sciences, can eliminate the interference of some social factors does not, however, mean that they can eliminate all the basic social conditions that participate in the production of the scientific knowledge. All science is alike on this basis. Indeed, reliance upon technical design facilities to eliminate social influences totally can and does lead to the elaboration of social inhibitions on the advance of a discipline.[10] The scientist who decides to rely on technical features for the full elimination of nonscientific social influences upon science actually participates in building up a social and cultural structure that limits the content and form of the knowledge that the workers in that structure will produce. It may be said that to rely upon the progressive elimination of the social and cultural interpenetration of scientific values and ideas with other values and ideas is to participate blindly in an infinite regression series toward a more and more limited view of the phenomena of the scientific discipline in question. Breaking out of that series is the price of the fundamental discovery and revolutionary advance in science that occurs whenever problems and phenomena become redefined in spite of the resistances of social and cultural forms created by the preceding scientific work.

In sum, my study does not imply that the improvement of scientific operations in psychiatric research requires reliance

---

10. The argument is conclusively made in A. H. Maslow, *op. cit.*

upon increasingly strenuous efforts to eliminate the participation of all social factors. Rather, the psychiatric researcher must accept the burden and responsibility of making explicit the social pressures that inevitably affect his work. Perhaps having been made explicit, *some* of these pressures can be handled in such a way as to decrease or even eliminate their influence entirely. But as a psychiatrist, sophisticated in the observation and formulation of human behavior, surely he can never expect that scientific knowledge will be obtained by eliminating the influences of the basic processes of the human mind and life— the processes of social interaction and cultural allegiance. These, he must realize, are not inimical to knowledge and science; they are a part of it.

Scientific Ideas as Behavior

I am going to set out now a rather personally oriented perspective on this problem of truth within the human reality of science. Only by doing so, by making some comments that clearly indicate some of the participation of personal matters in what I can see and think about in research, is it at all possible for the next person to make an adequate evaluation of the usefulness of my observations and speculations for his own work. It will also serve to show how my conclusions on the human nature of science in psychiatric research are quite generally applicable. In the remainder of this book, then, I shall try to set out in the simplest terms the relationship between some of the scientific perspectives that we can and do use and the personal, human, historical influences upon the choices to be made between and within those perspectives—with myself and this study as a case in point.

In the course of doing this I shall sketch in a rather new area of scholarly interest in social science.[11] The quickest way

11. Although the field of study (what has been called empirical epistemology) is fairly new in contemporary social science, of course many of its problems are ancient philosophical issues.

to describe this area is to call it the study of ideas as behavior. That is, it is the study of the behavior that produces and constitutes communicated conceptions of experience and reality—for example, scientific ideas. Increasingly acute studies in the patterns and development of cognition,[12] in ethnoscience,[13] and in the social process of research,[14] call today, it seems to me, for a generalized statement of the study of ideas as behavior. Although I shall not be able here to present such a statement in the formal and systematic terms it requires, I want to set out the perspective in at least an introductory way, in informal and programmatic terms.

The study of scientific ideas as behavior has been historically formulated in the conceptions of the sociology of knowledge and the sociology of science. The former, however, has connotations of a limited nature (usually referring to societal and not to microsocial processes) and does not include a wide variety of studies that might otherwise be considered as directly relevant to the growth and development of scientific ideas in the primary groups of researchers, for example.[15] By contrast, the sociology of science has not been concerned with ideational development so much as with relevant social and organizational structures, although it includes many studies of the small work groups of scientists. Moreover, a study of the human contextual influences

---

12. Piaget's work of course stands out here, and there is also the recent work of psychologists like Bruner and Mandler and the whole social psychological tradition of work in perception. See Charles M. Solley and Gardner Murphy, *Development of the Perceptual World*, New York: Basic Books, 1960.

13. Ethnographers like Conklin, Frake, and others, especially students of language, like Goodenough, have begun the process of theoretical and conceptual analysis of cultural components of knowledge. A. Kimball Romney and Roy Goodwin D'Andrade, eds., "Transcultural Studies in Cognition," *Amer. Anthro.* (1964) 66, part 2: 1-253.

14. A book of readings, recently published, samples the contemporary work: Bernard Barber and Walter Hirsch, *op. cit.*

15. So far as I am aware, the only work that has considered seriously the microsocial processes in the context of the sociology of knowledge is Werner Stark's *The Sociology of Knowledge*, New York: Free Press, 1958. See also Werner Stark, *The Fundamental Forms of Social Thought*, London: Routledge and Kegan Paul, 1962.

on the development of scientific ideas certainly requires investigations of cultural and psychological processes as well as social ones. I believe that psychologists, psychiatrists, anthropologists, and sociologists—social scientists in general—will have to begin to organize their interest in scientific ideas as human data in a broader frame of reference. Thus, it seems appropriate to define the field more generally as the study of scientific ideas as behavior, rather than as the sociology of science or as cognitive psychology, and so on.

The problem of definition is quite germane here, for of course definition is itself a fundamental idea, created wittingly or unwittingly by the behavior of persons doing the defining. In the 1930s in what was in America a real hey-day of social science—before it underwent certain undigested influences as a consequence of its part in World War II—the exciting eddies, tides, whirlpools, and cross-currents of ideas and methodologies tossed up on the sands a relevant dictum: *Define, if you must, but define operationally and qualify your definition with an autobiographical statement.*[16] I take this dictum here as a guide and also as an introduction to the basic problem that the very business of studying ideas as behavior is addressed to.

This dictum arose out of the philosophical problems that were recognized again in social science when Bridgman's concept of operationalism had filtered into it.[17] I am afraid that we in the social sciences often lose sight of the kind of problem that that dictum refers to. We generally feel or act as if we have

---

16. See Leonard S. Cottrell, Jr., and Ruth Gallagher, *Developments in Social Psychology, 1930-1940* (Sociometry Monograph No. 1), New York: Beacon House, 1941.

17. I am sure it will be clear that when I talk about operationalim, I am very far from what came to be the form when Bridgman's insights were perverted in psychology and in sociology as mere instrumentation. Insofar as I myself define operationally here, I do so only sketchily by trying to say *how I approach* the study of ideas as behavior. Those familiar with the conception of science used by Bridgman will know that I have adapted and adopted many of his other insights. See esp. P. W. Bridgman, *The Logic of Modern Physics*, New York: The Macmillan Company, 1927; and P. W. Bridgman, *The Way Things Are*, Cambridge, Mass.: Harvard University Press, 1959.

solved it, or at least know exactly how to go about solving it. I mean the basic problem of that sensory and conceptual consensus with his fellows which is ever the goal of the scientist but never his achievement. The process of reaching this consensus is a crucial problem in the study of ideas as behavior.

Because no one can feel with my fingers, see with my eyes, think with my brain, use my concepts, or work with my theories, but only with his own fingers, eyes, brain, concepts, and theories—because of this, each of us is concerned to report what occurs to us in a way that allows another to approximate that same experience—or at least to believe he approximates it. In short, one tries to make one's private experience a matter of public record. There can be no quarrel with this conventional statement of the scientific process, but its complications, as Bridgman has pointed out, must be made explicit.

For example, I can satisfy myself, under some circumstances, that I know what is going on "in" someone else—for example, I can translate his anxiety into palmar sweat indices. I can even hook myself up to the same machine and grind out similar indices on myself. But in fact my anxiety is not the same as those palmar sweat indices, *and I know it*, because I am the one who is anxious. Quite the most considerable part of science is in the realm of what I know because I am going through it; only a smaller part of it is made up of such things as palmar sweat indices that I am sometimes willing to take as someone else's adequate judgment of what is going on. In fact, I must depend upon my own judgment, even when it disagrees with what others say, *even when I am willing to use my judgment to say that my judgment is incorrect* and that I accept someone else's judgment. Science thus is this sort of private matter.

Bridgman in speaking about this problem says:

It may be objected that it would lead to impossible complication to insist on the differences between public and private—that a strict application of this point of view would mean that there are as many "sciences" as there are people engaged in "sciencing." This may indeed be the case, but if it is we can do nothing about it but accept it. The first consideration must be "what is true?" not "what is simple?" I believe that nearly always the first results of a careful operational analysis will be to bring complication rather than simplification. The conceptual structure which we have inherited is a conventionalized and simplified structure, in which we usually do not know what the simplifications are or what are their consequences. The first task of the operational approach is usually to recover the full complexity of the primitive situation.[18]

It is the "primitive situation" implicit in the scientist's attempt to make public what is essentially private that is at stake in the study of ideas as behavior. The scientist's attempt gives rise to the same kinds of events that one ordinarily studies in the behavioral sciences. As soon as the scientist tries to get his experience publicly ratified by his fellows he is engaging in a range of activities which must come under the scrutiny of the social scientist. When we as scientists want to arouse the sympathetic and agreeable consensus of our fellow scientists for what we are trying to say scientifically, we try to couch our statements in the most socially acceptable terms, which are ordinarily the most understandable terms. The process of making public what is our private experience is the social-cultural-psychological act in science. The necessity to share and to reach a consensus implies an engagement in interaction—with some combination of fantasied or physically embodied others. In the process of interaction the scientist's communicated ideas become socialized as human components of that interaction.[19]

There is another fundamental component of the primitive situation of knowledge-creation, but it is not apt, under ordinary circumstances, to be subjected to the explicit socialization process although it is nevertheless part of the social understanding that permits the scientist to communicate with his colleagues. This part of the understanding is silently acknowledged as if it

18. P. W. Bridgman, "Rejoinders and Second Thoughts," *Psychol. Rev.* (1945) 52: 281-84; see p. 282. Cf. P. W. Bridgman, *Reflections of a Physicist* (second edition), New York: Philosophical Library, 1955.

19. I am indebted here to Virginia L. Olesen who coined the phrase "the socialization of ideas" to describe the process by which a scientific paper, before publication, undergoes revision under the critical assault of friendly (or unfriendly) colleagues.

had long ago been so clearly accepted that it need not even be referred to. I speak here, of course, of the initial conceptual structure of reality, preliminary to the scientist's work—the epistemological and ontological assumptions without which no one can think scientifically. Problems in scientific research on occasion will reveal suddenly the existence of these prior assumptions, and the whole structure of epistemology and ontology will be challenged. This is precisely what happened with the Einsteinian revolution in physics, which was translated generally by Bridgman into the methodological concept of the operator.[20] These preliminaries to scientific thought are distinguishable when they are brought into the light for scrutiny, and they (or their reformulated substitutes) are an inherent part of scientific thought.[21]

The existence of these nonempirical aspects of science has a behavioral as well as a philosophical significance, for they are habits of thought. Recognized or unrecognized, they are sanctioned by social acceptance. As Bunge has pointed out,[22] it was the great gift of the phenomenologists that they taught us that these were indeed habits rather than fundamental intuitions of basic truths. The so-called a priori concepts loom important in a behavioral analysis of the scientific process in much the same way as any evaluative statement in a preliterate culture is a clue to the total structure of thought in that culture.[23] They do not determine that structure but as an interactive element in it, they are constituent influences.

---

20. F. S. C. Northrup provides a swift and illuminating historical summary of Einstein's epistemological quandary and how it was solved. See his "The Raison d'Etre of the Inquiry," Chap. 1, in F. S. C. Northrup and Helen H. Livingston, eds., *Cross-Cultural Understanding: Epistemological Anthropology*, New York: Harper & Row, 1964.

21. Even the most determined empirical scientists recognize today that they cannot escape using these nonempirical tools as fundamental parts of their work. See, for example, George A. Lundberg, "The Place of Supra-Empirical Statements in Sociology," *Sociol. Inquiry* (1961) 31: 117-27.

22. Mario Bunge, *Intuition and Science*, Englewood Cliffs, N.J.: Prentice-Hall, 1962.

23. See Gregory Bateson, *Naven* (second edition), Palo Alto: Stanford University Press, 1958.

In summary, the simplest situation of scientific behavior includes a conventional frame of reference which, as a set of habits, exerts an influential force upon the development of a science; and the situation includes a process of seeking consensus which is also more or less conventionalized in standard ways of behavior. These two features alone should alert us to the necessity of examining closely all possible constituent elements of the human nature of science. To discover what aspects of the scientific process still need operationalizing one must return to the primitive situation of science, as Bridgman called it, and recognize the variety of social, cultural, and psychological operations that the scientist engages in willy-nilly in order to be a scientist.

The particular role-maintaining maneuvers and the roles themselves made use of by the clinical psychiatrists in research at the Center must be viewed as inherent components of the scientific process in the study of clinical psychiatric problems. In such a study, as in any study, the essence of science cannot be a reaching for truth independent of the ties of the time, place, society, or person concerned, but rather must be an operational explication of that reaching, including the social, personal, cultural, and other human elements in it. For this reason, I must indicate in at least a sketchy form something of these same elements in the investigative process constituting this book. My views, my analysis, and my presentation of the observations detailed in this book are perhaps understandable if I explicitly qualify my definitions with an autobiographical summary. As in my comments on the psychiatrists and their work, I shall describe only relatively public aspects of the social situation of my research activity, and I shall inattend any personality factors, however important these, too, may be.

In a sense, I face the task of being a social scientist with a basic, pervading, inalterable pessimism that colors whatever I do. I begin, as may already be gathered, with the pessimistic idea that I (like all other scientists) am basically alone in this world and that what I have always to do is to try to transcend that aloneness, to get others to feel with me, to experience with me, to think with me—*even though I can never fully succeed in that task.* The way in which I try to encode my experience so that I can, in approximation at least, share it with others is bound up with the rules of science that I also hope I share. Those rules we presumably share are our hope for partially transcending time, place, and personality so that we may communicate or share not only with colleagues today but colleagues to come, building on what colleagues of earlier days have already laid down. But my pessimistic assumption must apply to these rules of science, as well as to the intellectual products of these rules. That is, I cannot fully share the meaning of those rules as I experience them.

This pessimism that I carry around with me is not, of course, part of the baggage of many other social and other scientists. I mark that down right away as one source of what separates us all, another illustration to tell me again that each of us is alone. There are indeed many in social science who would begin with quite the opposite assumption that basically, pervadingly, inalterably colors everything they do: the optimistic assumption that experience (that is, knowledge) is in its essence a general commodity unlinked to individual being. I might paradoxically call that the social assumption about knowledge while the pessimistic view is somehow the asocial assumption! At any rate, on the basis of the *optimistic assumption*, the scientist can happily set about doing what the pessimist is trying to do much less happily, that is, formulate what one finds out so that someone else can share it in some significant sense. In other words, both the optimist and the pessimist are engaged in the same task, but they go about it in different ways.

For example, the optimist assumes that he and I are in such good agreement that he often starts off right away with trying to answer what seems to him a clean, simple question by clean and simple methods. If he starts out that way, we may be already even further apart than before he started, and by the time he has finished his work—and particularly the report of his work—we are still further apart. Far from having carried me along with him in his journey of discovery, he has, in fact, left me blind and stumbling a good long way back.

The pessimist, by contrast, knowing from long experience that he himself is so often left behind, is less sanguine about the community of rules and experience he himself hopes to use and help create. Being less hopeful, he is forced to try that much harder, I believe, to ensure a modicum of community. By no means does that suggest that he succeeds more often than the optimist. Perhaps he truly succeeds less frequently and so confirms his pessimism. But he is more wary of the pseudo community of selective inattention to all the ways in which, in fact, each scientist is on his own, however much he needs and relies on each other scientist in their common quest. The pessimist is not satisfied with the easy and swift recognition, among the members of his discipline, of the common verbalisms of, for example, a "high statistical significance level." Such a shared rule is valuable, to be sure, but often tangential; too often it offers a distraction from paying atention to all the ways in which the other scientists may have already been left behind before it is time to invoke a rule of "point-oh-one."

Also, the pessimist, since he does not expect to achieve full and complete community, seems more ready to undertake a research that promises a good deal less, right from the beginning. The optimistic scientist, by contrast, usually picks out a problem that he expects will lead to a complete sharing of the knowledge or experience he will gain and pass on.

These, then, are some of the differences in the approach to the task of being a social scientist that can arise out of the first, basic choice of assumption of the nature of one's world, one's life, one's work. There are undoubtedly others, but I hope that I have given enough of an insight into the meaning of the proto-scientific pessimism I embrace, so that we can share it somehow. It is merely an instance of the class of assumptions or orientations or definitions, any choice of which ontogenetically precedes scientific behavior and is incorporated in it, but also comes to be formulated by it.[24] The study of scientific ideas

---

24. It is this interaction that complicates the simple notion that there are basic intuitions preliminary and defining of scientific truth. Cf. Bunge, *op. cit.*

as behavior, then, can itself be defined as beginning with the primitive situation of encountering the attempt to make public what is private and as therafter moving to any other stage in the process of publicizing the private.

I have defined a bit again, because I must, but now I should qualify with a more clearly autobiographical statement. In other words, why do I think this way, behave with ideas this way? Perhaps the answer lies in the particular history of how I was inducted into the role of the social scientist, and if I describe something of this, I emphasize that I do so as an illustrative analysis; I am applying the inquiry into ideas as behavior—in my own instance—as illustration but also as a necessary operational description of the definition of the field, as I set it out.

My selection of the pessimistic posture as being more appropriate than what I would criticize as the optimistic imposture probably arises out of the way in which I was socialized into the social scientist role. As distinguished from the usual contemporary course of socialization from which one emerges with the status of a certified scientist by means of certain rather well established, orderly, and progressive stages, marked by standard initiation and welcoming ceremonies, I was in many ways informally plopped into the role, without a great deal of ado, when I began my study at the Center. My relevant academic preparation had been in fact very irregular, for it had consisted mainly of work at the Washington School of Psychiatry. The Washington School was not then associated with any university but, to be sure, I had had the advantage of studying with a brilliant collection of scholars, clinicians, and scientists, of whom any university might have boasted. The intellectual frame of reference that I took on at the School was much more thoroughly an interdisciplinary matter, however, than would be possible in the university setting where the departments carve up what is known or to be known. At the School, the various disciplines of anthropology, psychoanalysis, sociology, psychology, neurology, and so on, together with a variety of professional outlooks from psychiatry, medicine, teaching, social work, law, nursing, and so on, were melded in one perspective: the study of interpersonal relations, especially as it might be applied to the remedy of current problems in living, whether those problems concerned relations with a legal client, a minority group member, a primary school student, a physically ill patient, a hostile foreigner, a mental patient, or whatever.[25] I was therefore not trained as a sociologist, a social psychologist, or any other specialist, and I certainly was not a psychiatrist or even a psychotherapist by virtue of this learning experience. Rather, the seminars, lectures, and "intensive personality inventory" (that is, personal psychotherapy as a tool for assessing one's assets and liabilities for professional work) simply presented concepts and techniques designed to sensitize one for observing what goes on in an interpersonal context. What was for others—the psychiatrists, social workers, and so on—a postgraduate program was my first introduction to the scientific approach to human behavior in all its social, cultural, and psychological variety.

Five years after my first work at the School, when I joined the staff at the Center, I was clearly the most junior research person there, and I think this is the crucial social status characteristic that shunted my work in the direction it took. First of all, I was too soon entered into research to be already committed to a particular research problem, and I was too inexperienced to decide swiftly what I might do in the freedom that was offered by the new program. What more obvious way to learn something than to watch others at work? My interest then became research on the processes engaged in by my colleagues, who were senior to me.[26] I did not clearsightedly plan out such a program, and there were times when I wandered from it in the next five years I was at the Center. Yet to study what the psychiatrists were doing rather than to study some substantive problem in social science rather obviously fitted the perspective of a very junior staff member. I could, as in the fondest dreams of all graduate

---

25. The perspective of the School is illustrated in Harry Stack Sullivan, *The Fusion of Psychiatry and Social Science, op. cit.*

26. As a matter of fact I was steered in this direction on the suggestion of two colleagues, a psychiatrist and a sociologist, who would have liked to take the time to do the sort of study that I did.

students, watch and criticize from a safe distance the work of those senior to me, who, simply by working, were concurrently providing me with the most valuable instruction I could obtain.

Second, my junior status exempted me from some of the responsibilities that others had to shoulder, and since I was, at first, the only nonpsychiatrist with a full-time commitment to the new clinical program, I could wander easily from one context of the work to another without any restrictions by senior social scientists, who were otherwise engaged. Sometimes, perhaps, I was a bright mascot, and at others, a burdensome questioner. I doubt if someone in that sort of role could have been tolerated except in the free atmosphere of a broad new program, in which everyone was so busy developing his own ways of working at the Center that no one would feel the necessity to explicitly train a junior person from another discipline.

Looking around me during those five years, I noticed that I seemed to be the only social scientist who stayed on with the clinical research program. Others came but most seemed to find it necessary to ply their skills elsewhere than in the hurly-burly of the emotionally charged clinical setting. Perhaps life there did not fit easily the requirements of the techniques and concepts they brought with them; at any rate, they generally resigned shortly or found ways of doing studies peripheral to or outside the clinical setting of the Center. Social science research in an action setting puts considerable limits upon the exercise of the academic skills, but I did not realize that then, for I had never known anything different or easier.

My unconventional training and my junior status combined with still another feature of my early experience to shape the perspective I use. Because of the very great range of disciplines represented in the Research Center program, whose members were supposed to find ways of working together, I was forcibly struck by the vigorous competition between different scientific positions, ideologies, methodologies, disciplines, and so on, that characterized the entire program.[27] The competitions were

---

27. Some of this state of the field of psychiatry in general is most recently described in Strauss, *et al., op. cit.*

fought out between different conceptions of psychiatric reality —for example, between somatists and psychoanalysts, between medical and nonmedical perspectives, between the methodological camps of, as one person called them, "the counts versus the no-'counts," and so on. And of course all these perspectives combined into all the possible combinations and permutations, so that a veritable Tower of Scientific Babel was constructed. Moreover, of course, the politics and the psychology, the organization and the culture, the personalities and the loyalties, the honesties and something other than honesty, swirled around within the scientific brew giving it a rather conglomerate character by no means visible in the neat little papers that began to be turned out.

With such an experience it is perhaps no wonder that I came to be concerned with intellectual ideas as behavior—especially scientific ideas. I have now very little sense of science as some grandly independent and inexorable progression toward truth and knowledge, as so many scientists, both natural and social, conceive it. Certainly, I must in a way hold to that ideal view of science, but I regard all our scientific ideas as personal and social constructions in the course of the urge of all of us to commune with each other.

Does this mean that there is no point in trying to be scientific? By no means. We must have ways to encode our experience for communal living. Science, as distinguished from other sorts of encoding processes such as religion or art, should claim the first allegiance of the sociologist, the anthropologist, the psychiatrist, and so on. Moreover, it seems for them to be a more successful coding process than other systems. So, as a sociologist, for example, I want to pursue the goal of sorting out *my* experience in such a way that it becomes meaningful somehow for others, through science—that is, through a more or less self-correcting and systematic program of observation for the development and testing of a generalized theoretical perspective.

Science works out as a way of achieving a community of experience because basically it appears to our sensing and perceiving apparatus that there is a certain regularity in things and people. And the regularities in the world are continuous with regularities in our means of sensing, perceiving, and organizing it. For example, although some of us may be color blind, for most of us the optic nerve and all the related paraphernalia of vision articulates regularly with the radiations of color that we can see, so that we are very often in agreement in labeling something red or green or blue or even tangerine. We are even more likely to be in agreement—that is, to have a shared bit of knowledge—about the length of a line, for example, or its relative placement in relation to other lines. Thus we find it somewhat easier to read a dial for a colorimeter than to recognize the colors themselves. Yet, as careful studies have shown in the last few years, the opportunity for consensus on the length of a line or even the existence of a color (much less its distinction from another color) is a cultural and social opportunity that may be denied an entire group or a single individual.[28]

The reason that we can tell that color or length judgments are culturally and socially defined under certain conditions is because we have some sort of transcultural and transsocial standard against which to compare the variant judgments. As scientists, we might throw up our hands in complete despair if we could not believe in the possibility of such transcultural standards, but in fact, we have to recognize that simply because we can sometimes obtain regularities, that does not mean that those regularities are not a cultural product—that is, they must be understood as a product of a *transnational culture* of scientists and scholars.

The consensus that is established at least to some degree within that transnational culture, within that confraternity of coders of experience, is by no means a universal consensus. That is, it is imperfectly and spottily accepted or shared by many within the culture—not to speak of those outside it. Insofar as the scientific consensus is not universal it must always remain

28. Roger W. Brown, *Words and Things,* New York: Free Press, 1958. Solomon E. Asch, "Studies of Independence and Conformity: I. A Minority of One Against a Unanimous Majority," *Psychol. Monogr.* (1956) 70, No. 9 (Whole No. 416). Publications like the *Journal of Human Factors* examine certain of the individual and group physiological concomitants of knowledge.

challenged as not fully true. Only by recognizing that the partial consensus is a cultural and social product and not an achievement of universal and essential truth can each individual member of the scientific culture continue to search effectively for that truth. Deviations from the consensus and variants of it, at different times and places, are the clues to achieving increased consensus. That is, they are signals that something is askew, but they are not necessarily evidence of error or willfulness or ignorance among the deviants, whatever their status or role within and without the scientific culture. For example, if my expereince or judgment does not check with someone else's or with that of a large number of other people, that is a signal for further research, not an indication that I should accept the others' view, or they mine.[29]

Deviations from the standards, rules, and agreements on reality set by the international subgroup of scientists and scholars must be studied for what they might provide in additional knowledge. These deviations cannot be examined merely as exotic or psychotic ways of coding, for so to do prejudices the inquiry from its beginning. The fact that there is a consensus among a group of scientists (or even among almost all scientists) provides a point of reference from which examinations of deviations from that consensus may proceed—nothing more than that. It does not define the deviations as outlawed; it acts as a point of departure for research. Moreover, the manner of proceeding from that point of reference and departure is itself a matter of consensus among some but not all who may be interested in the standard and deviations from it. Thus the rules of science themselves can prejudice the results, so that it is essential to recognize what sorts of directions of inquiry are ruled out if one adheres inflexibly to those scientific rules.

---

29. Joseph Ben-David has systematically examined the role of the deviant professional in the history of medicine. Ben-David, *op. cit.* In a remarkable and fruitful book, Kuhn has described the nature of the theoretical revolutions in the history of physics as the result of someone finally examining long-known but inattended observations that had all along not fitted current and fully accepted theory. Thomas S. Kuhn, *The Structure of Scientific Revolutions,* Chicago: University of Chicago Press, 1962.

The perspective that I have placed before the reader on the recordings, observations, interviews, and so on, builds a picture that undoubtedly deviates from that held by other participants in the research program at the Center. Certainly Dr. Richards, Dr. Thorpe, Dr. Lowe, and others would view these same events with different problems in mind, different questions to answer, and with a good deal of different information to flesh out some of the bones in my reports. In some respects, upon discussion with them, I should expect to revise my own thinking; I assume that they would revise theirs. The development of consensus however, never can be complete on these events, indeed, must be very much less complete than on other scientific matters. Our deviations from an agreement with each other do not mean that any one of us is engaged in an unscientific analysis of the experience, although they are an indication of the enormous complexity of the study of scientific human behavior *in vivo*. In part, we may be able to fit our various perspectives together in a patchwork quilt that will pass for warranted knowledge. If so, we can agree with each other that we have arrived at a temporarily acceptable truth, and that would not be different in kind from the truth that any scientific effort strives for.

The Fallacy of the Genetic Fallacy

The thesis of this book can be summed up in the fallacy of the genetic fallacy. To describe this fallacy is to encapsulate the lesson that the psychiatrists' experience at the Center teaches.

For hundreds of years, scholars have been cautioned about the so-called genetic fallacy. That is, they have been warned that just because one points to unrespectable sources of a truth does not affect the valid status of that truth. So it is, when the social scientist points to social sources of knowledge, science, truth— that is, sources presumably outside the realm of ideas per se— he is supposedly pointing to an unrespectable genesis of that knowledge. He is, as it were, impugning the legitimacy of its birth, asserting an act of conception unblessed by the proper marital ceremonies over the ideas involved. The logician attacks the sociology of knowledge, for example, as committing the genetic fallacy if it dares assert that its investigation casts doubt upon the universality of the truth being analyzed.

Mark: If the social scientist, as the result of his research, will never have anything whatsoever useful to say about the significance of the particular ideas he studies—in the sense of their significance according to the yardsticks of valid knowledge—then indeed his studies are largely jejune. All he can talk about is the facilitation or hindering of the rate of ideational development that comes from the social surroundings of the scientific ideas. I do not think the social scientist ought to be willing to settle for that. There is something wrong in the logician's objection to the more profound relevance of the sociology of knowledge in particular, and the study of ideas as behavior, in general. There is something wrong there that I should like to call *the fallacy of the genetic fallacy*.

A number of considerations suggest the fallacy of the genetic fallacy. First, there is the simple fact that validity at all times and places is still a matter of warranted knowledge, and warranties themselves are social constructions, privately reconstructed. The manner of these warranties tends to differ from time to time, so that one has to read the fine print, so to speak, to be sure whether labor as well as parts are guaranteed, and for how long. Two sorts of warranties are in use today. One of them is the pragmatic test (Does it work?) and the other is the more precise test of prediction or postdiction, a generative test (Does it produce more knowledge?). I do not think we are able to do without either warranty, but I am not concerned with that, nor with the question of exactly how different they are. My point here is merely that there are some differences in emphasis in the criteria by which we warrant something as true knowledge; these differences can be recognized as social constructions; and choices between them are socially dictated, personally dictated, and culturally dictated.

Next, there is the matter of method in the production of knowledge. I mean method in its most general sense, not the very particular techniques of investigation, although of course they also are liable to the same strictures. Here I again come back to the notion of the operator. The central figure of the operator, the producer of the knowledge, is described by the way in which he goes about producing, creating, the knowledge—that is, by his method in the most general sense. When one gets back to the really primitive situation of knowledge production, one comes ineluctably to the conclusion that the social, personal, and cultural circumstances of the production are a part of that production. True, the social situation, to take one example, leads to a choice of one over another formulation which is then to be labeled true knowledge; but in addition, as Weber suggested, the social situation permits only a limited range of possible conclusions or formulations to be seriously considered.[30] Hypothetical other formulations are simply irrelevant and do not come to mind, so to speak. Thus, while the social situation produces a bias that must be filtered out somehow, it also is part of the creation of different parts of the truth.

If one returns to the primitive situation of knowledge creation—that is, the situation before all conceptions and constructions are called into action or indeed themselves created—and starts out from that point (which is already an interesting problem), then method also includes a host of conceptual tools that most of us have not thought about at all, and some tools, I imagine, that none of us have yet recognized. The operator uses those tools, those cultural, social, and personal conceptual inventions, to manufacture the finished product. It is no wonder then that we will have to recognize that the product is shaped by the tools and stuff thus selected. Thus, indeed, the generation of truth must be examined as a means of determining what that truth is, and whether we even want to call it truth, whether we

30. Edward A. Shils and Henry A. Finch, trs. and eds., *Max Weber on the Methodology of the Social Sciences*, New York: Free Press, 1949. In his analysis of the child's selection of communicable ideas in the process of growing up, Schachtel has made much the same point. See Ernest G. Schachtel, "The Development of Focal Attention and the Emergence of Reality" and "On Memory and Childhood Amnesia," Chaps. 11 and 12 in *Metamorphosis*, New York: Basic Books, 1959.

want to put our guarantee behind it. On this basis alone, it seems to me that to raise the specter of the genetic fallacy is to set up an insubstantial phantom. I do not think the logician can any longer scare us with that ghost from the past.

So far as social science itself is concerned, there is still another important consideration that suggests the fallacy in the genetic fallacy. The process of investigation and analysis in the behavioral study of social science ideas, theory, and data will almost inevitably turn up additional relevant social science ideas, theoretical formulations, or data.

For example, if one studies the sociological generation of a piece of psychological science, some quite relevant additional psychological data will very likely come to light. Certainly they will not arise ordinarily by means of repeating the exact same psychological experiment that led to the original piece of psychological science. That presumably has already been done, and the results of replication have already been the same, so that indeed the piece of psychology has been warranted as scientific. No, additional data will not ordinarily come from the attempt to make an exact re-run of the experiment, but they are likely to come from an examination of the social generation of that experiment. This likelihood is illustrated, I believe, in my examination of the transference diffusion theory and its evolution, even though, of course, it was not an experimental study.[31] In a sense, then, the sociology of knowledge, for example, is apt to have a very significant impact upon the validity of the particular type of social science knowledge that is being investigated.

What, I believe, has generally disturbed scientists and others

31. For a discussion of the vulnerabilities of experimental sociology studies, see Theodore M. Mills, "A Sleeper Variable in Small Group Research: The Experimenter," *Pacific Sociol. Rev.* (1962) 5: 21-28. For some interesting discussions of similar problems in psychological science, see Raymond B. Cattell and John M. Digman, "A Theory of the Structure of Perturbations in Observer Ratings and Questionnaire Data in Personality Research," *Behav. Sci.* (1964) 9: 341-58; and, especially, Robert Rosenthal and Kermit L. Fode, "The Effect of Experimenter Bias on the Performance of the Albino Rat," *Behav. Sci.* (1963) 8: 183-89.

about this whole relational point of view on validity is the fact that it removes an absolute standard for judging the truth of something. Many critics of a relational perspective have pointed out that if one relativizes truth, it is nevertheless relativized to a particular standard, and to point out that that standard too is relative is merely to engage in an infinite regression series. This criticism, however, does not stand examination. The actual relativity of truth is akin to the solution of the Archimedes paradox of going each time only half the distance remaining to a particular goal. Practically speaking, the choices that relativize truth reach an end because their goal is reached in the process of choosing, *for those choices have themselves defined the goal.*

I cannot develop or criticize in technical and systematic epistemological terms the various positions that may be taken on this question; but one does not have to be a subtle philosopher of science to recognize that truth is essentially a matter of incomplete, mutual confirmation of an entire pattern of ideas.[32] The pattern idea itself may change, and then the means of mutual confirmation disappear and a new pattern is substituted. This transformation of truth has, it is true, a certain mysterious and magical quality to it. How awesome and unsettling it is when something we must depend upon daily suddenly disappears and in its place, as with the wizard's enveloping smoke, something else quite unfamiliar materializes. This is, in fact, the reality-transforming experience that the schizophrenic—or the person under LSD—undergoes, and it disturbs in an unearthly way.[33]

---

32. Without specifically concentrating on the issue of truth per se, Chambers ranges widely enough and writes so communicatively that he offers a stimulating introduction to the general problem of the philosophy of knowledge and its behavioral considerations. See Frank P. Chambers, *Perception, Understanding and Society*, London: Sidgwick and Jackson, 1961.

33. In the *Clinical Studies in Psychiatry, op. cit.*, Sullivan's exposition of the schizophrenic experience and its relation to the ordinary processes of life offers a significant clue to the limitations as well as the usefulness of the cognitive operations inherent in science. The compartmentalizations inherent in thought are broken in schizophrenic experience, and this sort of experience is the basis for the liberating effect that the artist, for example, can sometimes find in LSD.

But the conception of truth in science is not and cannot be an everlasting standard; it will change under the analytic eye of the philosopher, and it will change under the impetus of the empirically and theoretically derived ideas of the scientist when he turns up a startlingly different arrangement of the world he has studied. As Alfred North Whitehead warned, we must beware of "the fallacy of the perfect dictionary"—that is, the fallacy that somehow we already have all the basic ideas we need, including a sufficient variety of ideas as to what is truth, knowledge, science, and so on.[34]

This is what Bridgman was insisting when he urged the wholesale generalization of the operational approach. Probably he was insisting on this because he went through the Einsteinian revolution and he saw no reason to suppose that he, or his successors, would not undergo another revolution sometime later, and another, and another. Partly these revolutions must come about by derivations of accepted ideas; that is the ordinary process of scientific development. The logical, rational, and empirical implications of ideas (conceptualized experience) already floating around are followed out, and lo and behold! something quite different has turned up from what anyone had expected. I think what bothered Bridgman was that the process of scientific development might be left to that single possibility —using ideas' already floating around, ideas already accepted if only in the sense that they are definitely thought about as a part of a scientific field. Such ideas are a part of the cultural milieu of the scientist, but perhaps he ought not to be limited by that milieu. So I say, the study of scientific ideas as behavior may have a certain relevance for the validity of those ideas in the sense that such a study tries to transcend the particular cultural limits of the ideas floating around in the milieu, and thus points up the way in which the scientific formulations depend upon

---

34. See the Epilogue in Alfred North Whitehead, *Modes of Thought*, New York: Macmillan, 1938. The mathematization of concepts, however useful to avoid the greater degree of imprecision in verbal concepts, does not exempt one from this fallacy, of course.

the pre-selections made by the milieu that the scientist has grown up in.

Studying Scientific Ideas as Behavior

The model for the usual study of behavioral components in the constructions of science perhaps is exemplified originally in the discovery of the optic reaction time problem in astronomy. Different eyes simply saw different things. The development in astronomy of the so-called personal equation was a means of adjusting to the optic physiology of scientific observation, and Helmholtz in his general studies of reaction time was to opine that all observations might be subject to the necessity of a corrective personal equation. In one of those interesting historical convergences, Marx at the same time was insisting that incomplete or inaccurate knowledge about society was apt to be a matter of the social position of the observer. But in the instance of either Helmholtz' or Marx's problem, the truth could be achieved by some corrective action that would, as it were, purify it out of its mixture with behavioral contaminants.

There is still much to learn about constructions or ideas or observations in science that are, in a sense, distorted by personal, social, and cultural influences. For example, there are studies to be done in the physiology of perception and sensation by which we can understand better the "phi phenomenon" (seeing apparent movement where there is none), the correction of size relations in distance perception, and so on. Similarly, in the differential psychology of the individual, we must learn something about the ethology of ideas, the occurrence at critical periods in human development of differentially influential experiences that shape the future ideational behavior of the individual. And we have still much to learn about the relationship of social position and cultural bias in the selection and promotion of particular scientific theories.[35] Much of the penetration of "irrelevant" factors in the First LSD Project and in the "transference diffusion" theory can be understood this way.

There is another model within which some studies in this new field must be carried out. This second approach does not assume that there is a pure truth to be winnowed from the chaff of historical experience; it assumes rather that there is much— if not everything—about our knowledge of the world that is historically partial. Therefore we need to know as much as possible about the conditions under which historically—that is, in time and in space—a piece of knowledge was arrived at. With such knowledge, we can reinterpret and revise our codings for the world in an ever successive modification of the corpus of knowledge. This particular point of view about the study of ideas is epitomized in the disputes among scholars of history as to whether they ever arrive at a fairly final approximation of truth about an historical event—say, the American War of Independence—or whether the past must always be reinterpreted in the light of perspectives that change as the times change.[36] In the social scientific study of scientific ideas, we may not expect continual, swift change in the basic formulation of truths in science. A certain continuity, luckily, carries the world of science on in a relatively stable manner. The history of the great revolutions in science or its subfields clearly indicate that there are social and cultural forces that maintain old perspectives as well as lead to new ones. It is these forces that help to determine what the truth is in science, and if the truth is what the scientist seeks, then he must understand that it includes essential human components.

---

35. See, for example, Nicholas Pastore, *The Nature-Nurture Controversy*, New York: Columbia University Press, 1949.

36. For a recent symposium see Hans Meyerhoff, ed., *The Philosophy of History in Our Time*, New York: Doubleday, 1959.

Appendix

A BIBLIOGRAPHICAL NOTE

THE CONFLICT BETWEEN RESEARCH AND
TREATMENT IN CLINICAL PSYCHIATRY

✍

O F ALL THE potential contending allegiances with which the scientist conducting research with psychiatric patients must find some accommodation, his and others' commitment to the therapeutic welfare of the patient is probably the most salient and the most influential. Yet there are few published materials in psychiatry that even touch upon the potential conflict between research and treatment or between research and general considerations of the patient's therapeutic welfare.[1] There are, for

---

1. An idea of the undeveloped nature of materials on this topic can be gathered merely from the small number of references I shall cite. Although I cannot claim to be clearly exhaustive in this survey and particularly may have overlooked materials in the literature of clinical psychology, I include all items that I have any knowledge of. The briefest and thereby especially illustrative of the lack of elaboration of ideas in this problem area are the following: Harriet E. O'Shea, "Research and Training: Are They Sometimes Sirens Leading Therapy Astray?" *J. Psychol.* (1959) 48: 103-05; Gordon W. Olson, "Reactions to Unidentified Research Medication," *Psychiatry Digest* (1963) 24: 21-27. See also a two-page comment by Alfred H. Stanton, "Relations Between Therapist and Researcher," in Milton Greenblatt, *et al.*, eds., *The Patient and the Mental Hospital*, New York: The Free Press, 1957.

example, no systematic surveys or analyses of the problem and no intensive or extensive observational studies.[2]

The psychiatrist has been fully aware of the intimacy of relations between treatment and research and their potentialities for conflict. For example, Sullivan states: [3]

---

2. There have been significant studies of the problem in nonpsychiatric settings, however. Many such works can be reviewed with profit for possible applications to the problem as it occurs in psychiatric research, but I shall not attempt to analyze this literature. The best empirical study on the problem as it appears in medicine in general was conducted on a metabolic research ward. Renée C. Fox, *Experiment Perilous*, New York: The Free Press, 1959. A thorough survey, from a legal standpoint, of the conflict between research goals and medical responsibilities for patient welfare is provided by Irving Ladimer, "Ethical and Legal Aspects of Medical Research on Human Beings," *J. Pub. Law* (1954) 3: 467-511. This and a number of other useful studies are reprinted with a long bibliography in Irving Ladimer and Roger W. Newman, *Clinical Investigation in Medicine: Legal, Ethical, and Moral Aspects*, Boston: Law-Medicine Research Institute, Boston University, 1963. Listed but not included in this book is an article on the legal aspect of psychiatric drug research in which the authors merely advise the research psychiatrist to get the drug company to take legal responsibility for any malpractice suits. William Furst, M.D., and William Furst, LL.B., "The Medico-Legal Aspects of Psychiatric Research," *Dis. Nerv. Sys.* (1960) 21: 132-34.

The reader is also directed for bibliographies and especially useful treatments to the following: Henry K. Beecher, *Experimentation in Man*, Springfield, Ill.: Charles C Thomas, 1959; Renée C. Fox, "Some Social and Cultural Factors in American Society Conducive to Medical Research on Human Subjects," *Clin. Pharmacol. and Therapeutics* (1960) 1: 423-43; and a symposium in *Science*, "The Problem of Experimentation on Human Beings" (1953) 117: 205-15, which includes papers by Otto Guttentag, Alexander M. Kidd, Michael B. Shimkin, and others. Within the last year or so, considerable controversy has arisen over medical experimentation, and *Science* has maintained a close interest, publishing a number of comments and analyses. A short discussion and a useful bibliography on the topic of personal motivations for clinical research is provided in Robert E. Goldstein, "The Motivations and General Character Structure of the Medical Research Investigator," pp. 170-95, in Roger Hagan, ed., *Selected Papers From Social Sciences 136, 1959* ("*Character and Social Structure in America*"), Cambridge, Mass.: Harvard Printing Office, 1960.

3. Italics in original. Harry Stack Sullivan, "Notes on Investigation, Therapy, and Education, in Psychiatry and Their Relations to Schizophrenia," *Psychiatry* (1947) 10: 271-80. Sullivan's carefully formulated conception of psychiatry itself and of clinical research are of course implicit determinants of his particular point of view in this paper. See also especially his "Therapeutic Investigations in Schizophrenia," *Psychiatry* (1947) 10: 121-25; and *Schizophrenia as a Human Process* (with Introduction and

To those who can reasonably aspire to becoming psychiatric *scientists* let me say that there is no purely psychiatric research except it be therapeutic. No one can secure data on interpersonal relations by the route of uncorrected error.

He goes on to insist that mistakes are inevitable but that the worker must learn from them by trying a modification that can be successful the next time. He sees the schizophrenic patient as particularly important as a research subject but warns that this patient is terribly vulnerable to anxiety just when he may be most communicably lucid and that, therefore, disastrous accidents can occur. He concludes, "With the bitterest feeling about the human cost involved, I have to say that the testing ground" for psychiatry is nevertheless therapy with schizophrenics.

Despite such specific statements of the critical and excruciating situations in which the psychiatrist and his patient may find themselves, there are only a very few meaningful examinations of the conflict between the two sets of values, research and treatment. Among the most important of these are reports of various conferences in which the participants specifically addressed themselves to their common problems in this matter. Two conference reports in particular afford a broad range of points of view, and in the context of these, one can place the other scattered papers.

What I believe is the first extensive commentary on the problem appeared in the proceedings of a round-table discussion held at the American Orthopsychiatric Association meetings in 1946.[4] Five or six years later, under grants from the National

---

4. See "Problems in Clinical Research: Round Table, 1946," *Amer. J. Orthopsychiat.* (1947) 17: 196-230. I will refer to this hereafter as "Problems" (1947).

Commentaries by Helen Swick Perry), New York: W. W. Norton & Company, 1962. For a statement on experimenter-induced emotional disturbance, compare Bernard Bressler, *et al.*, "Research in Human Subjects and the Artificial Traumatic Neurosis: Where Does Our Responsibility Lie?" *Amer. J. Psychiat.* (1959) 116: 522-26. Robert A. Cohen and Mabel Blake Cohen describe frankly some of the problems that they have experienced in a number of research projects in which psychotherapeutic aims were important. Robert A. Cohen and Mabel B. Cohen, "Research in Psychotherapy: A Preliminary Report," *Psychiatry* (1961) 24: 46-61.

Institute of Mental Health, a series of conferences was held to discuss many problems of psychiatric research, including the conflict. These conferences were summarized and analyzed in a book by Margaret Barron Luszki.[5] In dealing with these two reports, for purposes of clarity, I shall refer to participants in the latter set of conferences as *NIMH conferees* and to participants in the orthopsychiatric round table discussion as *Orthopsychiatric discussants*, although some of the same people participated in both the NIMH and Orthopsychiatric Association meetings.

The NIMH conferees located the problem primarily in relations between team members;[6] by contrast, the Orthopsychiatric discussants located the problem primarily within the clinical researcher himself. The NIMH conferees saw the conflict of research vs. service (or more particularly research vs. treatment) as personified in competing team members, in which the medical members of the team ordinarily represented treatment values and the nonmedical members represented research values.[7] In other words, the NIMH conferees defined the conflict primarily as a replay of the long history of difficulties between clinicians and nonclinicians in medical research. Orthopsychiatric discussants recognized that there might be differences of approach among various clinical research personnel, but to the discussants the conflict mainly resided in the role of the clinical researcher. I would guess that the difference in the perspectives of the two

5. Margaret B. Luszki, *Interdisciplinary Team Research: Methods and Problems*, New York: New York University Press for the National Training Laboratories, 1958. I shall refer to this hereafter as Luszki (1958). NIMH also sponsored an "Institute on Training for Research of Psychiatric Residents," *q.v.*

6. Luszki summarizes the general feeling of the conferees: "Perhaps the most serious problem [in interdisciplinary collaboration], with the most far-reaching implications in the mental health field, is that of research versus service." Luszki (1958), p. 87.

7. Occasionally the interests of the patient might be more strongly upheld by nonmedical members, according to some conferees. Interestingly, one physician claimed that the medical psychiatrist would have no anxiety about doing research on patients if the nonmedical team members would not get anxious and transmit their anxiety to the psychiatrist. *Ibid.*, pp. 93*ff*. Cf. Howard E. Mitchell and Emily M. Mudd, "Anxieties Associated with the Conduct of Research in a Clinical Setting," *Amer. J. Orthopsychiat.* (1957) 27: 310-30.

reports is partly a function of increasing recognition of the complexity of the problem.

Depending upon where the problem was located, different solutions were proposed. Orthopsychiatric discussants, as one might expect, were likely to suggest solutions that depended upon adjustments made by the clinical researcher himself, that is, by the research psychiatrist primarily. For example, Lawrence S. Kubie at the Orthopsychiatric meeting felt that the researcher in psychiatry must give up most experimentation, more so than in internal medicine.[8] The NIMH conferees, by contrast, often suggested intrateam solutions, such as improved mutual understanding of team members' varying points of view, or lodging medical responsibility for patients in someone other than the team psychiatrist, so that the psychiatrist has no more authority on the team than other team members, and so on.[9]

The NIMH conferees began with the assumption that research functions and treatment functions were apt to be separated in situations in which the nonmedical researchers scrutinized either patients or the clinical setting itself, in collaboration with the psychiatrists and other clinicians carrying on treatment. Some of the Orthopsychiatric discussants came to the same point by concluding that the resolution of the conflict required separation of research and treatment functions so that the research psychiatrist would not have to experience the conflict.[10] Other Orthopsychiatric discussants maintained that such separation was impossible, even though they saw a basic conflict between therapeutic values and research values.[11]

The solutions proposed by workers in the field fall into two

---

8. In "Problems" (1947), pp. 202-203.

9. Luszki (1958), pp. 97ff. Another suggestion was that "research versus service problems can be largely overcome by knowing what the other person's business is, respecting it, and not being threatened by it," *ibid.*, p. 101.

10. For example, Lawrence S. Kubie and Margaret Mead, in "Problems" (1947). In one passage, Mead insists that one must not separate research and treatment, but by this she means that she opposes foregoing research about treatment, *ibid.*, p. 227.

11. For example, Kurt Goldstein, in "Problems" (1947). In the same round table, Margaret Brenman and Merton Gill also insist upon the concomitant conduct of research and treatment by the same practitioner.

classes: *technical* (that is, research maneuvers) and *social* (that is, organizational or interpersonal). Among the proposed technical recommendations are that the researcher (a) give up experimentation (Kubie, as previously mentioned); (b) conduct case studies in which the individual is studied statistically, rather than conduct a survey of groups (Henry A. Murray); [12] (c) use only naturalistic observation without any attempt to introduce changes for research purposes (Margaret Mead); [13] (d) avoid some types of rigorous basic studies, "such as Ph.D. theses," in favor of applied studies (George E. Gardner); [14] (e) restrict research to case studies, of a naturalistic sort (Brenman and Gill); [15] (f) complete the treatment before examining the patient's case for research purposes (Freud); [16] and (g) avoid manipulations of human behavior to obtain control cases and instead use natural control cases.[17] All these technical suggestions have a certain *ad hoc* quality. There is only one theme that seems to run through all of them: *Keep as much distance as possible between research functions and therapeutic functions.*

The other class of solutions—by social means—includes various recommendations that also seem to imply a clear separation of the two functions. Some NIMH conferees thought that there should be a redistribution of role functions for the research team whenever trouble arose; others emphasized that clinicians ought not to be expected to do very much to further a psychiatric research project and even that the research should be carried out entirely by nonclinicians. Margaret Mead at the Orthopsyciatric round table also held to this position. Kubie insisted at the Orthopsychiatric round table in 1946 and again at an institute in 1959 that research in psychiatry ought to be carried

---

12. "Problems" (1947), pp. 224f.
13. "Problems" (1947), p. 227.
14. George E. Gardner, "Clinical Research in a Child Psychiatry Setting," *Amer. J. Orthopsychiat.* (1956) 26: 330-39.
15. "Problems" (1947), p. 219.
16. Sigmund Freud, "Recommendations for Physicians on the Psychoanalytic Method of Treatment," pp. 312-22, in *Collected Papers*, Vol. II; London: Hogarth Press, 1933.
17. Luszki (1958), p. 99.

out by persons who had had therapeutic experience but who did not, while conducting research, have therapy obligations.[18] Birren warns from his experience in studies of aging that one should be "on guard against placing an investigator in an ambiguous position by requiring that he be both a clinician interested in the well-being of the specific patient and also in making a general contribution to the research." He urges, "So far as possible the dual role of clinician and researcher should be separated." [19] The same theme of distance runs through most of this second class of solutions for the conflict. At the same time, most commentators seem to take it for granted that at least some clinicians will continue somehow to conduct research in the course of carrying out therapeutic obligations. Dunbar urges certain operations by which the private practitioner can conduct research with his patients economically in the regular course of his practice.[20] Of course, most psychoanalytic research is carried out by private practitioners on their private patients, following the model provided by Freud, although it is doubtful that they follow his recommendation to postpone research until the patient is discharged.[21]

In summary, two types of solutions are proposed in the literature: technical and social. Which solution among these two types is emphasized appears to be related to the way in which the conflict is defined. If the conflict is seen as a problem that arises between professionals, then proposed solutions, technical or social, have to do with the distribution of functions among them. If the conflict is conceptualized primarily as a personal

18. "Problems" (1947); and Lawrence S. Kubie, "The Making of the Behavioral Scientist," paper prepared for and reported in "The Institute on the Training for Research of Psychiatric Residents," *op. cit.*

19. James E. Birren, "Problems in the Design of Multidisciplinary Research," paper presented at Veterans Administration Conference, Baltimore, May 11, 1956.

20. Flanders Dunbar, "Research in Private Practice," *Amer. J. Psychiat.* (1950-51) 107: 739-42.

21. Freud, *op. cit.* Cf., however, reports of the Menninger study of psychotherapy. Esp. Bernard H. Hall and Robert S. Wallerstein, "Operational Problems of Psychotherapy Research: II. Termination Studies," *Bull. Menn. Clin.* (1960) 24: 190-216.

experience of the researcher, quite apart from his colleagues, then the recommended solutions, technical or social, tend to emphasize adjustments that the researcher himself can make. Whatever the definition of the conflict and whatever the proposed solution, there is a tendency among most commentators to suggest by implication or by explicit formulation that the conflict should be minimized by solutions that keep research and treatment separate and distant from each other. This contrasts sharply with the formulations and recommendations I have proposed in this book.

The fact that most commentators tend toward a position on the conflict quite different from that taken in this book is not, I believe, particularly significant. No one has yet analyzed systematically the full range of potential clinical research activities and the full range of potential therapeutic activities to show how these two sets of activities offer potential combinations that are mutually antagonistic or mutually supportive.[22] Yet obviously the different kinds of research activity and of treatment procedures would have different implications for both the role relations of the researcher and the technical maneuvers in the research and in the treatment processes. For example, as my examination of the First LSD Project and the Permissive Ward Project indicated, a research technique (in that case, the use of a drug) has different meanings and different conflict potentials depending upon whether or not the technique is viewed as a therapeutic device as well as a research device. When the investigations

---

22. My own comments in this book do not represent a full and systematic analysis, which, in the first place, would require considerations of physiological and biological factors in which I am not competent. Yet even these factors are mixed up with social and psychological forces, as Jay L. Hoffman's comments on research upon the tranquilizers indicate. He takes the position, for example, that the use of tranquilizers is so demanding of time and services in a public hospital (just passing out the pills and keeping track of newly active patients) that no research should be attempted in many such hospitals. See his "Critique," in Jonathan O. Cole and Ralph W. Gerard, eds., *Psychopharmacology: Problems in Evaluation*, Washington, D.C.: National Research Council, 1959.

have no direct therapeutic meaning either for the patient immediately concerned or for patients in the future, the problems of conflict are much different.[23]

Rashkis comes closest to an examination of different possible combinations with different conflict potentials, but his remarks are of limited use. He distinguishes three types of clinical research in psychiatry: experimentation for the comparison of therapies, naturalistic observations of social relations on the psychiatric ward, and tests and measurements of psychophysical variables. There are certainly other types of investigations and investigative techniques that have been and are currently being used with psychiatric patients—as my case studies indicate. Nevertheless, Rashkis believes that only research with an experimental design for the evaluation of therapies will pose major conflict on actions with respect to the patients or the ward problems. By conflict, he seems to mean a difference in opinion between a psychiatrist conducting research and a psychiatrist charged with therapeutic responsibility for the research patient. This is, of course, the definition that some others have used of the conflict: a problem in team relations. Rashkis' solution is to put the research physician in total charge of the ward and patients. The summary I have given of other commentators on this problem alone demonstrates that the conflict is a good deal more complex than Rashkis would suggest.[24]

A differentiation of treatment techniques in the course of a particular research activity is as necessary as a careful differentiation of research techniques. For example, most psychoanalysts apparently conclude that psychoanalysis is automatically transformed into something else if certain systematic studies are undertaken upon it. Procedures like metabolic tests before and after the psychoanalytic hour or the use of one-way observational windows for viewing the analysis in progress will cause

23. Gardner, op. cit. See also Juliana Day, "The Role and Reaction of the Psychiatrist in LSD Therapy," J. Nerv. Ment. Dis. (1957) 125: 437-38.

24. Harold A. Rashkis, "Does Clinical Research Interfere with Treatment," Arch. Gen. Psychiat. (1961) 4: 105-108.

a degeneration of the treatment process, they believe.[25] Specifically then, there is a radical incompatibility, in their eyes, of psychoanalytic treatment, as a type of therapy, with any type of research procedure that involves actions other than those that the analyst ordinarily takes himself in the course of the treatment.[26]

Assuming that he has indeed discovered incompatibilities between a certain therapeutic procedure and a certain research procedure, the clinical researcher must then assess the relative merits and liabilities of substitute therapies or substitute research procedures that might be used as a means of handling the conflict. For example, the psychoanalyst may reason that pure psychoanalysis is the only psychotherapeutic technique indicated for the patient or preferred by the physician, and therefore the research procedures must be changed. Or he may reason that for certain cases, the form of psychotherapy into which psychoanalysis is transformed under certain research conditions is a fully acceptable substitute therapy.

---

25. For example, "a contaminated analysis," because of research procedures, is no longer psychoanalysis, according to L. J. Roose, "The Influence of Psychosomatic Research on the Psychoanalytic Process," *J. Amer. Psa. Assoc.* (1960) 8: 317-34. See also the following: H. M. Fox, "Effect of Psychophysiologic Research on the Transference," *J. Amer. Psa. Assoc.* (1958) 6: 413-32; T. R. Miles, "I. Experimentalists and Therapists: The Dynamics of a Conflict Situation," *Brit. J. Med. Psychol.* (1961) 34: 1-6; D. H. Malan, "III. On the Clinical and Objective Approaches to Psychodynamic Material," *Brit. J. Med. Psychol.* (1961) 34: 15-21. Cf. Rae Shifrin Sternberg, *et al.,* "Psychotherapy Research and the Problem of Intrusions on Privacy," *Psychiatry* (1958) 21: 195-203; and Kenneth Mark Colby, *An Introduction to Psychoanalytic Research,* New York: Basic Books, 1960. A good discussion of the reluctance of the psychotherapist to conduct research is given in Clyde H. Ward, "Psychotherapy Research: Dilemmas and Directions," *Arch. Gen. Psychiat.* (1964) 10: 596-622.

26. Early in the history of American psychoanalysis, in 1932, the incompatibility of research and psychoanalysis was apparently considered so complete that a member of the New York Institute was forbidden by his fellow psychoanalysts to continue his practice of recording his interviews. This story is reported by John Dollard and Frank Auld, Jr. (*Scoring Human Motives,* New Haven: Yale University Press, 1959), according to Ward, *op. cit.*

Technical distinctions such as these will enable the research psychiatrist to select from among technical responses to the conflict; and the differentiation of social responses will also make possible a more considered selection of the organizational and interpersonal means of dealing with the conflict. Facilitation of the participation of physician and patient in clinical research will require such distinctions, as a minimum. The literature on the topic does not supply this minimum.

REFERENCES CITED*

Alexander, Franz. "Evaluation of Statistical and Analytical Methods in Psychiatry and Psychology," *Amer. J. Orthopsychiat.* (1934) 4: 433-48.

American Psychiatric Association. *Training the Psychiatrist to Meet Changing Needs.* (Report of the Conference on Graduate Psychiatric Education, 1962.) Washington, D.C.: American Psychiatric Association, 1964.

Angell, Robert. "A Critical Review of the Development of the Personal Document Method in Sociology: 1920-1940," in Louis Gottschalk, *et al.*, *The Use of Personal Documents in History, Anthropology and Sociology.* (Social Science Research Council Bulletin 53.) Washington, D.C.: Social Science Research Council, 1945.

Asch, Solomon E. "Studies of Independence and Conformity: I. A Minority of One Against a Unanimous Majority," *Psychol. Monogr.* (1956) 70, No. 9 (Whole No. 416).

Atherton, Lewis. "The Research Center in Entrepreneurial History: A Personal Appraisal," *Explorations in Entrepreneurial History* (1954) 7: 105-10.

Back, Kurt W. "The Game and the Myth as Two Languages of Social Science," *Behav. Sci.* (1963) 8: 66-71.

Bakan, David. *Sigmund Freud and the Jewish Mystical Tradition.* Princeton, N.Y.: D. Van Nostrand Co., 1958.

Baldwin, Alfred. "The Study of Child Behavior and Development," in Paul H. Mussen, ed., *Handbook of Research Methods in Child Development.* New York: John Wiley and Sons, 1960. Also excerpted in Ladimer and Newman, 1963.

Barber, Bernard. *Science and the Social Order.* New York: The Free Press, 1952.

——, and Walter Hirsch, eds. *The Sociology of Science.* New York: The Free Press, 1962.

---

* The more accessible versions of these references are cited here. Initial publication dates are given, if these have been particularly relevant when they were cited in text.

Barzun, Jacques. *The House of Intellect*. New York: Harper & Row, 1959.

Bateson, Gregory. *Naven*. Second edition. Palo Alto: Stanford University Press, 1958.

Becker, Ernest. *Zen: A Rational Critique*. New York: W. W. Norton & Company, 1961.

Beecher, Henry K. *Experimentation in Man*. Springfield, Ill.: Charles C Thomas, 1959.

Ben-David, Joseph. "Roles and Innovations in Medicine," *Amer. J. Sociol.* (1959-60) 65: 557-68.

Bennis, Warren. "The Social Scientist as Research Entrepreneur: A Case Study," *Social Problems* (1955) 2: 44-49.

Beveridge, W. I. B. *The Art of Scientific Investigation*. New York: Random House, Vintage paperback edition, 1961.

Birren, James E. "Problems in the Design of Multidisciplinary Research." Paper presented at Veterans Administration Conference, Baltimore, May 11, 1956.

Blake, Robert R. "The Interaction-Feeling Hypothesis Applied to Psychotherapy Groups," *Sociometry* (1953) 16: 253-65.

Bottomore, T. B., and Maximilien Rubel. *Karl Marx: Selected Writings in Sociology and Social Philosophy*. London: Watts & Co., 1956.

Bressler, Bernard, *et al.* "Research in Human Subjects and the Artificial Traumatic Neurosis: Where Does Our Responsibility Lie?" *Amer. J. Psychiat.* (1959) 116: 522-26. Also excerpted in Ladimer and Newman, 1963.

Bridgman, P. W. *The Logic of Modern Physics*. New York: The Macmillan Company, 1927.

——. *Reflections of a Physicist*. Second edition. New York: Philosophical Library, 1955.

——. "Rejoinders and Second Thoughts," *Psychol. Rev.* (1945) 52: 281-84.

——. *The Way Things Are*. Cambridge, Mass.: Harvard University Press, 1959.

Brown, Roger W. *Words and Things*. New York: The Free Press, 1958.

Bunge, Mario. *Intuition and Science*. Englewood Cliffs, N.J.: Prentice-Hall, 1962.

Burnham, Donald. "Identity Definition and Role Demand in the Hospital Careers of Schizophrenic Patients," *Psychiatry* (1961) 24, Suppl. to No. 2: 96-122.

Cattell, Raymond B., and John M. Digman. "A Theory of the Structure of Perturbations in Observer Ratings and Questionnaire Data in Personality Research," *Behav. Sci.* (1964) 9: 341-58.

Caudill, William. *The Psychiatric Hospital as a Small Society*. Cambridge, Mass.: Harvard University Press, 1958.

Chambers, Frank P. *Perception, Understanding and Society*. London: Sidgwick and Jackson, 1961.

Chance, Erika, and Jack Arnold. "The Effect of Professional Training, Experience, and Preference for a Theoretical System upon Clinical Case Description," *Hum. Relat.* (1960) 13: 195-213.

Chance, Erika, *et al*. "Professional Background and Themes in Clinical Case Description," *Hum. Relat.* (1962) 15: 53-61.

C[obb], S[tanley]. " 'Too Scientific,' " *Amer. J. Psychiat.* (1950-51) 109: 935-36.

Cohen, Robert A., and Mabel B. Cohen. "Research in Psychotherapy: A Preliminary Report," *Psychiatry* (1961) 24: 46-61.

Colby, Kenneth Mark. *An Introduction to Psychoanalytic Research*. New York: Basic Books, 1960.

Cole, Jonathan O., and Ralph W. Gerard, eds. *Psychopharmacology: Problems in Evaluation*. Washington, D.C.: National Academy of Sciences-National Research Council, 1959.

Cole, Jonathan O., and Martin M. Katz. "The Psychotomimetic Drugs: An Overview," *J.A.M.A.* (1964) 187: 758-61. Reprinted in David Solomon, 1964.

Coser, Rose Laub. *Life in the Ward*. East Lansing, Mich.: Michigan State University Press, 1962.

Cottrell, Leonard S., Jr., and Ruth Gallagher. "Developments in Social Psychology, 1930-1940." (Sociometry Monograph No. 1.) New York: Beacon House, 1941.

Davis, Kingsley. "Mental Hygiene and Class Structure," *Psychiatry* (1938) 1: 55-65.

Day, Juliana. "The Role and Reaction of the Psychiatrist in LSD Therapy," *J. Nerv. Ment. Dis.* (1957) 125: 437-38.

de Grazia, Alfred. "A Concept of Scientists and Their Organization," *Amer. Behav. Scientist* (1962) 6: 30-34.

Devereux, George. "Cultural Thought Models in Primitive and Modern Psychiatric Theories," *Psychiatry* (1958) 21: 359-74.

——. "Practical Problems of Conceptual Psychiatric Research," *Psychiatry* (1952) 15: 189-92.

Dollard, John, and Frank Auld, Jr., *Scoring Human Motives*. New Haven: Yale University Press, 1959.

Dunbar, Flanders. "Research in Private Practice," *Amer. J. Psychiat.* (1950-51) 107: 739-42.

Dunlap, Jane, pseud. *Exploring Inner Space: Personal Experiences Under LSD-25*. New York: Harcourt, Brace & World, 1961.

Durkheim, Emile. *Division of Labor in Society*. George Simpson, tr. New York: The Macmillan Co., 1933. French edition, 1893.

Engels, Frederich. *Herr Eugen Dühring's Revolution in Science* [*Anti-Dühring*]. Emile Burns, tr. C. P. Dutt, ed. Moscow and Leningrad: Cooperative Publishing Society of Foreign Workers in the U.S.S.R., 1934.

Erikson, Erik H. "Ego Identity and the Psychosocial Moratorium," in Helen L. Witmer and Ruth Kotinsky, eds., *New Perspectives for Research on Juvenile Delinquency*. (Children's Bureau Publication No. 356.) Washington, D.C.: Department of Health, Education and Welfare, 1956.

[Faculty Committee]. *The Behavioral Sciences at Harvard*. Cambridge, Mass.: Harvard University, 1954.

Fox, H. M. "Effect of Psychophysiologic Research on the Transference," *J. Amer. Psa. Assoc.* (1958) 6: 412-32.

Fox, Renée C. *Experiment Perilous*. New York: The Free Press, 1959.

——. "Medical Scientists in a Chateau," *Science* (May 11, 1962) 136: 476-83.

——. "Some Social and Cultural Factors in American Society Conducive to Medical Research on Human Subjects," *Clin. Pharmacol. and Therapeutics* (1960) 1: 423-43. Also excerpted in Ladimer and Newman, 1963.

Freud, Sigmund. "Recommendations for Physicians on the Psychoanalytic Method of Treatment (1912)," in *Collected Papers*, Vol. II. London: Hogarth Press, 1933.

Furst, William, M.D., and William Furst, LL.B. "The Medico-Legal Aspects of Psychiatric Research," *Dis. Nerv. Sys.* (1960) 21: 132-34.

Galdston, Iago, ed. *Freud and Contemporary Culture*. New York: International Universities Press, 1957.

——, ed. *Man's Image in Medicine and Anthropology*. New York: International Universities Press, 1963.

Gardner, George E. "Clinical Research in a Child Psychiatry Setting," *Amer. J. Orthopsychiat.* (1956) 26: 330-39.

Gilbert, Doris C. "Ideologies Concerning Mental Illness." Unpublished doctoral dissertation, Harvard University, 1954.

Gill, Merton, *et al. The Initial Interview in Psychiatric Practice*. New York: International Universities Press, 1954.

Glaser, Barney G. *Organizational Scientists*. Indianapolis: The Bobbs-Merrill Co., 1964.

——. "Recognition in Scientists' Careers," *Social Problems* (1962-63) 10: 268-76.

Glover, Edward. "Research Methods in Psycho-analysis," *Int. J. Psa.* (1952) 33: 403-09.

Goffman, Erving. *Asylums*. Garden City, N.Y.: Doubleday & Company, 1961.

———. *The Presentation of Self in Everyday Life.* (Monograph No. 2.) Edinburgh: University of Edinburgh Social Sciences Research Centre, 1956. Garden City, N.Y.: Doubleday & Company, Anchor edition, 1959.

———. "Role Distance," in *Encounters: Two Studies in the Sociology of Interaction.* Indianapolis: The Bobbs-Merrill Co., 1961.

Goldstein, Robert E. "The Motivations and General Character Structure of the Medical Research Investigator," in Roger Hagan, ed., *Selected Papers From Social Sciences 136, 1959,* ("Character and Social Structure in America"). Cambridge, Mass.: Harvard Printing Office, 1960.

Greenblatt, Milton, *et al.,* eds. *The Patient and the Mental Hospital.* New York: The Free Press, 1957.

Gregg, Alan. "When to Change Jobs—And Why," *Harper's Magazine* (August, 1955) 211: 71-76.

Grinker, Roy R. "Lysergic Acid Diethylamide," *Arch. Gen. Psychiat.* (1963) 8: 425.

Gross, Neal, *et al., Explorations in Role Analysis.* New York: John Wiley & Sons, 1957.

Group for the Advancement of Psychiatry. *Some Observations on Controls in Psychiatric Research.* (Report #42.) New York: Group for the Advancement of Psychiatry, 1959.

Hagstrom, Warren O. *The Scientific Community.* New York: Basic Books, 1965.

Hall, Bernard H., and Robert S. Wallerstein. "Operational Problems of Psychotherapy Research: II. Termination Studies," *Bull. Menn. Clin.* (1960) 24: 190-216.

Henry, Jules. "The Formal Social Structure of a Psychiatric Hospital," *Psychiatry* (1954) 17: 139-51.

———. "Types of Institutional Structure," *Psychiatry* (1957) 20: 47-60.

Hill, Austin B. "Medical Ethics and Controlled Trials," *Brit. Med. J.* (1963) 1: 1043-49.

Hoffman, Jay L. "Critique," in Jonathan O. Cole and Ralph W. Gerard, eds., *Psychopharmacology: Problems in Evaluation.* Washington, D.C.: National Academy of Sciences-National Research Council, 1959.

Homans, George C. *The Human Group.* New York: Harcourt, Brace & World, 1950.

Hook, Sidney, ed. *Psychoanalysis: Scientific Method and Philosophy.* New York: Grove Press, Evergreen edition, 1960.

"The Institute on Training for Research of Psychiatric Residents (Fort Lauderdale, Florida, April 10-11, 1959)." Mimeographed for the National Institute of Mental Health, Bethesda, Maryland, 1960.

Joravsky, David. "Soviet Scientists and the Great Break," in Bernard Barber and Walter Hirsch, eds. *The Sociology of Science*. New York: The Free Press, 1962.

Kaplan, Abraham. *The Conduct of Inquiry*. San Francisco: Chandler Publishing Co., 1964.

Kaufman, M. Ralph. "Psychoanalysis in Medicine," *Bull. Amer. Psychoanal. Assoc.* (1951) 7: 1-12.

Kluckhohn, Florence R., and Fred L. Strodtbeck. *Variations in Value Orientations*. New York: Harper & Row, 1961.

Kubie, Lawrence S. "Some Unsolved Problems of the Scientific Career," *American Scientist* (1953) 41: 596-613; (1954) 42: 104-12. Reprinted in Barber and Hirsch, 1962.

——. "The Making of the Behavioral Scientist." Paper prepared for Institute on the Training for Research of Psychiatric Residents, Fort Lauderdale, 1959. Mimeographed with Institute proceedings, 1960.

Kuhn, Thomas S. *The Structure of Scientific Revolutions*. (Vol. II, No. 2, *International Encyclopedia of Unified Science*.) Chicago: University of Chicago Press, 1962. Phoenix paperback edition, 1964.

Labedz, Leopold. "How Free is Soviet Science? Technology under Totalitarianism," in Bernard Barber and Walter Hirsch, eds., *The Sociology of Science*. New York: The Free Press, 1962.

Ladimer, Irving. "Ethical and Legal Aspects of Medical Research on Human Beings," *J. Pub. Law* (1954) 3: 467-511. Also excerpted in Ladimer and Newman, 1963.

——, and Roger W. Newman, eds. *Clinical Investigation in Medicine: Legal, Ethical, and Moral Aspects*. Boston: Law-Medicine Research Institute, Boston University, 1963.

Landy, David H. "The Anthropologist and the Mental Hospital," *Hum. Org.* (1958) 17: 30-35.

Lasswell, Harold D., and Dorothy Blumenstock. *World Revolutionary Propaganda*. New York: Alfred A. Knopf, 1939.

Lerner, Max. *America as a Civilization*. New York: Simon and Schuster, 1957.

Lewin, Bertram D., and Helen Ross. *Psychoanalytic Education in the United States*. New York: W. W. Norton & Company, 1960.

Little, Ralph B., and Edward A. Strecker. "Moot Questions in Psychiatric Ethics," *Amer. J. Psychiat.* (1956) 113: 455-60.

Lundberg, George A. "The Place of Supra-Empirical Statements in Sociology," *Sociol. Inquiry* (1961) 31: 117-27.

Luszki, Margaret Barron. *Interdisciplinary Team Research: Methods and Problems*. New York: New York University Press for the National Training Laboratories, 1958.

Mainland, Donald. "The Clinical Trial—Some Difficulties and Suggestions," *J. Chronic Dis.* (1960) 11: 484-96.

Malan, D. H. "III. On the Clinical and Objective Aproaches to Psychodynamic Material," *Brit. J. Med. Psychol.* (1961) 34: 15-21.

Malinowski, Bronislaw. *Crime and Custom in Savage Society.* New York: Harcourt, Brace & World, 1926.

Mannheim, Karl. *Ideology and Utopia* (with Introduction by Louis Wirth). Louis Wirth and Edward Shils, trs. New York: Harcourt, Brace & World, 1936.

Marx, Karl. *A Contribution to the Critique of Political Economy.* N. I. Stone, tr. New York: International Library Publishing Co., 1904.

——, and Friedrich Engels. *The German Ideology.* R. Pascal, ed. New York: International Publishers Co., 1947.

Maslow, A. H. "Problem-Centering Vs. Means-Centering in Science," *Philos. Sci.* (1946) 13: 326-31.

May, Rollo, *et al.,* eds. *Existence: A New Dimension in Psychiatry and Psychology.* New York: Basic Books, 1958.

McEwen, William J. "Position Conflict and Professional Orientation in a Research Organization," *Adminis. Sci. Quart.* (1956) 1: 208-24.

——. *The Problem of Social Scientific Knowledge.* Totowa, N.J.: The Bedminster Press, 1963.

Merton, Robert K. "Introduction" to "Part IV: Studies in the Sociology of Science"; "Manifest and Latent Functions"; "Science and Economy of 17th Century England" (Based on publications in 1938 and 1939); and "The Sociology of Knowledge," all in *Social Theory and Social Structure.* Revised and enlarged edition. New York: The Free Press, 1957.

——. "The Role-Set: Problems in Sociological Theory," *Brit. J. Sociol.* (1957) 8: 106-20.

Meyerhoff, Hans, ed. *The Philosophy of History in Our Time.* New York: Doubleday & Company, 1959.

Miles, T. R. "I. Experimentalists and Therapists: The Dynamics of a Conflict Situation," *Brit. J. Med. Psychol.* (1961) 34: 1-6.

Mills, C. Wright. "The Professional Ideology of the Social Pathologists," *Amer. J. Sociol.* (1943) 49: 165-80.

Mills, Theodore M. "A Sleeper Variable in Small Group Research: The Experimenter," *Pacific Sociol. Rev.* (1962) 5: 21-28.

Mitchell, Howard E., and Emily H. Mudd. "Anxieties Associated with the Conduct of Research in a Clinical Setting," *Amer. J. Orthopsychiat.* (1957) 27: 310-30.

Mitscherlich, Alexander, and Fred Mielke. *Doctors of Infamy*. Heinz Norden, tr. New York: Henry Schuman, 1949.

Nagel, Ernest. "Malicious Philosophies of Science," in Bernard Barber and Walter Hirsch, eds., *The Sociology of Science*. New York: The Free Press, 1962.

Newland, Constance A. *My Self and I*. New York: Coward-McCann, 1963.

Nisbet, Robert A. "Conservatism and Sociology," *Amer. J. Sociol.* (1952) 58: 167-75.

——. "The French Revolution and the Rise of Sociology," *Amer. J. Sociol.* (1943) 49: 156-64.

Northrup, F. S. C., "The Raison d'Etre of the Inquiry," in F. S. C. Northrup and Helen H. Livingston, eds., *Cross-Cultural Understanding: Epistemological Anthropology*. New York: Harper & Row, 1964.

Olson, Gordon W. "Reactions to Unidentified Research Medication," *Psychiatry Digest* (1963) 24: 21-27.

O'Shea, Harriet E. "Research and Training: Are They Sometimes Sirens Leading Therapy Astray?" *J. Psychol.* (1959) 48: 103-105.

Parsons, Talcott. "Introduction" to Part Four, "Culture and the Social System," in Parsons, *et al.*, eds., *Theories of Society*. Vol. II. New York: The Free Press, 1961.

——. "On the Concept of Political Power," *Proc. Amer. Philos. Soc.* (1963) 107: 232-62.

——. *The Social System*. New York: The Free Press, 1951.

Pastore, Nicholas. *The Nature-Nurture Controversy*. New York: Columbia University Press, 1949.

Perry, Stewart E. "Notes on the Role of the National," *Conflict Resolution* (1957) 1: 346-63. Reprinted in James N. Rosenau, ed. *International Politics and Foreign Policy*. New York: The Free Press, 1961.

——. "Observations on Social Processes in Psychiatric Research," *Behav. Sci.* (1956) 1: 290-302.

——. "Social Processes in Psychiatric Research." Unpublished doctoral dissertation, Harvard University, 1963.

——, and Helen Swick Perry. "A Report on the Major Areas of Interest and Emergent Findings of the Institute on Training for Research of Psychiatric Residents." Mimeographed with Institute proceedings, 1960.

Perry, Stewart E., and Gertrude N. Shea. "Social Controls and Psychiatric Theory in a Ward Setting," *Psychiatry* (1957) 20: 221-47.

Perry, Stewart E., and Lyman C. Wynne. "Role Conflict, Role Redefinition, and Social Change in a Clinical Research Organization," *Social Forces* (1959) 38: 62-65.

Polansky, Norman, Ronald Lippitt, and Fritz Redl. "An Investigation of Behavioral Contagion in Groups," *Hum. Relat.* (1950) 3: 319-48.

"The Problem of Experimentation on Human Beings," (A Symposium), *Science* (1953) 117: 205-15. Also excerpted in Ladimer and Newman, 1963.

"Problems in Clinical Research: Round Table, 1946," *Amer. J. Orthopsychiat.* (1947) 17: 196-230.

"Psychoanalytic Education," *J. Amer. Psa. Assoc.* (1962) 10: 118-65.

Pumpian-Mindlin, E., ed. *Psychoanalysis as Science.* New York: Basic Books, 1956, new edition.

Rapoport, Robert N. *Community as Doctor: New Perspectives on a Therapeutic Community.* Springfield, Ill.: Charles C Thomas, 1961.

——. "Notes on the Disparagement of 'Sociologizing' in Collaborative Research," *Hum. Org.* (1957) 16: 14-15.

Rashkis, Harold A. "Cognitive Restructuring: Why Research Is Therapy," *Arch. Gen. Psychiat.* (1960) 2: 612-21.

——. "Does Clinical Research Interfere with Treatment?" *Arch. Gen. Psychiat.* (1961) 4: 105-108.

Reid, John R., and Jacob E. Finesinger. "Inference Testing in Psychotherapy," *Amer. J. Psychiat.* (1950-51) 109: 894-900.

Richfield, Jerome. "The Scientific Status of Psychoanalysis," in Philipp Frank, ed., *The Validation of Scientific Theories.* Boston: Beacon Press, 1957.

Riesman, David. *Constraint and Variety in American Education.* Lincoln, Nebr.: University of Nebraska Press, 1956.

Riessman, Frank, *et al.*, eds. *Mental Health of the Poor: New Treatment Approaches for Low-Income People.* New York: The Free Press, 1964.

Romney, A. Kimball, and Roy Goodwin D'Andrade, eds. "Transcultural Studies in Cognition (Report of a Conference Sponsored by Social Science Research Council Committee on Intellective Processes Research)," *Amer. Anthro.* (1964) 66, Part 2: 1-253.

Roose, L. J. "The Influence of Psychosomatic Research on the Psychoanalytic Process," *J. Amer. Psa. Assoc.* (1960) 8: 317-34.

Rosenthal, Robert, and Kermit L. Fode. "The Effect of Experimenter Bias on the Performance of the Albino Rat," *Behav. Sci.* (1963) 8: 183-89.

Ruesch, Jurgen. "The Trouble with Psychiatric Research," *Arch. Neurol. Psychiat.* (1957) 77: 93-107.

——, and Gregory Bateson. *Communication: The Social Matrix of*

Psychiatry. New York: W. W. Norton & Company, 1951.

Ruesch, Jurgen, and A. Rodney Prestwood. "Anxiety: Its Initiation, Communication and Interpersonal Management," *Arch. Neurol. Psychiat.* (1949) 62: 527-50.

Sarbin, Theodore R. "Role Theory," in Gardner Lindzey, ed., *Handbook of Social Psychology.* Vol. I. Cambridge, Mass.: Addison-Wesley Publishing Co., 1954.

Savage, Charles. "LSD: A Clinical-Psychological Study," *Amer. J. Psychiat.* (1952) 108: 896-900.

——. "The LSD Psychosis as a Transaction between the Psychiatrist and Patient," in Louis Cholden, ed., *Lysergic Acid Diethylamide and Mescalin in Experimental Psychiatry.* New York: Grune & Stratton, 1956.

——. "Variations in Ego Feeling Induced by LSD," *Psychoan. Rev.* (1955) 42: 1-16.

Schachtel, Ernest G. "The Development of Focal Attention and the Emergence of Reality" and "On Memory and Childhood Amnesia," in *Metamorphosis.* New York: Basic Books, 1959.

Schaffer, Leslie, and Leila C. Deasy. "Deference, Social Mobility, and Conflict in Psychiatric Settings." Paper presented at the meetings of the American Sociological Society, Washington, D.C., 1957.

——. "Social Mobility and the Value Context of Psychiatry." Paper presented at the meetings of the American Psychiatric Association, San Francisco, 1958.

Schoenfeld, C. G. "Three Fallacious Attacks Upon Psychoanalysis as Science," *Psychoan. and the Psa. Rev.* (1962) 49: 35-47.

Searles, Harold F. "The Informational Value of the Supervisor's Emotional Experience," *Psychiatry* (1955) 18: 135-46.

Seely, John R. "Social Values, the Mental Hygiene Movement and Mental Health," *Annals Amer. Acad. Pol. Social Sci.* (March, 1953) 286: 15-25.

Selye, Hans. *From Dream to Discovery: On Being a Scientist.* New York: McGraw-Hill Book Company, 1964.

Shepard, Herbert A. "Patterns of Organization for Applied Research and Development," *J. Business* (1956) 29: 52-61.

——. "Superiors and Subordinates in Research," *J. Business* (1956) 29: 261-67.

Shils, Edward A., and Henry A. Finch, trs. and eds. *Max Weber on the Methodology of the Social Sciences.* New York: The Free Press, 1949.

Shryock, Richard H. *The Development of Modern Medicine.* New York: Alfred A. Knopf, 1947.

Smith, Alfred G. "The Dionysian Innovation," *Amer. Anthro.* (1964) 66: 251-65.

Smith, Harvey L. "Psychiatry: A Social Institution in Process," *Social Forces* (1954-1955) 33: 310-16.

——. "Psychiatry in Medicine: Intra- or Inter-Professional Relationships?" *Amer. J. Sociol.* (1957) 63: 285-89.

Solley, Charles M., and Gardner Murphy. *Development of the Perceptual World.* New York: Basic Books, 1960.

Solomon, David, ed. *LSD: The Consciousness-Expanding Drug.* New York: G. P. Putnam's Sons, 1964.

Sorokin, Pitirim A. *Fads and Foibles in Modern Sociology and Related Sciences.* Chicago: Henry Regnery Co., 1956.

Spiegel, John P. "The Resolution of Role Conflict Within the Family," *Psychiatry* (1957) 20: 1-16. Also in Milton Greenblatt, *et al.*, 1957.

——. "The Social Roles of Doctor and Patient in Psychoanalysis and Psychotherapy," *Psychiatry* (1954) 17: 369-76.

——. "Some Cultural Aspects of Transference and Countertransference," in Jules Masserman, ed., *Individual and Familial Dynamics.* New York: Grune & Stratton, 1959.

"Standards for the Training of Physicians in Psychoanalysis," *Bull. Amer. Psa. Assoc.* (1950) 6: 1-5.

Stanton, Alfred H. "Psychiatric Theory and Institutional Context," *Psychiatry* (1954) 17: 19-26.

——. "Relations Between Therapist and Researcher," in Milton Greenblatt, *et al.*, eds. *The Patient and the Mental Hospital.* New York: The Free Press, 1957.

——, and Morris S. Schwartz. "Medical Opinion and the Social Context in the Mental Hospital," *Psychiatry* (1949) 12: 243-49.

——. *The Mental Hospital.* New York: Basic Books, 1954.

Stark, Werner. *The Fundamental Forms of Social Thought.* London: Routledge and Kegan Paul, 1962.

——. *The Sociology of Knowledge.* New York: The Free Press, 1958.

Stefansson, Vilhjalmur. *The Standardization of Error.* London: Kegan Paul, Trench, Trubner, 1928.

Sternberg, Rae Shifrin, *et al.* "Psychotherapy Research and the Problem of Intrusions on Privacy," *Psychiatry* (1958) 21: 195-203.

Stouffer, Samuel A. *Communism, Conformity, and Civil Liberties.* New York: Doubleday & Company, 1955.

Strauss, Anselm, *et al. Psychiatric Ideologies and Institutions.* New York: The Free Press, 1965.

Sullivan, Harry Stack. *Clinical Studies in Psychiatry.* Helen Swick Perry, Mary Ladd Gavell, and Martha Gibbon, eds. New York: W. W. Norton & Company, 1956.

——. *The Fusion of Psychiatry and Social Science* (with Introduction and Commentaries by Helen Swick Perry). New York: W. W. Norton & Company, 1964.

——. *The Interpersonal Theory of Psychiatry*. Helen Swick Perry and Mary Ladd Gavell, eds. New York: W. W. Norton & Company, 1953.

——. "Notes on Investigation, Therapy, and Education and Their Relations to Schizophrenia," *Psychiatry* (1947) 10: 271-80.

——. "Psychiatry: Introduction to the Study of Interpersonal Relations," *Psychiatry* (1938) 1: 121-34. Reprinted as "The Data of Psychiatry" in Sullivan, 1964.

——. *Schizophrenia as a Human Process* (with Introduction and Commentaries by Helen Swick Perry). New York: W. W. Norton & Company, 1962.

——. "Therapeutic Investigations in Schizophrenia," *Psychiatry* (1947) 10: 121-25.

Szasz, Thomas S. *The Myth of Mental Illness: Foundations of a Theory of Personal Conduct*. New York: Harper & Row, 1961.

Toby, Jackson. "Some Variables in Role Conflict Analysis," *Social Forces* (1952) 30: 323-27.

Villiers de L'Isle-Adam, P. A. M. de. "The Heroism of Doctor Hallidonhill," E. O'Neil, tr., in Max Lieber and Blanche Colton Williams, eds., *Great Stories of All Nations*. New York: Tudor Publishing Co., 1933.

Ward, Clyde H. "Psychotherapy Research: Dilemmas and Directions," *Arch. Gen. Psychiat.* (1964) 10: 596-622.

Watson, David Lindsay. *Scientists Are Human*. London: Watts & Co., 1938.

Whitehead, Alfred North. *Modes of Thought*. New York: The Macmillan Company, 1938.

Wilson, John Rowan. *Margin of Safety*. Garden City, N.Y.: Doubleday & Company, 1963.

Wolff, Kurt H. "Notes Toward a Sociocultural Interpretation of American Sociology," *Amer. Sociol. Rev.* (1946) 11: 545-53.

Wolstein, Benjamin. *Transference: Its Meaning and Function in Psychoanalytic Therapy*. New York: Grune & Stratton, 1954.

Wyatt, Frederick. "Climate of Opinion and Methods of Readjustment," *Amer. Psychol.* (1956) 11: 537-42.

Znaniecki, Florian. *The Social Role of the Man of Knowledge*. New York: Columbia University Press, 1940.

indexes

NAME INDEX

SUBJECT INDEX

adjustive techniques: *see* role-maintaining techniques
administration of ward, 40; *see also* insulation
American Psychoanalytic Association, research training in, 151*n*.
anxiety
  contagion of, 91-92*n*.
  and humor, 92-92*n*.
  and LSD, 29*n*.
  and reassurance of patients (illus.), 79
  in research, 89, 89*n*.
Archimedes, paradox of, 251
author's participation, 238-44

competition in science, 162, 243-44
conflict; *see also* role conflict schema
  for resolution of, 143
consensus in science, 235-36; *see also* science, truth in as culturally determined, 245-46
  deviations from, 246, 246*n*.
conversion, 164

decontamination, 135-38, 142; *see also* segregation
de-differentiation, of values, 62
defenses: *see* role-maintaining technique
depersonalization, 31*n*.

diagnosis
  hypothesis of error in (illus.), 205-206
  and ward setting, 200*n*.
drugs
  for controlling behavior, 2*n*.
  criteria for use of, 9*n*.

epistemology, 230
  empirical, 232*n*.
ethics: *see* values
evasion, 52-54
extenuation, 27, 132-33

fallacy, genetic, 247-52; *see also* science, truth in
friendliness, as value, 61-62, 99, 139

genetic science, Russian studies in, 8-9
good-bad dilemma, in therapy *vs.* research, 99-100; *see also* therapy *vs.* research

hierarchy of roles, 109-10, 142-43; *see also* integrating process; role conflict; Therapy Observation Project

ideas: *see also* science, ideas in, as behavior